ATLANTIC STUDIES

BROOKLYN COLLEGE PROGRAM ON SOCIETY IN CHANGE

No. 29

Editor-in-Chief Béla K. Király

City of Cracow's Coat of Arms. Codex Picturatus Balthasaris Behem, Cracovia 1505.

SZCZEPAN K. ZIMMER

THE BEGINNING OF CYRILLIC PRINTING
CRACOW, 1491
FROM THE ORTHODOX PAST IN POLAND

Edited by
Ludwik Krzyżanowski and Irene Nagurski
with the assistance of Krystyna M. Olszer

A POLISH INSTITUTE OF ARTS AND SCIENCES OF AMERICA BOOK
SOCIAL SCIENCE MONOGRAPHS, BOULDER, COLORADO

distributed by
COLUMBIA UNIVERSITY PRESS

New York, 1983

EAST EUROPEAN MONOGRAPHS, No. CXXXVI

Cover: Engraving from *Chronicon Mundi,* 1493 by Hartman Schedel.

Library of Congress Card Catalog Number 82-62806
ISBN 0-88033-027-9

Printed in the United States of America

To
My Wife Halina

Contents

Illustrations

Acknowledgments

The author would like to express his gratitude to those who generously helped and advised him during the various stages of his studies for this book. I wish to extend thanks to: Czesław Miłosz, University of California, Berkeley; Doyce B. Nunis, Jr., University of Southern California, and Rev. Jacek Przygoda, Loyola University, Los Angeles; Ludwik Krzyżanowski, *The Polish Review,* and Vitaut Tumash, Belorussian Institute of Arts and Sciences in America, New York; Zora Kipel, New York Public Library, Msgr. Walerian Meysztowicz, *Antemurale,* Rome, Italy; Rev. Emil Manastersky, St. Basil's College, Stamford, Connecticut; Irene Nagurski, The Polish Museum, Chicago; Rev. Alexander Nadson, The Francis Skaryna Byelorussian Library and Museum, London; Danuta Peters, Pergamon Press, Oxford; Eliza Szandorowska, National Library, Warsaw; Tadeusz Zapiór, Cracow.

Acknowledgment is also made to the three distinguished institutions without whom this book's publication would not have been possible: The Polish Institute of Arts and Sciences of America for the attention given to the manuscript and its recognition of the scholarly value of this publication, to the California Chapter of the Polish American Historical Association for its generous financial assistance, and to the Brooklyn College Program on Society in Change for including this book in its series.

Brooklyn College Program on Society in Change conducts research, organizes conferences and publishes scholarly books. The Program has been commissioned, encouraged and supported by Dr. Robert L. Hess, the President of Brooklyn College. The National Endowment for the Humanities awarded the Program a research grant for 1978–1981, which was renewed for another three-year term (1981–1984). Without these substantial and much appreciated supports, the Program could not realize its goals, indeed could not exist.

In addition, I wish to thank all those who have supported this publication by their patronage.

do y otorgado todos inuocada la gracia del espiritu santo q̃ eligẽ dela dicha orden a fulano: ⁊ assi fecha la dicha elecciõ todos capitularmente ⁊ cada vno por si la reposieran ⁊
le entregarã los pẽdones del maestrazgo y se acostũbra de cãtar. Te deũ laudamus. ⁊c.

¶ Presentacion de carcel.

¶ Señor alcalde. ⁊c. Yo hulano hago saber a vuestra merced que a noticia mia nueua
mente es venido que vosotros señores me mandays enplazar por carta y mandado de
los dichos señores rey y reyna por vosotros librada a pedimiento de hulana sobre ra-
zon dela muerte de fulano su marido en que dize que yo soy culpante ⁊ con protestaci-
on que hago de no vos hauer por mis juezes enla causa presente saluo en quanto de derecho lo seays ⁊ porque soy ynocente ⁊ sin culpa dello me vengo a presentar ante vosotros señores ⁊ a vuestra carcel: ⁊ caso que fuessedes juezes para conoscer desta dicha cau
sa yo entiẽdo ⁊ quiero prouar ante vos cerca dela dicha muerte ⁊ de como soy ynocente ⁊ sin culpa della no me obligando a prueua superflua ni impertinente ⁊ vos pido señores q̃ recibays esta dicha presentacion que yo assi hago ante vos ala dicha carcel ⁊ a-
si recebida me mandeys dar copia ⁊ traslado de qualquier acusacion o pedimiento que
por mi ante vos sea fecha por parte del dicho fulano o fulana porque pueda dezir ⁊ ale
gar de mi derecho cõtra ellos ⁊ porq̃ yo soy ombre hõrrado ⁊ hijo dalgo o cauallero de
linaje o señor de vassallos o rico ⁊ abonado vos pido q̃ me deys lugar a q̃ yo ande suel
to sobre mis bienes segũ q̃ la ley del fuero deste reyno lo requiere ⁊ dispone o alomenos
me mãdays dar sobre fiadores carceleros comentarienses los quales yo estoy presto de
dar ante vos: ⁊ lo qual digo ⁊ pido enla mejor forma ⁊ manera que puedo ⁊ deuo de de
recho ⁊ para lo necessario ⁊ cõplidero inploro vr̃o noble oficio pido ⁊ protesto las costas.

Deo gracias.

¶ Acabado ⁊ impremido fue el p̃sente tractado de forma libellã
di. Enla muy noble ⁊ muy leal ciudad de seuilla: por Stanislao
polono Año del señor de mill ⁊ quinientos. a. xix. de março.

Stanislaus Polonus. Last page: colophon and printer's device, 1500.

List of Patrons

Mrs. Mae Theodora Abel, Hemet, California
The University of Alberta Library, Edmonton, Alberta, Canada
Mr. and Mrs. Maroun Atallah and Family, Los Angeles, California
Prof. Thomas E. Bird, Little Neck, New York
Book House, Inc., Jonesville, Michigan
Dr. Witold Borysiewicz, Chicago, Illinois
Mr. Adam Bryl, London, England
Leonard Brzozowski, D.D.S., Erie, Pennsylvania
Ms Alice Burkhardt, Chicago, Illinois
University of Southern California Doheny Library, Los Angeles, California
H. E. Bishop John Chedid, Los Angeles, California
J. T. Chodaczyńska and C. M. Peters, Hallandale, Florida
Dr. V. C. Chrypiński, Flat Rock, Michigan
Kazimierz and Henryka Cybulski, Alhambra, California
Mr. Andrew M. Czyżewski, Passaic, New Jersey
Mr. W. Dembski, Fitzroy, South Australia
Mr. Bogdan Deresiewicz, Santa Barbara, California
Mrs. Wanda K. Dezwol, Huntingdon Valley, Pennsylvania
Ms. Helen Ernst Dosik, Northridge, California
M and C. Drozdowski, Santa Monica, California
Zbigniew K. Dworak, MD, SC.D, Hollywood Hills, California
Mrs. Cecilia Filipowicz, Fort Erie, Ontario, Canada
Mr. Roman E. Friedel, Fayetteville, North Carolina
Andrzej and Lila Furman, Seaton, South Australia
Kazimierz and Irena Furman, Woodville West, South Australia
Maria Aleksandra Furman, Woodville West, South Australia
Ms Halina Gawlińska, Los Angeles, California
Mr. John W. Gembala, Rio Rancho, New Mexico
Mr. Longin Głogowski, Los Angeles, California
Mr. Mieczysław Goździkowski, San Fernando, California
Mr. Edmund Graczyk, Petersham, N.W., Australia
Lt. Colonel Mitchel Haifter, San Bernardino, California

Mrs. Isabella Hamilton, Los Angeles, California
Hamilton Library, University of Hawaii, Honolulu
Mr. and Mrs. M. G. Henzel, Lakewood, California
Ms Matylda Zurowska-Hudak, Havertown, Pennsylvania
C. Olechno-Huszcza, Los Angeles, California
Zygmunt and Wanda Ipohorski-Lenkiewicz, London, England
A. Jaskiewicz, Mt. Clemens, Michigan
Mr. Jerzy Jawa-Jasielski, Hot Springs, Arkansas
Mr. and Mrs. Jan W. Jaźwiński, Los Angeles, California
Mrs. G. Kafrouni, La Canada, California
Ms Melanie J. Kamińska, Madison, Wisconsin
General and Mrs. S. Karpinski, Los Angeles, California
S. Kasprowick, Chicago, Illinois
Mr. Arthur E. Knoff, Detroit, Michigan
Mr. J. G. Knothe, London, England
Edgar C. Knowlton, Jr., Honolulu, Hawaii
T. F. Korleske, Butte, Montana
Mrs. Stanley Kornelak, Torrington, Connecticut
Ms Sophia Kotowski, Los Angeles, California
Ms Zofia Kowalska-Głodowski, Brooklyn, New York
Z. S. Kowalski, Monrovia, California
Jeanette L. and Marian Kozien, Bellflower, California
Mrs. Wanda H. Krans, Oak Park, Illinois
Rev. Dr. Stjepan Krasić, Rome, Italy, Istituto per le Opere di Religione
Ms Casimira Krawczyński, Glen Ellyn, Illinois
H. E. Cardinal John Król, Archbishop of Philadelphia, Pennsylvania
Mr. Adam Krzemuski, Hollywood, California
Mrs. Fran Lieberman, Los Angeles, California
Rev. Eugene R. Linowski, St. Mary's Byzantine Catholic Church, Van Nuys, California
Mr. Victor Londzin, Los Altos, California
Los Altos Public Library, California
Mrs. E. Luberski, La Sierra, California
Aleksander and Izabella Macander, Rockville, Maryland
Rev. Dr. M. J. Madaj, St. Mary of the Lake Seminary, Mundelein, Illinois
Gregory and Rosalie Madejski, Clarence, New York
Roman and Irene Makarewicz, Gardena, California
H. E. Cardinal Timothy Manning, Archbishop of Los Angeles, California
Jerome F. Mancewicz, M.D., Grand Rapids, Michigan
Z. and W. Marcinkowski, North Hollywood, California
Mrs. Mieczysława S. Maricz, Rosemead, California
Ms. Monica Mieroszewska, Washington, D.C.

Ms Carolyn A. Mills, Los Angeles, California
Bernard Mrozek, Pontifico Istituto Orientale, Rome, Italy
Doyce B. Nunis, Jr., Los Angeles, California
O.L.Q.A. Seminary Library, Mission Hills, California
Mr. Stanley E. Orbacz, Congers, New York
Mr. Stanley J. Paszek, Newington, Connecticut
Joseph and Mildred Peskin, Los Angeles, California
Poland's Millenium Library, Los Angeles, California
The Polish Catholic Mission in Greater Washington
The Polish Library, London, England
Polish Teachers Association in America, Chicago, Illinois
Polish University Club of Los Angeles, California
Legion of Young Polish Women, Mount Prospect, Illinois
Mr. Stanislas Potulicki, Culver City, California
Rev. Jacek Przygoda, San Fernando, California
Polish American Historical Association, California Chapter, Los Angeles
Mr. Janusz Pyter, Los Angeles, California
Theodore S. Ramond, Arlington Hts, Illinois
Ms Alice Reinhardt, Van Nuys, California
H. E. Cardinal Władysław Rubin, Vatican City
Sr. M. Ruth, IHM, St. John's Seminary College, Camarillo, California
Rev. Joseph C. Rutkowski, Chagrin Falls, Ohio
Judge Anthony Rutkowski
Mr. Francis Rutkowski
Ms Stella Kazmierski
Mr. Stephan Siemborski
Mr. Julian Sak, Chicago, Illinois
Dr. Stephen Sawruk, Allentown, Pennsylvania
H. E. Thaddeus Shubsda, D.D., Bishop of Monterey, California
Mr. and Mrs. Chester Sonta, Chicago, Illinois
Ms Alice Sparrow, Harwood Hts, Illinois
Olgierd and Helena Staniewicz, Greenwich, Connecticut
Mr. and Mrs. Ben S. Stefanski, Shaker Hts, Ohio
Ms Gail M. Stefanski, Shaker Hts, Ohio
Dr. Maria M. Święcicka-Ziemianek, Washington Crossing, Pennsylvania
Mr. and Mrs. Joseph B. Sypniewski, Calumet City, Illinois
Mrs. Sabina Szechowycz, Evanston, Illinois
Mr. S. M. Szymanski, San Pedro, California
Mikołaj and Łucja Szyndler, Brooklyn Park, South Australia
Mr. Marian Talarczyk, Port Augusta West, South Australia
Mr. Henryk S. Toczylowski, Topanga, California
Mr. Sigmund M. Toczyski, Chicago, Illinois

Rev. Z. Ostrowski, Towarzystwo Chrystusowe, Los Angeles, California
Mr. Anthony F. Turhollow, Los Angeles, California
Mr. A. Tybulewicz, Scientific Translations and Information, London, England
Hanna and Adam Tyszkiewicz, Los Angeles, California
Rudolf and Waclawa Veit, Salem, Wisconsin
Alexander Wallace III, MD, Los Angeles, California
Mr. Leon C. Walling, Capistrano Beach, California
Mrs. M. W. Wegner, Los Angeles, California
Dr. Bernard Wichlenski, Chicago, Illinois
Mr. Bernard Wielewinski, Tuscon, Arizona
Msgr. W. A. Wnuk, Windsor, Ontario, Canada
Dr. Sophie Mae Wolanin, Girard, Ohio
Mr. Wilhelm A. Wolny, Polish American Variety Hour, San Jose, California
Dr. Zygmunt Wygocki, Bridgeview, Illinois
Tatiana Rannit, Curator, Yale University, Slavic and East European Collections, New Haven, Connecticut
Mrs. Lottie Zajkowski, Calumet City, Illinois
Dr. Edwin L. Zebroski, Los Altos, California
Dr. Kazimir Pierre Zaleski, Paris, France
Krystyna and Zbigniew Zielkiewicz, Pasadena, California

Introduction
Cyrillic Incunabula

In recent years a significant change in the attitude of Western scholars toward the history of early printing and bookmaking has emerged. Many works on various aspects of the development of the printed book have been published and have found an enthusiastic response. As Douglas C. McMurtrie pointed out in his monograph, *The Book: The Story of Printing and Bookmaking,* "In the cultural history of mankind there is no event even approaching in importance the invention of printing with movable types."[1]

Printing, even printing with movable types, had been practiced in China and other Oriental lands long before its appearance in Europe. The first appearance of the printed word in Europe about the middle of the fifteenth century was so unobtrusive that no clear record of its beginning exists; hence, we do not know definitely how and where printing was first begun in the Western world.

However, Johann Gutenberg, born in Mainz, Germany, about 1400, is credited as the inventor of the art of printing. On the basis of historical evidence it is agreed that he did indeed invent printing with movable types of metal cast in matrices (which constitutes the invention of printing) at Mainz some time between 1440 and 1450 using both Latin and Gothic alphabets.

Of course, rival claimants to the honor sprang up. Among them, for example, was Laurens Janszoon Coster of Haarlem in the Netherlands, who, it is said, began to print with movable types sometime about 1430. But it is not the purpose of this work to argue the merits of the various claimants to the invention or in fact even to list them. Our intent here is to present a history of the development of the first Cyrillic printing press in the world established in Cracow, Poland, by Szwajpolt Fiol less than half a century after Gutenberg's invention.

Before turning our attention to Fiol and the Cyrillic press, it is important to understand the rapid dissemination of the new art of printing. We speak of incunabula, a term which applies to all books, pamphlets, broadsides, and leaflets produced in the fifteenth century up to and including 1500. The term is taken from

[1] Douglas C. McMurtrie, *The Book: The Story of Printing and Bookmaking* (New York, 1943), p. 136.

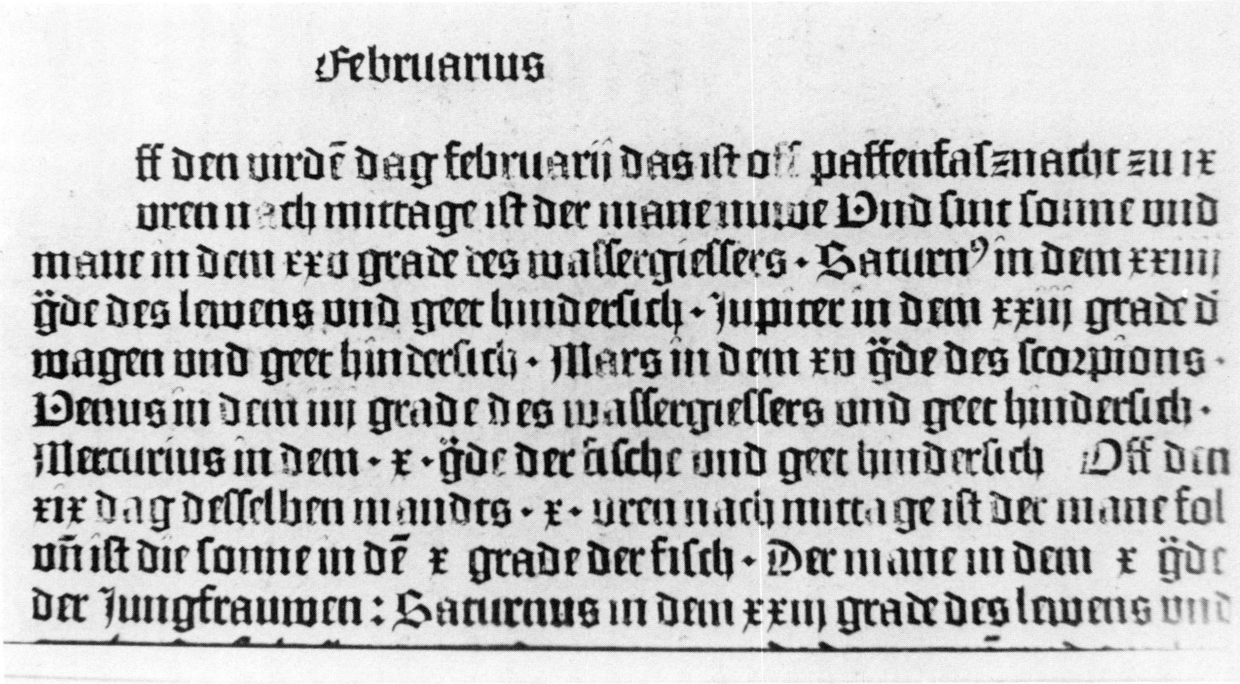

Februarius

ff den virdē dag februarij das ist off paffenfasznacht zu ix
uren nach mittage ist der mane nuwe Und sint sonne und
mane in dem xxv grade des wassergiessers · Saturnus in dem xxiij
g̃de des lewens und geet hindersich · Jupiter in dem xxiij grade d̃
wagen und geet hindersich · Mars in dem xv g̃de des scorpions ·
Venus in dem iiij grade des wassergiessers und geet hindersich ·
Mercurius in dem · x · g̃de der fische und geet hindersich Uff den
xix dag desselben mandes · x · uren nach mittage ist der mane fol
unñ ist die sonne in dē x grade der fisch · Der mane in dem x g̃de
der Jungfrauwen : Saturnus in dem xxiij grade des lewens und

Almanach ad a. 1448. German. Mainz, J. Gutenberg. Fragment 118×217 mm. Johannes Gutenberg. Calendarium astronomicum recte tabula siderum. Lewicka-Kamińska, Anna. Inkunabuły Biblioteki Jagiellońskiej. Kraków, 1960. p. 33.

The oldest pull sheet from Gutenberg's printing shop. Unique document of his first trial in printing.

the Latin word *incunabulum,* or cradle, and implies the period of infancy of the book industry, a subject of special interest to bibliophiles and to the branch of library science which can be referred to as the science of incunabula, similar to French *science des incunables*; German—*Inkunabelkunde*; Polish and Russian—*inkunabulistyka.*

Prior to Gutenberg's death sometime just before the year 1468, rival printers were already at work in Germany, mostly in and around Mainz. Conrad Sweynheym and Arnold Pannartz, Germans who had been apprentices in Mainz, established themselves as printers in Italy at Subiaco in 1464–1467 and in Rome, 1467–1472. By 1472 they had produced forty titles in editions of 275 to 300 copies, mostly works of the Latin classics. Johann Spira, a goldsmith from Mainz, published the first book in Venice in 1469.

Itinerant printers soon roamed throughout Europe taking their knowledge of the infant art with them. During the next decade typography spread throughout Central and Western Europe. A press was established in Pilsen (Plzen), Bohemia, soon after 1468; at Cracow in 1473–74; at Budapest in 1473; and Wrocław (Breslau), Silesia, in 1474.

Typography was introduced in Switzerland, France and Holland, and at Bruges in the southern region of the Low Countries comprising approximately the area of present-day Belgium in 1470. William Caxton and Colard Mansion printed the first book in the English language, *The Recuyell of the Historyes of Troye,* in 1474. While the first incunabula were predominantly printed in Latin, printing in Western native languages quickly followed. Types were developed for printing in Greek in 1465 and for Hebrew in 1474; Arabic and other languages soon afterwards.

Szwajpolt Fiol from Neustadt-an-der-Aisch in Franconia moved to Poland and settled in Cracow in 1479. There he enlisted in the goldsmith guild, although his specialty was doing fine embroidery work with gold thread and pearls on rich church vestments. Fiol was a fascinating man, an inventor, a shrewd businessman and not one to let an opportunity go wanting. Through a mysterious set of circumstances this German Catholic established the first Cyrillic printing press in the world and produced the first Cyrillic incunabula in 1491. Fiol's feat is remarkable for several reasons, not the least of which was his residence in the capital of a Roman Catholic Poland at a time when the Catholic Church preserved its effective control over doctrine. Given the time and the place, Fiol's printing of religious books using the Cyrillic alphabet (as opposed to the Latin) for use by followers of the Eastern or Orthodox Church could be considered nothing less than heresy. But, being himself a Catholic, Fiol was not motivated by religious fervor, as we shall see.

Cyrillic is one of two Slavic alphabets, the other being the Glagolitic. According to tradition, St. Cyril and St. Methodius, brother missionaries to the Slavs, invented the alphabets in the ninth century for the purpose of teaching Holy Scrip-

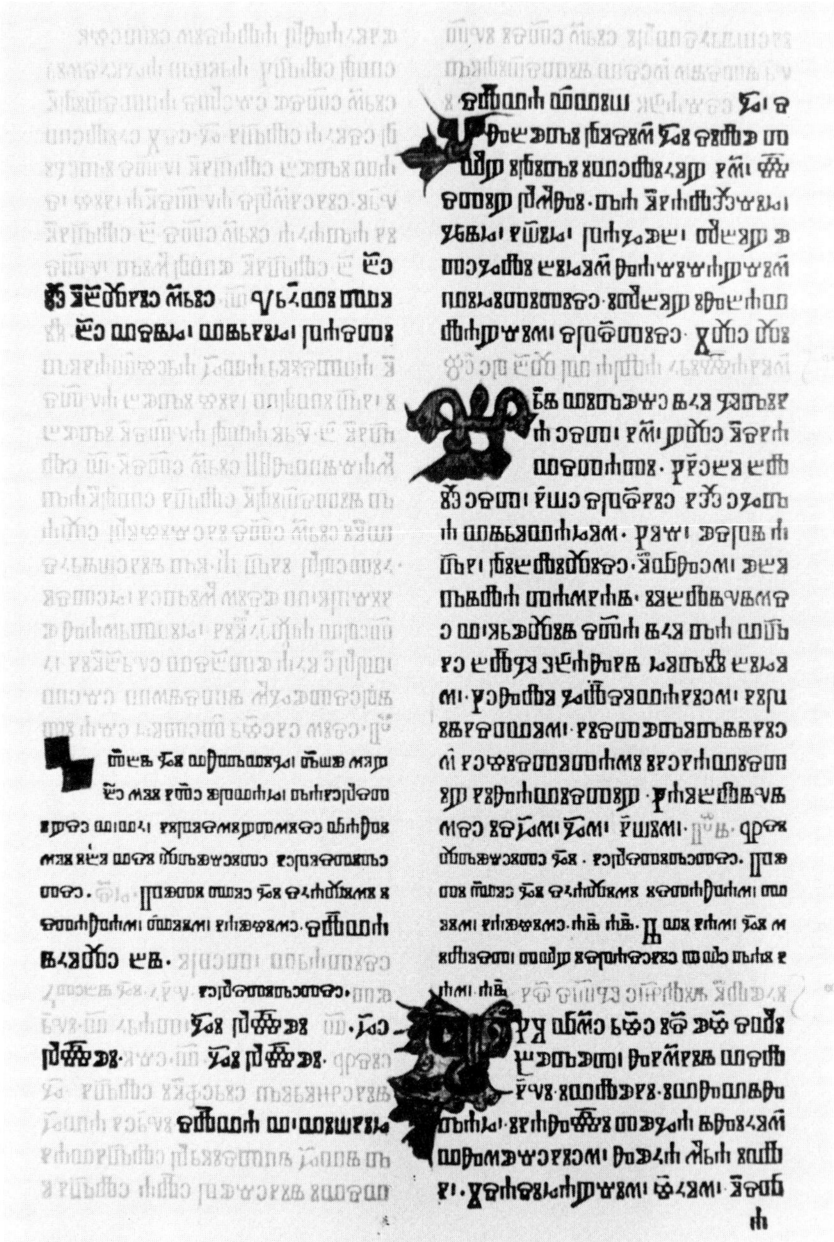

MISSAL — First page. Venice, 1483. Glagolitic print.

ture to the converts. The Slavist Horace G. Lunt, professor at Harvard University, has described their origin as follows:

> The Glagolitic (from glagol = word) was invented by St. Cyril perhaps with the aid of his brother Methodius in or about 863 A.D. It is a unique and homogeneous system, despite reminiscences from various styles of Greek, Coptic and other alphabets.... A second less esoteric alphabet was soon devised for Slavic, probably at the beginning of the tenth century in Bulgaria. . . . Utilizing Greek letters whenever possible, the new alphabet adapted the Glagolitic symbols for typically Slavic sounds to the current majuscule style of Greek writing.[2]

This second alphabet, associated with the name of St. Cyril, became known as Cyrillic.

Very soon the Cyrillic alphabet dominated in all the Slavic nations which had accepted Christianity from Byzantium, in Eastern Europe the Belorussians (also referred to as Byelorussians or White Russians), Ruthenians (the Ukrainians or Little Russians) and Russians (Great Russians), as well as the Bulgarians, Macedonians, and Serbians of the Balkans. The Croatians and Slovenians, as Roman Catholics, first used the Glagolitic and later the Latin alphabet. The Western Slavic nations, the Poles, Czechs and Slovaks, who closely identified with Western Roman culture, adopted the Latin alphabet from the beginning, although Glagolitic was used in the ninth and tenth centuries in the territories (now Czechoslovakia) which then formed the Great Moravian State.

Very few Cyrillic incunabula were produced. When compared to that produced in Latin, the amount is only a fraction of one percent. Two printing shops devoted exclusively to Cyrillic printing are known to have existed in the latter part of the fifteenth century. Foremost was Fiol's workshop in Cracow, Poland, where four books were produced not later than 1491. The second Cyrillic printing shop was established in 1493 in Obod, near Cetinje, Montenegro in the Balkan peninsula. There a monk named Makarije (Makarios) printed five books under the auspices of the ruler of Montenegro, Gjurgje Crnojević (George the Black). It is believed by some scholars that yet another Cyrillic press was active in Braşov (Kronstadt) in Hungary at the very close of the century. This press allegedly produced a *Psalter*. However, no copy of it has ever been uncovered and no concrete evidence proving the existence of the press has been presented to date.

A case has been made for extending the framework of Cyrillic incunabula until the year 1525. In accepting that date we must also acknowledge three ecclesiastical books printed at Târgovişte in Wallachia (now Rumania) between 1508 and 1512 as Cyrillic incunabula. The printer was also a monk and also named Makarije (Makarios), but identity with Makarios of Cetinje has not been proved. The books produced in Târgovişte were destined for the Rumanian Eastern Orthodox Church

[2] Horace G. Lunt, *Old Church Slavonic Grammar* (2nd ed.; The Hague, 1959), p. 14.

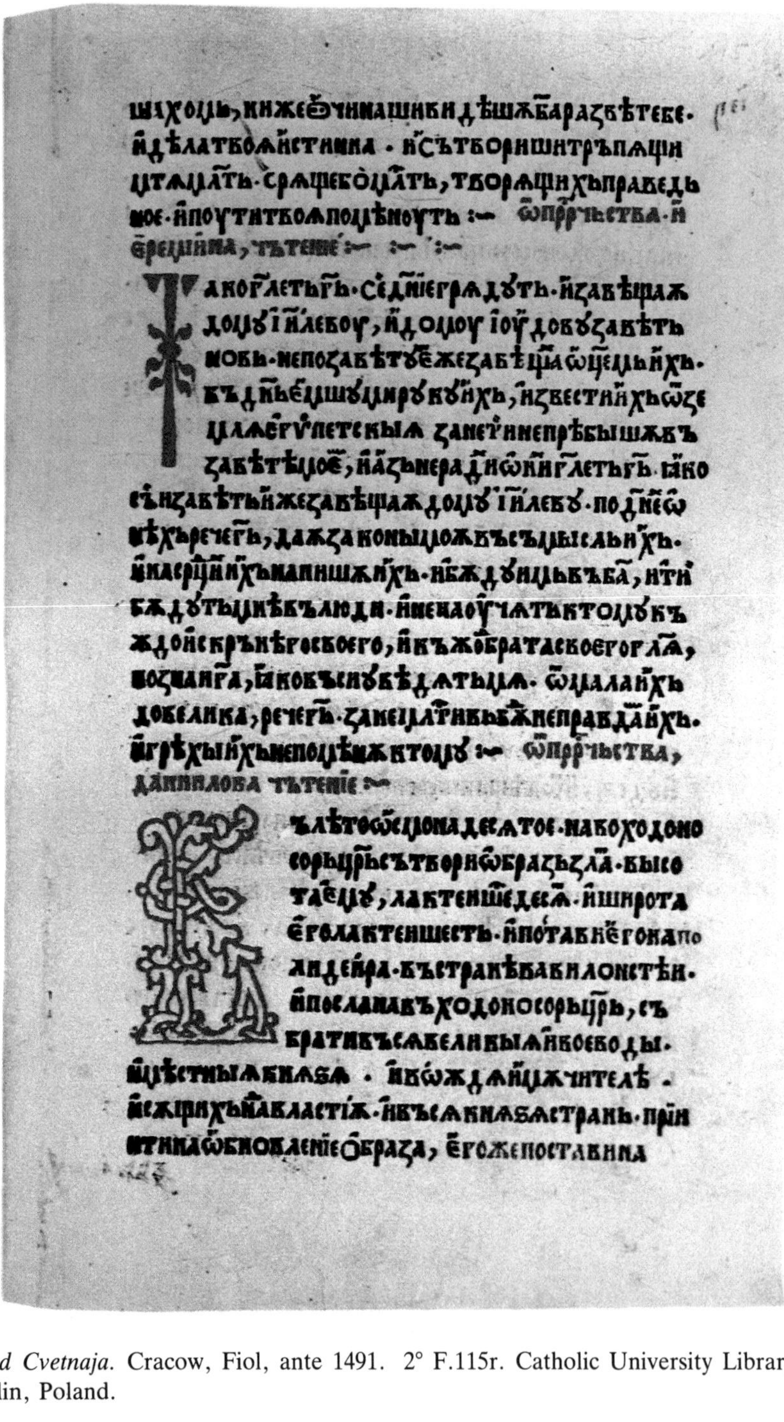

Triod Cvetnaja. Cracow, Fiol, ante 1491. 2° F.115r. Catholic University Library in Lublin, Poland.

which, over the centuries, used the Old Church Slavonic language just as Latin was used by the Roman Catholic Church.

Two Catholic prayer-books, *Officia Beatae Mariae Virginis* and *Officia Sanctae Brigittae,* adapted under the name of *Molitvenik* by Franjo Micalović-Ratković were printed by Georgio Rusconi in Venice in 1512. They were printed in a special type called *bosančitsa,* a Cyrillic cursive type with some Glagolitic elements. There two other printing shops, one owned by B. Vuković, the other by Djurdje and Tadore Ljubović, produced Orthodox ecclesiastical books in Cyrillic for the Balkan peninsula about 1519. Approximately in 1521 the Ljubović shop was transferred to Goražde in Herzegovina, presently the republic of Bosnia-Herzegovina in Yugoslavia.

Obviously the development of Cyrillic printing was a rapid process. The efforts of Fiol and his followers were finally crowned by the production of prints which fully deserve to be designated as modern books which no longer looked like reproduced manuscripts. Certainly among these should be the prints produced by Dr. Francišak Skaryna, the first Belorussian printer and the most prominent pioneer of Cyrillic printing who worked in Prague, 1517–1519 and between 1520–1525 in Wilno (Lithuanian: Vilnius; Russian: Vilna).

These four printing shops—Fiol's in Cracow, that of Makarios in Cetinje, of Makarios in Tărgovişte, and Dr. Skaryna in Prague-Wilno, existing during a span of about thirty-five years from 1490 to 1525, established the shape and form of a new branch of printing: the Cyrillic.

For the next three centuries Cyrillic typography was used in Eastern and Southern Europe by all Eastern Orthodox nations, whether Slavic or, in the case of Wallachia and Moldavia (now Rumania), non-Slavic.

Poland's Cyrillic incunabula deserve special attention. Not only were they the first of their kind, but it seems obvious that the other Cyrillic printers of the fifteenth and sixteenth centuries followed the pattern established by Fiol in Cracow or were at least inspired by him to continue the same form of printing. Moreover, as mentioned, an aura of mystery surrounds the Cracow initiative. To date it has not yet been explained how it had come about that the first Cyrillic printing press was established in the capital of Catholic Poland at a time when no printing presses existed in the Polish language, although Latin printing presses had been active in Cracow for nearly two decades. This work will endeavor to shed some light on this question.

Fortunately, sufficient documentary information pertaining to the Cracow Cyrillic printing press and the printer himself prevents any challenge to their existence, place, date of printing or the identity of the printer. Interest in Fiol and the Cracow Cyrillic incunabula was awakened much sooner than in the case of "The Printer of *The Turrecremata*" who produced the first Cracow Latin incunabula between 1474 and 1477. Extensive literature pertaining to the first Cyrillic press is available not only in Polish but also in Belorussian, Ukrainian, Russian, German and, recently, in Croatian and Rumanian.

American bibliophiles and scholars have not shown much interest in Fiol's Cyrillic incunabula, perhaps because only one copy was known to exist in the United States, the one owned by the New York Public Library. The description of this copy was first cited by M. B. Stillwell in 1940, and Frederick Richmond Goff lists it in the 1964 edition of the union list of Incunabula in the U.S.A.[3]

Many Western scholars tend to believe that if Muscovite Russia had no printing presses in the fifteenth century, then nothing of interest existed in other Slavic countries. This attitude is so prevalent that the prominent scholar Lawrence C. Wroth stated, "There was no printing press in Russia or the Balkans."[4] While Russia had no printing shop, actually several printing shops were functioning in the Balkans in the fifteenth century. Three of them were producing Glagolitic books, and one printed books using the Cyrillic alphabet.

Such oversights can be explained up to a point because little or no mention of Cyrillic or Glagolitic incunabula is found in such important reference books as Ludwig Hain's *Repertorium Bibliographicum,*[5] *The Catalogue of Books Printed in the XVth Century Now in the British Museum,*[6] or *Gesamtkatalog der Wiegendrucke.*[7]

Until a few years ago only two lists of Cyrillic incunabula existed: Vasilij Sopikov's *Opyt rossiĭskoĭ bibliografii* (Outline of Russian Bibliography) from 1813,[8] in which he included the incunabula; and Ivan Karataev's *Opisanie slaviano-russkikh knig napechatannykh kirillovskimi bukvami, 1491–1730* (Description of Slavic-Russian Books Printed in Cyrillic, 1491–1730), published in 1878 and republished in 1883.[9] Both are too dated to be of real value.

In 1969 the Russian historian Evgeniĭ L. Nemirovskiĭ published in German a list of seventy-five copies of Fiol's Cyrillic incunabula which are still in existence: *Slavische Inkunabeln in kyrillischer Schrift, Die Geschichte ihrer Erforschung*

[3] Margaret B. Stillwell. *Incunabula in American Libraries. A Second Census of Fifteenth Century Books Owned in the United States, Mexico and Canada.* New York, 1940. Frederick Richmond Goff, *Incunabula in American Libraries: a Third Census of Fifteenth Century Books Recorded in North American Collections* (New York, 1964).

[4] Lawrence C. Wroth, *A History of the Printed Book* (New Jersey, The Limited Editions Club, 1938), p. 394.

[5] Ludwig Hain, *Repertorium bibliographicum* (Stuttgartiae, Lutetiae Parisiorum, 1826–1838). 2 vols.

[6] *Catalogue of Books Printed in the XVth Century Now in the British Museum* (London, 1908–1962), Part 1–IX.

[7] *Gesamtkatalog der Wiegendrucke* (Leipzig, 1925–1940), Vols. 1–7, 8- /Lief. 1/.

[8] Vasiliĭ Sopikov, *Opyt rossiĭskoĭ bibliografii* (Outline of Russian Bibliography), (Sanktpeterburg, 1813; reprint ed. 1904), Part 1.

[9] Ivan Karataev, *Opisanie slaviano-russkikh knig napechatannykh kirillovskimi bukvami, 1491–1730* (Description of Slavic-Russian Books Printed in Cyrillic from 1491 to 1730), (Sanktpeterburg, 1878).

und die noch erhaltenen Exemplare.[10] This publication gives valuable data about Fiol's prints up to 1961. In a later book, *Nachalo slavianskogo knigopechataniia* (The Beginning of Slavic Printing)[11] published in 1971, he presented three new discoveries raising the total to seventy-eight. In this new monograph Nemirovskiĭ added more descriptive details which enhanced his study and also facilitates the location of all of Fiol's prints throughout the world, and allows us to determine their state of preservation. However, Nemirovskiĭ does not give all the data pertaining to the provenance of every single book: the original owner, the various owners over the centuries, purchase deeds, prices, consecutive locations and dates, etc. Nemirovskiĭ cites all those with Russian notations, disregarding most of the others. As a result his list has limited value. A complete, unrestricted catalogue of Cyrillic incunabula remains still to be compiled.

The study of Cyrillic incunabula is limited because of the difficulty in obtaining access to the books themselves. Most of the Cyrillic incunabula are in the U.S.S.R. which, for the time being, makes it practically impossible for many non-Russian scholars to study them *in situ.*

While deprived of the opportunity to examine all Fiol's incunabula due to their inaccessibility, the author has, nevertheless, attempted to present a comprehensive study based on what is available in copies and fragments located outside the U.S.S.R. and also based on the extensive literature on this subject, Russian and otherwise.

In 1972 a copy of *Triod Cvetnaja* was located in Braşov, Rumania, and a fragment of twenty-nine leaves, also of *Triod Cvetnaja,* was found in the United States. The latter had been in America for quite some time. However, it has never been mentioned in any catalogue or publication dealing with incunabula. Details of these two discoveries will be presented in Chapter IX and XII.

To facilitate an understanding of the four Cyrillic incunabula published in Cracow by Fiol, a short description of their contents follows:

(1) *TRIPĚSNEC* (Tripesnets) also known as *Triod Postnaja* (Postnaya, Postnaia) or *Triodon* in Greek. A liturgical book in the Eastern Rite containing the variable portions of the services from the Fourth Sunday before Lent through the Sunday before Easter. We will refer to it as *Triod Postnaja.*

(2) *TRIOD CVETNAJA* (Tsvetnaya, Tsvetnaia). A liturgical book containing the variable portions of the services from Easter Sunday to the eighth day after Pentecost. We will refer to it as *TRIOD CVETNAJA.*

(3) *ČASOSLOVEC* (Chasoslovets), in our transcription, *Chasoslovec* (referred

[10] Evgenij L. Nemirovskij, "Slavische Inkunabeln in Kyrillischer Schrift. Die Geschichte ihrer Erforschung und die noch erhaltenen Exemplare," *Beiträge zur Inkunabelkunde* (Berlin, 1969), Dritte Folge. pp. 81–111.

[11] E. L. Nemirovskiĭ, *Nachalo slavianskogo knigopechataniia* (Beginning of Slavic Printing), (Moscow, 1971).

to as such in the text which follows), a liturgical book containing the unchangeable parts of daily offices extending throughout the whole year.

(4) *OSMOGLASNIK* (Oktoikh, Oktoix), from the Greek *Octoechos.* A liturgical book containing the variable parts of the services from the first Sunday after Whitsun to the tenth Sunday before Easter. Subsequent references to this work will be to Osmoglasnik.

These four books cover the basic needs of the Eastern Orthodox Church in conducting services throughout the whole of the ecclesiastical year.

Johannes Kochanowski and Franciscus Skaryna Portrait in the University of Padua.

1
Szwajpolt Fiol's Cracow Printing Press

Cracow was already several centuries old when Szwajpolt Fiol moved there from Franconia and became its citizen in 1479. The first historical mention of the city under its present name can be found in an account written in 965 by Ibrahim Ibn Jakub, a Jewish Arab merchant, who referred to caravans of "Slavs and Ruthenians, journeying from the town of Cracow to the town of Prague." Long before the Arab traveler recorded that name for history, towns had existed there by other names. The Avars, nomads of Mongolian descent notorious for their savagery and cruelty, gained mastery over the region in the mid-sixth century and annihilated the populous settlements on Wawel Hill. Archaeologists have found evidence that man occupied the area along the Vistula River for thousands of years.

Thus, the Cracow that Fiol found in 1479 had already been an important trade, political and cultural center for almost five hundred years. The Polish state had its beginnings during the ninth and tenth centuries when the Polanians (dwellers in the field) obtained hegemony over the other Slavic tribes that occupied the country. Duke Mieszko I, founder of the Piast dynasty, began the conversion of Poland to Christianity in 966. The Piasts expanded their domain in wars against the German emperors, Hungary, Bohemia, Pomerania, Denmark, and Kiev, and in 1025, Bolesław I took the title of king. When Bolesław III died in 1138 the kingdom broke up and was not restored until Władysław I was installed as king of a unified Poland at Cracow in 1320. Thereafter Cracow became the coronation city, the temporal residence and burial place of the kings, the hub of political and cultural life and the center of trade for all Poland.

Under Casimir III, the Great (1333–1370), an enlightened ruler who befriended the peasants, extended protection to the Jews and codified the laws, Cracow attracted crowds of settlers—mostly Germans drawn by the prospect of the material success that the city offered. In 1364 King Casimir III founded (with Pope Urban V's consent) the second oldest university in Central Europe (after that in Prague) and consolidated Cracow's cultural supremacy. The university was extended and reorganized during the reign of Queen Jadwiga and her consort, King Władysław II Jagiełło (1384–1434) who was the founder of the Jagellonian dynasty which ruled Poland and Lithuania until 1572.

The Lithuanians had formed a strong unified state in the thirteenth century to protect themselves from the Teutonic Knights who had conquered the region comprising East Prussia. The combined forces of Poland and Lithuania defeated the German Order at Grunwald and Tannenberg in 1410, and the Teutonic Knights finally became vassals of the Polish kings by 1466, in the second Treaty of Toruń.

Eventually, Lithuania became one of the largest states of medieval Europe and included all of Belorussia, a large part of Ukraine and sections of Russia proper. With the marriage of Władysław II of Lithuania to Jadwiga, daughter of Louis I of Poland and Hungary, the union between Poland and Lithuania was formalized, and the Jagellonian dynasty established. The following period which lasted through the sixteenth century can be called Poland's golden age. The closely allied Polish and Lithuanian states maintained an empire which reached from the Baltic to the Black Sea, with Cracow as its capital.

The university, with the encouragement of Jadwiga and Władysław II, spread scholarship and knowledge throughout the United Polish-Lithuanian Kingdom and beyond its borders. It attracted such scholars as Nicholas Copernicus, who was a student there in 1491, and the Italian Philippo Buonaccorsi, known as Callimachus. Although Callimachus was exiled from Italy, in Cracow the enlightened and liberal King Casimir IV (1447–1492) put him in charge of educating his four sons. Callimachus, who lived in Cracow at the same time as Fiol, was a champion of the new progressive ideas of Humanism. The modern attitude of such men, and that of the Jagellonian kings, played an important role in Szwajpolt Fiol's pioneering of Cyrillic printing.

The art of printing preceded Fiol's arrival in Cracow by six or more years. During the years 1473–1476 in the Polish capital a printing shop existed in which four incunabula, including the *Explanatio in Psalterium* by Cardinal John de Turrecremata, were printed in Latin. None of the prints produced by the Cracow printing shop was signed by the printer, and his identity has not been firmly established.[1] The Cracow archives of this period mention printers: Caspar de Bavaria (1476)[2] and Casper druker (1477) identified by the Polish scholar Józef Seruga with Casper Strawbe von Dresen, Casper Strawbe von Leypczke, Caspar Straube.[3] It is possible that they were all the same man whom we name: "The Printer of *Turrecremata.*"

Court documents (dated 1483 and 1484) reveal the existence of two printers, Johannes Kriger and Johannes Pepelau, whose names appear in the files on two

[1]Szczepan K. Zimmer, "Cracow's First Printing Press," *Antemurale* (Rome and London, 1970), XIV: 173–192.

[2]Johannes Ptaśnik, "Cracovia Impressorum XV et XVI saeculorum," *Monumenta Poloniae Typographica XV et XVI saeculorum* (Leopoli: Sumptibus Instituti Ossoliniani, 1922) I: 4. 6.

[3]Józef Seruga, *Jan Haller, wydawca i drukarz krakowski (1467–1525)* (Jan Haller: Cracow Publisher and Printer, 1467–1525)., (Cracow, 1933), pp. 86–89.

separate occasions: once when they sued each other and later when one of them sued his employees named Paulus and Albertus.[4] No details are available regarding their printing achievements.

Cracow was not a prominent typographical center during the incunabular era, although four books produced there by the unknown printer between 1473 and 1476 are among the earliest printed in Central Europe. Economic and technical conditions were excellent for the development of typography: Poland had her own paper mills; bookbinding was a highly developed art; books were in great demand; nevertheless, there was no real incentive for the development of the new art. First of all, at that time the Polish language was passed over in favor of Latin in matters of education and literature. Latin, as in all Catholic countries, was the official church and literary language. Poland was well supplied with manuscript books. Her scribes were prospering and thus had a vested interest in not promoting printing. With the coming of the printing press social and religious leaders found it more convenient to order books from abroad than to produce them at home. Businessmen found little reason to chase the small profits to be derived from the new art.

Nonetheless, printing was attempted throughout the Commonwealth. Besides the early shop in Cracow, presses were established at Wrocław, Gdańsk, Malbork, and Chełmno. These produced little and soon disappeared. However, the shop in Wrocław directed by a priest was successful. Productive for about eight years, it printed eleven books and closed only because of the death of the owner, Canon Caspar Elyan.[5]

Elyan was a native of Silesia and, strangely, while printing was getting off to a slow start in Poland, this particular district was to produce several early printers who gained fame abroad such as Stanislaus Polonus, Maynard Ungut and Johannes Adam de Polonia. All were associated with the monk Matheus of neighboring Moravia, a prominent printer, and according to recent findings an alumnus of the Jagellonian University.[6]

Matheus Moravus was born in Četkovice in the vicinity of the town of Olomouc in Moravia (now Czechoslovakia). Between 1450 and 1468 he worked in Venice as a copyist. Manuscripts are preserved in his tiny readable Gothic script of Cicero's *Rhetorica,* and also in the beautiful antiqua (a particular Roman script) in which he copied Saint Jerome's *Letters.* Later in 1475 he applied the antiqua to the type in which he printed the works of Seneca. Sometime between 1473 and 1475 Moravus had learned the art of printing and organized his first shop in Genoa.

[4] Ptaśnik, "Cracovia Impressorum," *op. cit.,* pp. 9–10.

[5] Szczepan K. Zimmer, "Pierwszy polski drukarz—Kaspar Elyan" (The First Polish Printer—Kaspar Elyan) *Polish Congress of Contemporary Science and Culture in Exile* (London, 1970), pp. 315–321.

[6] Tadeusz Ulewicz, *Wśród impresorów krakowskich doby renesansu* (Among Cracow Printers in the Renaissance Period) (Cracow, 1977), p. 248.

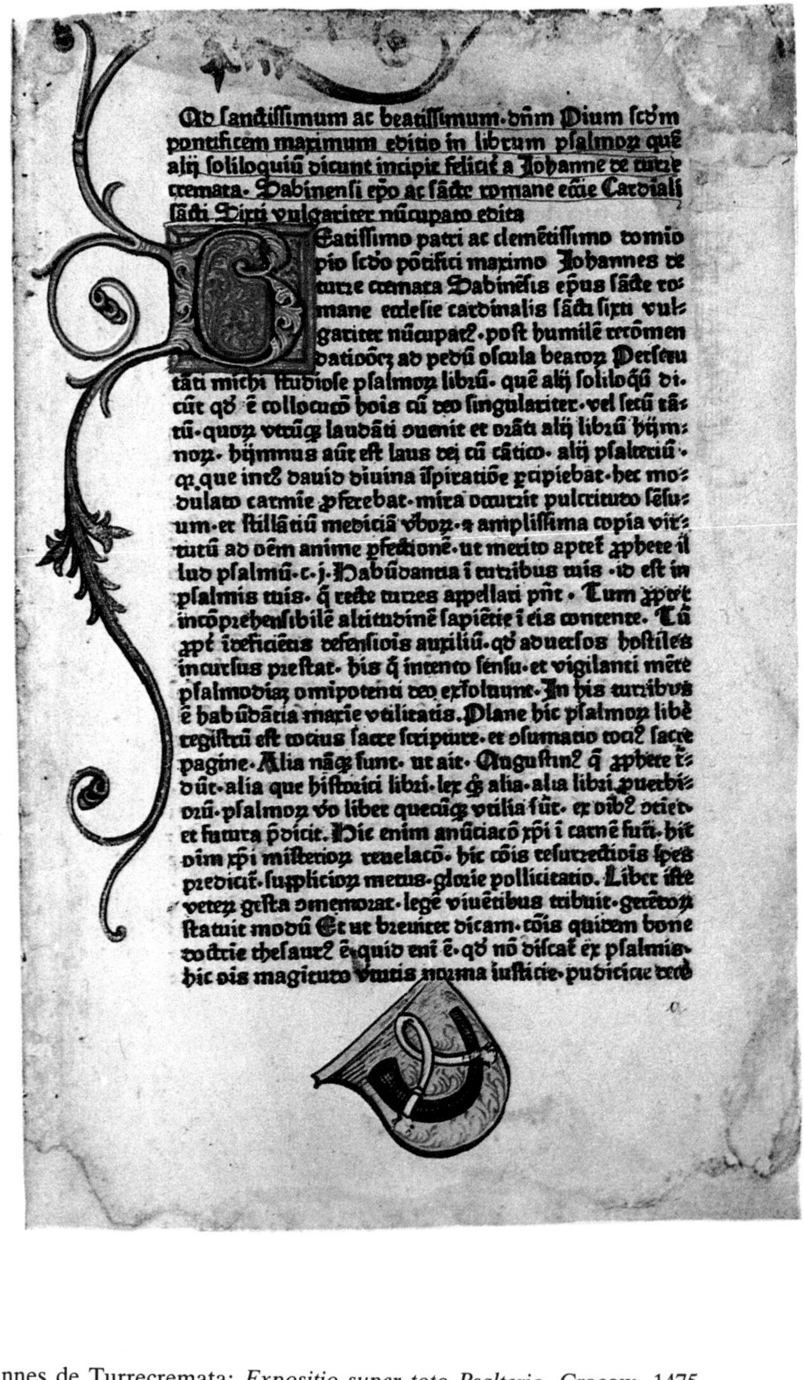

Ad sanctissimum ac beatissimum. dñm Pium scd'm
pontificem maximum editio in librum psalmorꝝ quē
alij soliloquiū dicunt incipit feliciť a Johanne de turre
cremata. Sabinensi epo ac sācte romane ecc̄ie Cardiali
sācti Sixti vulgariter nūcupato edita
Beatissimo patri ac clemētissimo domio
pio scd'o pōtifici maximo Johannes de
turre cremata Sabinēsis epus sācte romane ecclesie cardinalis sācti sixti vulgariter nūcupatꝰ. post humilē recōmen
dationēꝫ ad pedū oscula beatorꝝ Persču
tāti michi studiose psalmorꝝ librū. quē alij soliloqū di-
cūt qd' ē collocucō hois cū deo singulariter. vel secū tā-
tū. quorꝝ vtrūqꝫ laudāti ouenit et orāti alij librū hym-
norꝝ. hymnus aūt est laus dei cū cātico. alij psalteriū.
qꝛ que intꝰ dauid diuina īspiratiōe ꝯcipiebat. hec mo-
dulato carmie ꝓferebat. mira decurrit pulcritudo sēsu-
um. et stillātiū medicinā vborꝝ. ꝛ amplissima copia vir-
tutū ad oēm anime ꝑfectionē. vt merito aptet ꝓphete il
lud psalmū. c. j. Habūdantia i turribus tuis. id est in
psalmis tuis. q̄ recte turres appellari pnt. Tum ꝓpť
incōprehensibilē altitudinē sapiētie i eis contente. Tū
ꝓpť īdeficiētis defensiois auxiliū. qd' aduersos hostiles
incursus prestat. his q̄ intento sensu. et vigilanti mēte
psalmodiāꝫ omipotenti deo exsoluunt. In his turribus
ē habūdātia maxie vtilitatis. Plane hic psalmorꝝ libē
registrū est totius sacre scripture. et ꝯsumatio totiꝰ sacre
pagine. Alia nāqꝫ sunt. vt ait. Augustinꝰ q̄ ꝓphete ꝯ-
dūt. alia que historici libri. lex q̄ alia. alia libri ꝓuerbi-
orū. psalmorꝝ vo liber quecūqꝫ vtilia sūt. ex oibꝰ ꝯtiet.
et futura ꝓdicit. Hic enim anūciacō xpi i carnē futi. hic
oim xpi misteriorꝝ reuelacō. hic cōis resurrectiois spes
predicit. suppliciorꝝ metus. glorie pollicitatio. Liber iste
veterꝝ gesta ꝯmemorat. legē viuētibus tribuit. gerēdorꝝ
statuit modū Et vt breuiter dicam. cōis quidem bone
doctrie thesaurꝰ ē. quid eni ē. qd' nō discať ex psalmis.
hic ois magitudo vtutis norma iusticie. pudicicie decꝰ

Joannes de Turrecremata: *Expositio super toto Psalterio*. Cracow, 1475.

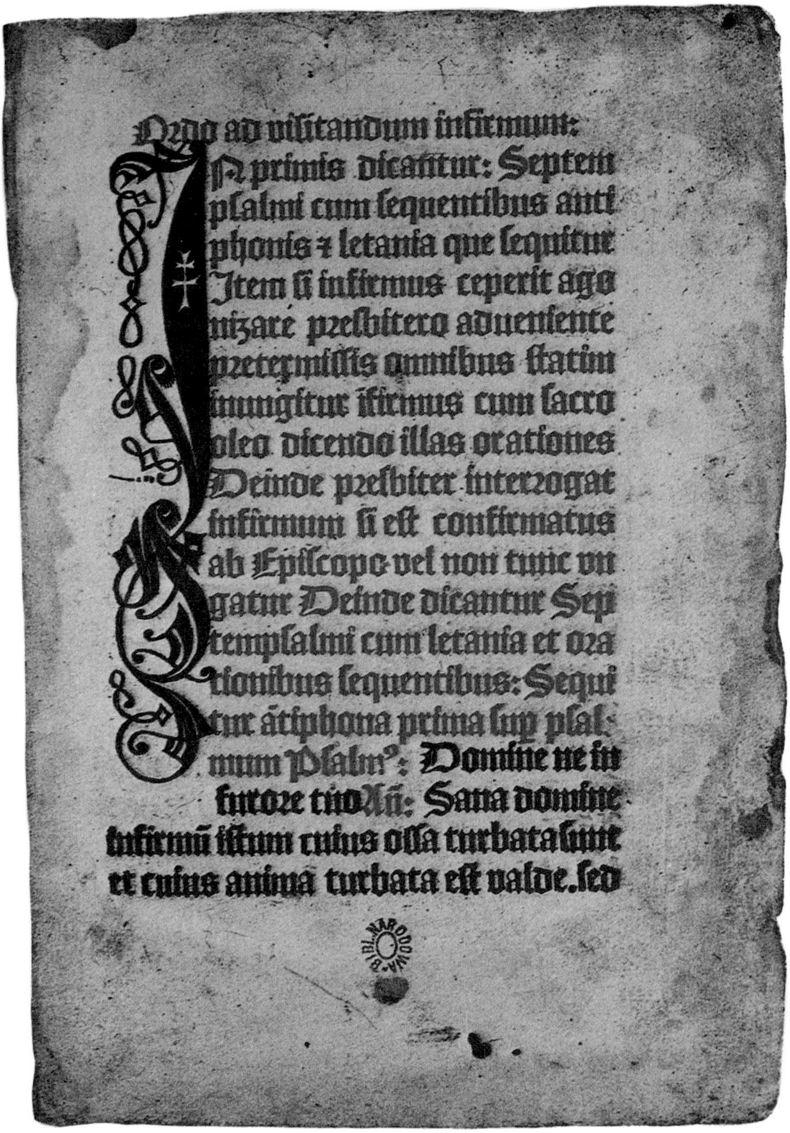

Ordo ad visitandum infirmum:
In primis dicantur: Septem
psalmi cum sequentibus anti
phonis ₇ letania que sequitur
Item si infirmus ceperit ago
nizare presbitero adueniente
pretermissis omnibus statim
inungitur ĩfirmus cum sacro
oleo dicendo illas orationes
Deinde presbiter interrogat
infirmum si est confirmatus
ab Episcopo vel non tunc vn
gatur Deinde dicantur Sep
tempsalmi cum letania et ora
tionibus sequentibus: Sequi
tur ãtiphona prima sup psal
mum Psalm⁹: Domine ne in
furore tuo An: Sana domine
infirmũ istum cuius ossa turbata sunt
et cuius anima turbata est valde. sed

Agenda sive Exsequiale sacramentorum, Gdańsk, 1499. 4°. Leaf 1 r. Printer: Konrad Baumgart.

From 1475 his shop in Naples was known for the production of beautiful prints and books that were, for the most part, religious in content.

The types from his last work, *Officia Beatae Mariae Virginis,* were used by Maynard Ungut and Stanislaus Polonus in Seville where they established their printing office in 1491.[7] This shop was organized and equipped with everything necessary for printing by Matheus Moravus at the request of the King of Spain. Konrad Haebler, the great authority in the science of incunabula, has this to say about those pioneers of Seville printings:

> Meinard Ungut and Stanislaus (Polonus) of Poland had been induced by the granting of many privileges to establish themselves in Seville. From their press came a large number of the most charming Spanish incunabula; and in all branches of printing, in the designing of types, the cutting of initials and woodcut illustrations, they displayed remarkable skill. Meinard Ungut died in the year 1499 and Stanislaus managed to print alone and, at the beginning of the sixteenth century when Jacob Cromberger became his partner. Under his management and that of his son, the press existed for decades in Seville and was the first to open a branch in the New World, in Mexico.
>
> These printers also were influenced by Italy. But the very peculiar design of their earliest types prove that they were not indebted for their training to the great center of the book trade, Venice, but that they were pupils of Mathias de Moravia of Naples.[8]

Another Polish printer, Jan Polonus (Johannes Adam de Polonia), was working in Naples at the same time in partnership with Nicolaus Jacobi de Luciferis. The book, *Antoninus Florentinus: Confessionale,* printed in 1478, has the Johannes Adam de Polonia signature. That same year he also printed the *Psalterium* with the same type, and that is all that remains. We do not have any knowledge of his later whereabouts, but it is assumed that he moved to England where he was known as John Lettou or John of Lithuania. The change of name was simple. As a subject of the Polish-Lithuanian Commonwealth, he could have used both names Johannes de Polonia or John of Lithuania. Belorussian scholars are currently engaged in research aiming to answer the question whether John Lettou was a Belorussian from Lithuania. This enigma may, perhaps, be solved through their efforts. Lithuanian scholars abroad are stressing that John Lettou was Lithuanian, a native of Wilno. They believe that his name was John Kuntrym and that he got his training in the art of printing in Mainz, as an apprentice of Gutenberg.

L. I. Vladimirov, while accepting the theory of the Lithuanian origin of John Lettou, does not agree that Kuntrym and Lettou are one: "In spite of all efforts, the

[7] Aloys Ruppel, *Stanislaus Polonus. Polski drukarz i wydawca wczesnej doby w Hiszpanii* (Stanislaus Polonus: An Early Polish Typographer and Publisher in Spain), Enlarged Polish edition prepared by Tadeusz Zapiór (Cracow, 1970).

[8] Konrad Haebler, *German Incunabula Text. West-European Incunabula. 60 Original Leaves.* Described by Konrad Haebler and translated from German by André Barbey. (Munich, 1928), p. 51, plate 54.

author of this statemet could not find any indisputable source which could support his version, or reveal Kuntrym in Gutenberg's environment and link his name with John Lettou."[9]

Vladimirov, in accord with Konrad Haebler, rejects also E. G. Duff's supposition expressed in his study of early English printing that Lettou is the same person as Johann Bremer, alias Bulle, who printed two books in Rome in 1478 and 1479 with type identical to that which John Lettou used in London.[10] Vladimirov's statements have been accepted by the majority of scholars.

The latest findings about John Lettou were presented by Colin Clair:

> Three years after Caxton had set up his press at Westminster a foreigner introduced the art of printing into the City of London. We call him Johannes or John Lettou, and the name suggests that he was a native of Lithuania. He was evidently a practised printer, though where he learned the art one will probably never know. . . . The workmanship of Lettou was in advance of that of any printer in England at that time. He was the first in England to make use of quire signatures and to set his page in two columns. . . . Lettou's first work in London was to print in 1480 John Kendale's *Indulgence* asking for aid against the Turks, an edition of which had been recently printed by Caxton. . . . Two other indulgences in the same year were followed by the only book printed by Lettou in 1480—*Questiones Antonii Andreae super XII libros metaphysice Aristotelis,* a small folio of 106 leaves, 49 lines to the page. In the following year appeared a folio volume of 348 leaves—Thomas Wallensis *Expositiones super Psalterium,* and probably during the same year a book on ecclesiastical procedure known only from two leaves found in a binding at Corpus Christi College Cambridge.[11]

Lettou was joined in 1482 by William De Machlinia [Machelen, Belgium?]. After printing five lawbooks in partnership, Lettou dropped out of sight and Machlinia continued the business alone.

The first prints of Lettou indicated his interest in church affairs so characteristic of all Polish printers in Poland and abroad. Many of them published books, pamphlets and broadsides dealing with the growing power of the Turkish Empire. The Polish Lithuanian Commonwealth was in peril. Lettou joined the ranks and printed a few indulgences. Three of these issued by Pope Sixtus IV have been preserved. That could be his link with Moravus and the Polish printers in Naples.

[9] L. I. Vladimirov, "Litovets Dzhon Lettov—londonskii pervopechatnik" (The Lithuanian John Lettov—London's Early Printer), *Kniga: Issledovaniia i materialy* (The Book: Research and Source Materials), (Moscow, 1973), XXVI, 184, footnote 10.

[10] Konrad Haebler, *Die deutschen Buchdrucker des XV Jahrhunderts im Auslande* (München, 1924), pp. 276–277; E. G. Duff, *The Printers, Stationers and Bookbinders of Westminster and London from 1478 to 1535* (Cambridge, 1906), p. 42; L. I. Vladimirov, "Litovets Dzhon Lettov . . . ," p. 184. Vladimirov does not mention the name of the author because he was from émigré circles.

[11] Colin Clair, *A History of Printing in Britain* (London, 1965), pp. 31–32.

We have already mentioned that printing had developed very early in Bohemia. There, under the auspices of Ladislaus II Jagello (1456–1516), King of Bohemia and Hungary, a great patron of printing, a magnificent Bible was printed at Kutná Hora. It is entirely possible that a group of men from the Polish-Lithuanian Commonwealth traveled to Bohemia, where printing was flourishing, to learn the art. Most of them were from Silesia which at the time was part of Bohemia.

It is characteristic that they did not use their family names. Instead they employed the name of their country of origin, with the exception of Ungut, who was of German extraction. The others appear to be bachelors and that gives substantiation to the theory that they were associated with the Church. We know for certain that Moravus was a monk and Caspar Elyan was also an ecclesiastic. The others could have been monks, priests or clerics who, like the monks, used only their first names.[12] While abroad they would use the name of their country as their last name.

There is also the possibility they were associated with the Cracow printing shop and/or with the anonymous printer called "Typographus Leonis I papae Sermones" who published seven incunabula between 1470–1478 of which fifty-one copies are known to exist. The majority of them are of Polish provenance. Based on this and other findings, Eliza Szandorowska surmises that "Typographus Leonis I papae Sermones" was working in Poland possibly in Chełmno or Cracow. Her three articles initiated further studies of this anonymous printer in Poland.[13]

Anna Lewicka-Kamińska, in her recent publication "The Riddle regarding the Printer of Pope Leon I Sermons," after a thorough investigation of 43 of the 51 preserved copies in libraries both in Poland and abroad, comes to the conclusion that Silesia, most likely Wrocław, was the territory of this printer's activities. Lewicka-Kamińska found close connections between the "Typographus Leonis I papae Sermones" and Caspar Elyan, a Wrocław printer, during the years 1474–1483. To quote Lewicka-Kamińska: "The anonymous printing house remained in some affiliation with the Wrocław printing shop of Caspar Elyan, because the paper used was the same, and very often prints of both shops were bound together."[14] Both printers published the same book, Poggius Florentinus: *Facetiae.*

[12] John M. Lenhart, *Introduction to Check-Lists of Names*... (St. Louis, 1959), p. VIII. The institution of clerics has been described as follows: "In the shops of our earliest fellow-printers, priests, monks and clerics were employed. The clerics were married men in minor orders, who wore the tonsure and the cassock like priests and enjoyed legal exemptions and immunities also like priests. They could not be drafted for military service nor could they be arrested by the civil police. They were exempt from certain taxes."

[13] Eliza Szandorowska, "Tajemnicza oficyna drukarska XV w." (A Mysterious Fifteenth-Century Press). *Rocznik Biblioteki Narodowej* (Yearbook of the National Library), 3 (1967) and "Czy w Chełmnie nad Wisłą drukowano inkunabuly?" (Were Incunabula Printed in Chelmno-on-the-Vistula?). *Ibid.,* 4 (1968), 23–49; and "A Dutch Printing-Office in Fifteenth Century Poland," *Quaerendo* (Amsterdam), Vol. II/3 (July 1972) 162–172.

[14] Anna Lewicka-Kamińska, "Zagadka drukarza Kazań papieża Leona I, tzw. Typographus Leonis I Papae *Sermones*" (The Riddle Regarding the Printer of Pope Leon I's *Sermons*) *Roczniki Biblioteczne* (Library Annals), XX, (Wrocław, 1976) 517.

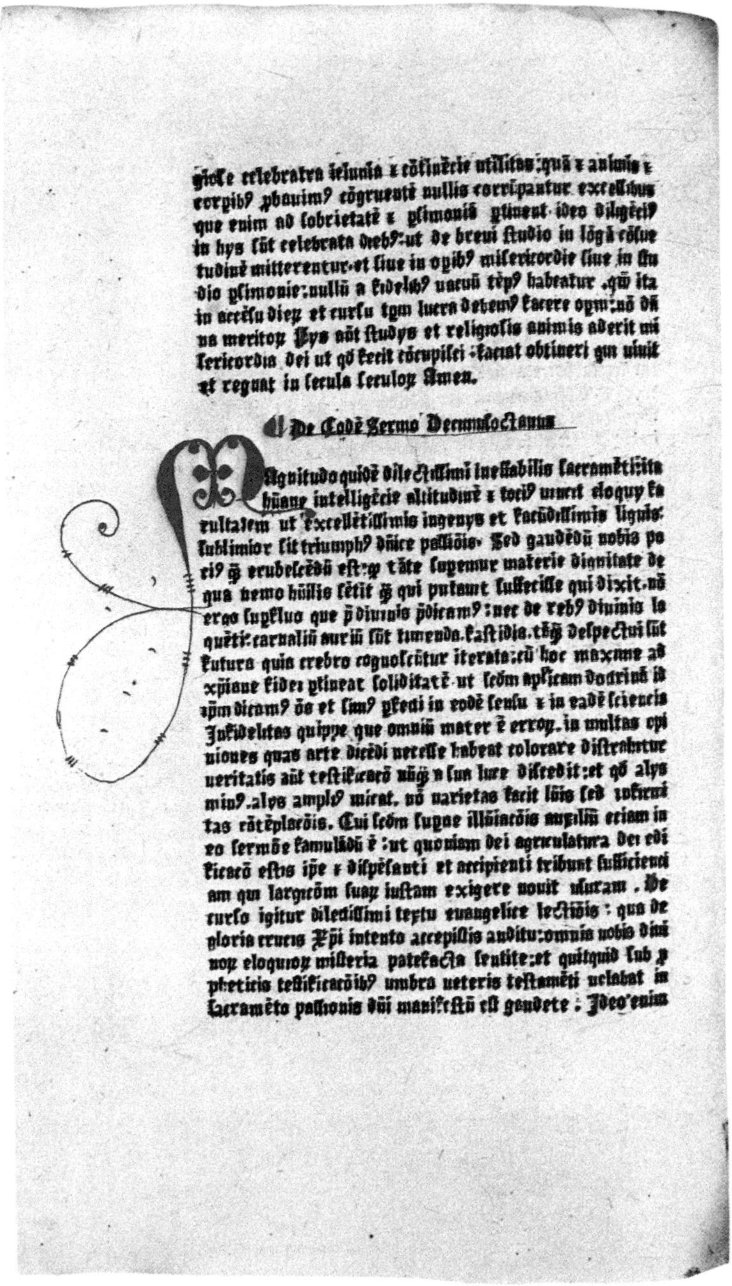

giose celebrata ieiunia & cōtinēcie utilitas: quā & animis & corpib⁹ pbauim⁹ cōgruentē nullis corripantur excessibus que enim ad sobrietatē & ꝯtinencia ꝯtinent ideo diligēci⁹ in hys sūt celebranda dieb⁹: ut de breui studio in lōgā cōsuetudinē mitterentur. et siue in opib⁹ misericordie siue in studio ꝯtinencie: nullū a fidelib⁹ uacuū tēp⁹ habeatur. quō ita in accēsu dieꝝ et cursu tēꝑm lucra debem⁹ facere opm: nō dn̄a meritoꝝ. Hys aūt studys et religiosis animis aderit misericordia dei ut qd̄ fecit cōcupisci: faciat obtineri qui uiuit et regnat in secula seculoꝝ Amen.

De Eodē Sermo Decimusoctauus

Magnitudo quidē dilectissimi ineffabilis sacramēti: ita hūane intelligēcie altitudinē & toci⁹ uincit eloquy facultatem ut excellētissimis ingenys et facūdissimis linguis sublimior sit triumph⁹ dn̄ice passiōis. Sed gaudēdū nobis potius q̄ erubescēdū est: q̄ tāte supemur materie dignitate de qua nemo hūilis sētit q̄ qui putauit sufficisse qui dixit. nō ergo superfluo que p̄ diuinis p̄dicam⁹: nec de reb⁹ diuinis loquēti: carnaliū auriū sūt timenda fastidia. tā q̄ despectui sūt futura quia crebro cognoscūtur iterata: cū hoc maxime ad xp̄iane fidei ꝯtineat soliditatē. ut scd̄m aplicam doctrinā id ip̄m dicam⁹ ōs et sim⁹ ꝑfecti in eodē sensu & in eadē sciencia. Infidelitas quippe que omniū mater ē erroꝝ. in multas opiniones quas arte dicēdi necesse habeat colorare distrahitur ueritatis aūt testificacō nūq̄ a sua luce discedit: et qd̄ alys minus. alys ampli⁹ mirat. nō uarietas facit lōis sed infirmitas cōtēplacōis. Cui scd̄m supne illūiacōis auxiliū eciam in eo sermōe famulādū ē: ut quoniam dei agricultura dei edificacō estis ip̄e & dispēsanti et accipienti tribuit sufficienciam qui largicōm suaꝝ iustam exigere nouit usuram. De curso igitur dilectissimi textu euangelice lectiōis: qua de gloria crucis xp̄i intento accepistis auditu: omnia nobis diuinoꝝ eloquioꝝ misteria patefacta sentite: et quitquid sub ꝑphetiris testificacōib⁹ umbra ueteris testamēti uelabat in sacramēto passionis dn̄i manifestū est gaudete: Ideo enim

Leon I, papa: *Sermones*. [Poland, ca. 1477–1478]. 2°. Leaf 98 v. Printed by Typographus Leonis papae I Sermones.

"Typographus" printed it first; its execution was crude. Elyan a few years later published it with considerable improvements. Both Szandorowska and Lewicka-Kamińska noticed some similarities in the mechanics of workshop production of Caspar Elyan, Casper Straube, alias Printer of Turrecremata and "Typographus Leonis I papae Sermones."

Though both scholars differ in small details, Szandorowska's and Lewicka-Kamińska's theories coincide in the most important aspect: that the anonymous printer worked in Poland and was in some way connected with other printers in this same area. The convergence of dates: 1470–1475 "Typographus Leonis I papae Sermones," 1473–1475 Printer of *Turrecremata*, and 1474–1483 Caspar Elyan, proves that printing was established and active in Cracow and Wrocław in the same period in which Fiol acquired his Cracow citizenship.

Fiol was originally an embroiderer of fine cloth. After moving to Cracow in 1479 he turned his hand to other endeavors. He became a goldsmith, a wine merchant, an inventor of mining machinery. Ten years after arriving in Cracow, Fiol invented a new system for draining water out of the Olkusz silver mine and was rewarded with special privileges by King Casimir IV. The King's generosity ensured Fiol a steady income and an elevated position in the kingdom. "*Consensus regiae maiestatis datus provido Sweipoldo Feyol, civi Cracoviensi, super plumbifodinas montium in Olkusz. . . .*"[15]

Surviving documents which mention Fiol refer to his financial status and court proceedings with clients, partners, and his brother-in-law in questions of inheritance and other matters. We are able to determine from these documents that after his arrival in Cracow Fiol married a Polish girl, the daughter of a butcher, Nicolaus Lubschicz. Eventually he established business connections abroad, as well as in Poland, and as a result traveled extensively, but Cracow was his domicile and there he lived most of his life.

Polish scholars have not shown as much interest in the documents pertaining to Fiol's various activities as they have in his occupation as a printer. Oddly, among the more than sixty documents collected in the span of one hundred years, from Jerzy Samuel Bandtkie to Jan Ptaśnik and K. Kaczmarczyk, only one directly relates to his printing activities. However, two others indirectly shed information which can be assumed to relate to his establishment of a printing press. On December 13, 1483, he rented, together with one Hannus Jakel, a barn and furnished it with various utensils and household furniture such as beds, tables and other items.[16]

Jan Ptaśnik assumed that this activity was in preparation for the establishment

[15] Joannes Ptaśnik, "Cracovia impressorum XV et XVI saeculorum," *Monumenta Poloniae Typographica XV et XVI saeculorum* (Leopoli, 1922) No. 43, p. 15, quoted from *Matriculae Regni Poloniae*, 14, f. 278, Latin document of March 9, 1489.

[16] *Ibid.*, No. 23, p. 10 quoted from *Consularia Cracoviensia*, 430, p. 9.

of a large printing shop, but due to the mention of beds, tables, and other utensils, some scholars have suggested he opened a hostel. However, none of the existing documents indicates that he ever entered the hostel business and in many he is called *impressor librorum,* that is a printer. Also, a barn would not be an appropriate facility for a hostel while it would suffice for a printing shop with accommodations for workers; i.e., beds, tables, etc. Basing his argument on this document, Ptaśnik accepted the year 1483 as the date on which Fiol began his printing activities.

Ptaśnik's theory is logical. To accomplish his pioneering task of printing books in Cyrillic, Fiol would have needed time to organize the physical plant, to prepare type, build presses, collect paper, ink, and to teach and instruct personnel. Printing consists of five different processes: designing, engraving, casting, composing and impressing. We know from various existing documents that while printers were living in Cracow at that time, they would not have been fluent in Cyrillic and would have needed to be taught this new specialty in typography, a time consuming project. Too, there was the matter of manuscripts to be printed which demanded specialists in Eastern Orthodox ecclesiastical literature. Fiol had to assemble editors, proofreaders, illuminators and other employees. To find them in the Polish-Lithuanian Commonwealth was not particularly difficult, but the possibility of their already being acquainted with the printing process was slight. In any case Fiol's helpers had to be trained. The entire process, from renting the facilities to the actual production and distribution of prints, certainly took longer than a single year; a minimum of two or three years and perhaps much longer was required.

This logical conclusion led the Ukrainian scholar Zeno Kuziela, among others, to support the theory of Ptaśnik. Kuziela underscores:

> Ptaśnik, Popov, and Hrushevskiĭ assume that Fiol had to commence the organization of his printing shop in 1485 at the latest. Taking into consideration that Fiol's engraver, Ludolf Borchtrop de Brunswyk, was already registered in the year 1485 at Cracow University as a student of astronomy and available at any time, there is no obstacle to regard Ptaśnik's opinion as most probable.[17]

However, due to the lack of supporting documented details, a majority of scholars seem unable to accept Ptaśnik's theory. They, therefore, have disregarded the

[17] Zeno Kuziela, "Der Deutsche Schweitpold Fiol als Begründer der ukrainischen Buchdruckerkunst (1491)," *Gutenberg-Jahrbuch* (Mainz, 1936), pp. 76–77. The original German text reads: "Es wird daher sowohl von Ptaśnik wie auch von Popow und Hrushchewskyj angenommen, dass Fiol spätestens in Jahre 1485 mit dem Setzen seiner Werke anfangen musste . . . Wenn wir noch bedenken, dass sein Schriftzeichner 'Ludolf Ludolfi Borchtrop de Brynswyk' bereits im Jahre 1485 als 'Studiosus astronomiae' an der Krakauer Universität inskribiert war und ihm zu Verfügung stehen konnte, so steht nichts im Wege, diese Annahme als äusserst wahrscheinlich zu betrachten."

date of 1483 or 1485 as the starting date of Fiol's printing enterprise. A second starting date—1489—is given credence by the *Consularia Cracoviensia* of 1490, where it is recorded that someone stole Fiol's paper. In the latter part of the fifteenth century a very long time was required for the accumulation of a large quantity of paper. A conclusion, based upon this assumption, would indicate Fiol had been in the printing business at least since 1489. We know from numerous documents that Fiol's shop closed and Cyrillic printing ceased in Cracow at the end of 1491. Given the time and place, three years is the absolute minimum time necessary to accomplish the printing of four books.

A most important document dated February 4, 1491, which pertains to Fiol's engraver, Borsdorf, fails to shed any light on the problem. The document states that Rudolphus [Ludolf] Borsdorff von Brawncwigk (Borchtrop de Brunswyk) prepared type for Fiol on order which the printer found very satisfactory. Fiol accepted the type with approval and offered Borsdorf a new order. This document was first reported by Jerzy S. Bandtkie and later by Ptaśnik.[18]

Based solely on this document, it was assumed that in February, 1491, Borsdorf delivered to Fiol a set of Cyrillic type with which he printed all four books by the end of that year, at which time, the press was ordered to cease all printing activity. This would have required Fiol to produce over 2460 pages in folio and in quarto, with at least 200 copies of each, in only eleven months. The technical limitations of the times render this supposition preposterous even if we were to accept Soviet scholar E. L. Nemirovskiĭ's theory that Fiol had two presses. The printing shop in Montenegro with four presses and eight printers in the charge of an Orthodox monk who had no problem with the language was not able to produce half that much print in one year. Again, the indications are that a minimum period of three years was required for Fiol to produce his four books after he organized the operation.

The Borsdorf contract with Fiol is the single most important document pertaining to Cyrillic incunabula. It is so important, in fact, that we cite a portion of it in the following word for word translation:

> Rodolphus Borsdorff von Braunczwigk declares in behalf of himself and his heirs, that he had drawn up a lawful and honest agreement and firm understanding with the honorable Sweybolt Veyl, our fellow townsman, which in essence is as follows: After he had engraved a certain amount of letters [type] for the above mentioned Sweybolt and delivered them in right appearance to the said Sweybolt, and also accomplished some other commissions he, hereby of his own free and good will, gives his solid promise to Sweybolt he shall never prepare, engrave and adapt for anyone even for himself *Rewsische* (Ruthen-

[18] Jerzy Samuel Bandtkie, *Historia drukarń krakowskich* (History of Cracow Printing Presses), (Cracow, 1815), pp. 136–139.

ian) characters, also he would not give anyone instructions in this matter nor teach, . . . under the threat of the loss of his entire property.[19]

In turn, outlined in the latter part of the agreement, Fiol promised to deliver all the necessary means of livelihood to Borsdorf, indicating that the engraver was employed by Fiol's printing shop. Borsdorf was given other meaningful and noteworthy responsibilities by Fiol. Under the threat of anathema he was obliged to guard and protect certain equipment. It may be assumed this pertained to the equipment used for casting the type, and Borsdorf was probably also given the duty of guarding and protecting the typecases and matrices.

Analysis of the document of February 4, 1491, indicates that it is, in fact, an agreement between employer and employee, divided into two parts. The first part deals with the past, and most pertinently, it does not actually state that the type was delivered on that date; the indication is only that it had been delivered. When the type was actually delivered cannot be determined. It could have been the day before, or it could have been a year, or for that matter, three years earlier. However, Fiol did express satisfaction with the completed job and promised Borsdorf future assignments.

The second part is a contract by which Fiol obtains an oath from Borsdorf to the effect that the engraver shall not reveal the secret of the Cyrillic type, nor shall he teach anyone else to make it; Borsdorf shall accept the condition that he will work exclusively for Fiol, that he will not work for anyone else nor will he open his own Cyrillic printing shop.

Such agreements were typical in matters of trade during the fifteenth and sixteenth centuries and were in accord with Guild laws. This document also reveals Fiol was expecting a large volume of work in his shop since in February, 1491, he engaged a type engraver for his exclusive use, a very expensive undertaking. Evidently, Fiol's business was flourishing and his intention obviously was to publish additional Cyrillic books beyond the four for which the type had already been delivered.

Unexpectedly the tables turned for Fiol. The bright, promising future of Cyrillic printing in Cracow was but a mirage. By the end of 1491, or at the very beginning of 1492, Fiol's printing shop—a well-organized and equipped operation producing a sizable number of books—was suddenly closed and disappeared from Cracow without a trace. Other than the four incunabula, the only evidence of its existence is a proofreading sheet which was found as lining in the binding of a book. It is now in the Jagellonian Library in Cracow, listed as Incunabulum No. 2051 a and b.[20]

[19] Ptaśnik, "Cracovia impressorum . . ." No. 48, pp. 19–29, quoted from *Consularia Cracoviensia,* 430, p. 286.

[20] Anna Lewicka-Kamińska, *Inkunabuły Biblioteki Jagiellońskiej* (Jagellonian Library Incunabula) (*Ibid.,* , 1962), pp. 58–59.

¶ Qui rem coherentē clerico aufert aut rem de manu ei9 arripit aut vestes q̄bus indutus ē scindit. ¶ x

¶ Qui arestat vl aufert rez clerico postq̄ ipe peruenerit ad locū suū et adept9 fuerit plene possessionez illius. ¶ xi

¶ Qui ordinat cū vxore sua vt clericū inuitet ad turpitudinem si p9ea percutiūt sūt ambo excoīcati. ¶ xij

¶ Mulier que percutit clericum inuitantem eam ad turpitudinem si solū vbis ipetat: secus si in facto. ¶ xiii

¶ Qui persequitur clericum et ipse quasi coactus proicit se in aquam vl ad periculum vt euadat. ¶ xiiii

¶ Si quis animo iniuriandi capit clericum p capillos dicens nisi esses clericus percuterem te. ¶ xv

¶ Mādās clericū vberare si seq̄t effect9 tam mādās q̄ verberās ē excoīcatus. ex de sen. ex. mulierēs. §. fi. ¶ xvi

¶ Qui ratam habet percussionem clerici eius nomine factam. De sen. exco. Cum quis. ¶ xvii

¶ Qui procurando dixit q̄ libēter vellet vindicari de tali clerico si p9 hec vba q̄s vberet illū licet non nomīe ei9.

·Finis.

¶ Anno Natiuitatis Domini Jesu. M. CCCC. LXXV ¶

Fransiscus de Platea, Cracow, 1495.

2
Fiol's Trial

History does not reveal what became of Fiol's printing press although theories and suppositions abound as to its eventual fate. Fortunately, various documents have survived pertaining to Fiol himself, and one of them reveals that the Catholic authorities in Cracow wished to squelch the printer's activities. In November, 1491, Fiol was charged with heresy and imprisoned. By the twenty-first of that same month he was released under a thousand golden ducat bail with the stipulation that he would not leave Cracow and that he would present himself before the ecclesiastical court at any time he was ordered to do so.

The bail was delivered by two prominent citizens of Cracow, Jan Turzo and his brother-in-law, Jan Tesznar. The bail document reveals more than appears on the surface and answers the nagging question of exactly where Fiol obtained the money for such a large printing operation. Fiol was not a rich man, but Jan Turzo was. Turzo, from Levoča, now in Slovakia, then a part of Hungary, was Fiol's sponsor, protector and financier of the publishing endeavor.

A businessman with many interests, especially in mining and banking, Jan Turzo was a citizen and councilman of the city of Cracow and his influence reached the highest echelons of the royal court. While Fiol was awaiting trial, Turzo approached the Archbishop of Gniezno, Primate of Poland, Zbigniew Oleśnicki,[1] with a request for permission to distribute the Cyrillic books which had already been printed, and further, authorization to print new ones. The Archbishop, after consulting the Chapter of which Turzo's son was a member, refused to grant the request and further issued a decree prohibiting the printing and distribution of "*Ruthenicos*" (Cyrillic) books. No explanations were given.[2]

[1] This Zbigniew Oleśnicki (1430–1493) should not be confused with his uncle Cardinal Zbigniew Oleśnicki, Bishop of Cracow (1389–1465), not only a powerful lord spiritual but foremost statesman, incidentally instrumental in implementing the Union of Florence, 1439 in Poland in an agreement with Isidore, Eastern Orthodox Metropolitan of Kiev. In connection with the religious background it should be noted that in 1443 King Władysław III, who was to die at the battle of Varna a year later, issued a privilege granting the Eastern Orthodox church complete equality with the Roman Catholics.

[2] Bolesław Ulanowski, ed. "Acta capitulorum nec non iudiciorum ecclesiasticorum selecta, Vol. I. Acta capitulorum Gneznensis, Poznaniensis et Vratislaviensis. (1408–1530)." *Monumenta*

This interdict is considered to be the first act of censorship in Poland.[3] Five years earlier, November 17, 1487, Pope Innocent VIII had issued a bull, *Imprimatur,* which decreed that no book could be printed without previous approval of the censors. Obviously Turzo's request was made with the intent of publishing additional books. The denial by the Archbishop was final, but no judgment was rendered pertaining to the four books which had already been printed other than the one prohibiting their distribution. Turzo apparently accepted the Archbishop's decision, from which no appeal was possible, and resigned from further publishing Eastern Orthodox liturgical books in Cracow. This did not mean, of course, that he was obliged to cease printing in other countries.

Fiol's sponsor, Jan Turzo, owner of Bethlefalva in Spisz (Zips), had acquired Cracow citizenship in 1464. Scion of a very old Hungarian family, he was a master of the art of separating silver and gold from copper. His purpose in moving to Cracow was to establish a central depot there for the main product of his mines—copper.[4] The location was ideal since the city was on the Vistula River road to Silesia through Wrocław to the west, and nearer to his base of operations—the mines in northern Hungary. To the north the Vistula connected Cracow with Gdańsk and the Baltic Sea. Other routes led south to Hungary, then to Augsburg and Vienna, east to Lwów and the Black Sea countries.

An educated man who had learned smelting in Venice while studying at Padua, Turzo used his knowledge to accumulate a huge fortune and begin a dynasty of copper magnates. The sixteenth century Polish historian Biernat (Bernard) Wapowski wrote that Turzo "could compete with the most wealthy merchants in the world."[5] Jan Turzo entered into a partnership with Jacob Fugger, a prominent European banker, in 1495.

Turzo could easily have gained political power as did his friend Fugger who purchased the Emperor's crown for Charles V of Habsburg and speculated for the papacy with indulgences (one of the main causes of Luther's "heresy"), but he apparently had little interest in such matters.[6] In Poland the Turzos were only

---

Medii Aevi Historica res gestas Poloniae illustrantia," Vol. XIII (Cracoviae, 1894) Nr. 2329. "Ibidem ex parte honesti . . . Turzo civis Cracoviensis rogatum est, quatinus libros per eum impressos Ruthenicos et alios imprimendos sua Rma Ptas cum suis dnis admitteret ad publicandum, qui dnus Rmus Archiepus examinatis votis dnorum inhibuit et persuasit, ne publicarentur nec imprimerentur decetero."

[3] Jan Fijałek, "Początki cenzury prewencyjnej w kościele rzymsko-katolickim i w Polsce" (The Beginnings of Preventive Censorship in the Roman Catholic Church and in Poland"), *Studia staropolskie* (Studies of Ancient Poland) (Cracow, 1928), pp. 127–144.

[4] Jan Ptaśnik, "Turzonowie w Polsce i ich stosunki z Fuggerami. Kartka z dziejów Krakowa w epoce humanizmu" (The Turzos in Poland and Their Relations with the Fuggers in the Age of Humanism), *Przewodnik Naukowy i Literacki* (Scholarly and Literary Guide), XXXIII. Lwów, 1905.

[5] Bernard Wapowski, *Scriptores rerum polonorum* (Cracovia, 1535), Vol. II. Cited from J. Ptaśnik, "Turzonowie w Polsce . . . ," p. 825. See footnote 3, chapter III, p. 35.

[6] R. Ehrenberg, *Das Zeitalter der Fugger* (Jena, 1896) I: 111.

merchants, albeit wealthy and influential ones, but later in Hungary they became princes and a decisive power in political life for generations.

In Cracow Turzo became Polonized and developed an interest in art and the sciences. He was one of the patrons of the famous artist Wit Stwosz, and co-sponsor of Stwosz's greatest achievement, the main altar of the Church of the Virgin Mary in Cracow. Because of Turzo's intellectual curiosity it was not out of character for him to promote Cyrillic printing, to finance and protect it. The often stated theory that he sponsored Fiol solely for profit has very little validity. Certainly he was no Medici; nevertheless, he did show some inclination toward promoting cultural enterprises. It is impossible to determine exactly what caused Turzo's interest in the printing of books in Cyrillic. Considerable Belorussian and Ruthenian influence existed at the court of Polish King Casimir and the theory that such influence extended to Turzo's circle is not far-fetched. At some point he sponsored the endeavor but whether before or after Fiol was engaged, it is impossible to determine. Fiol had developed a new system for draining the Olkusz silver mine, which eliminated the use of horses for this purpose, and Turzo used the innovation in his many mines. This point is stressed by Alfred Swierk: "It is not astonishing that next to Fugger, the greatest entrepreneur in European mining, John Turzo and his brother-in-law, John Tesznar in Lwów, were interested in these inventions."[7] Turzo also knew Fiol as a very able embroiderer in gold, which was then a part of the goldsmith trade. Many printers came from this profession because as goldsmiths they made seals, engravings and signets. Given the various interests of both men, it seems a natural progression that Fiol organized the first Cyrillic printing press and was subsidized by Turzo.

Fiol appeared in ecclesiastical court on March 22, 1492. His case was discharged after he made his declaration of purification and his confession of faith:

March 22, 1492. The Confession of Swajbold, printer in Cracow, "*in causa fidei.*"

I, Swaybold, citizen and resident of the city of Cracow, before the Passion of our Lord Jesus Christ, the Crucifix and the Holy Gospel, do sign and swear that I detest, curse and abhor all heresies brought forth against the Catholic faith. I confess by word of mouth and from my heart that I believe in all the articles of faith and uphold in them what our Mother, the Holy Roman Catholic Church, asserts, makes known and teaches, especially in those articles which I was accused of denying. By word of mouth and from my heart, I confess that only in the true Holy Church and in the Catholic Christian faith there is the sole salvation of the soul, and not in any religious sect. If I have said something contradictory, it was done not from my heart, but from flightiness, a slip of the tongue, or to get rid of intruders.

Also, by word of mouth and from my heart, I confess that in the Holy Sacrament of the Eucharist is the true God; that Communion in only one substance, bread, is sufficient to

[7] Alfred Swierk, "Der krakauer Buchdruck im 15 Jahrhundert," *Börsenblatt für den Deutschen Buchhandel* (Frankfurter Ausgabe), Nr. 43, May 29, 1970, p. 1197.

the Christian people for salvation; and that if ever in the future I should say anything against it, I will submit myself to the severity of canon law.

I also swear that because of this court case against me, I shall not be offensive nor revengeful toward anyone. If I should meet any enemies or blasphemers against the Christian religion, I shall inform the Church and Prelates in my religious eagerness and zeal. May God and the agony of Jesus Christ help me.[8]

The Church authorities accepted Fiol's confession. Two days later court official Andrzej Jeżowski, in the name of the Ecclesiastical Court, announced before the town council that the accusations brought forth against Szwajpolt concerning his disdain of the Catholic faith appeared not to be true—*testimonia in secreto adducta*—all depositions secretly obtained were found insufficient and therefore the Inquisitorial Commission, not finding any guilt, acknowledged him as a just and faithful Catholic.[9]

This, even though Poland was then a relatively liberal state, appears almost too good to be true, but the suspicion that hidden factors and powers caused Fiol's case to move so rapidly, smoothly and easily is not warranted. The Church had acted very cautiously, arranging the situation so that Fiol could not resume printing and repeat his "mistakes." The last paragraph of Fiol's pledge, which in reality has nothing to do with faith or religious wrongdoings, is especially revealing; there Fiol promised under oath never to take revenge against his denunciators. If he should try, he would automatically be summoned before the court again. Evidently the court intended to protect the informer or some important person who used the informer to instigate the inquiry. Furthermore, in spite of being cleared of the charges before the civil authorities, four Cracow citizens were obliged to give their guarantee in court and put up 1,000 ducats bail for Fiol.

What heresy was in question? Various scholars have associated Fiol with all the known heresies of the day.[10] While each has offered his own concept, most agree that the accusation of heresy was really a cover-up, a smoke screen, used by the Church to close the printing shop and stop the production of Orthodox liturgical books.

[8] Ptaśnik, "Cracovia impressorum . . . ," No. 56, pp. 22–23.

[9] *Ibid.*, No. 57, p. 24.

[10] J. S. Bandtkie twice imputes that Fiol favored Huss: *De primis Cracoviae in arte typographica incunabilis* . . . (Cracoviae, 1812), p. 6; *Historia drukarń krakowskich* (History of the Cracow Printing Presses), (Cracow, 1815), p. 133. The following scholars suspect that Fiol was persecuted for printing Eastern Orthodox books: J. F. Golowatzkij, "Sweipolt Fiol und seine Kirillische Buchdruckerei in Krakau . . . ," (Wien, 1876), p. 437. K. Morawski, *Historia Uniwersytetu Jagiellońskiego* (History of Jagellonian University) (Cracow, 1900), pp. 183–184. G. Bauch, *Deutsche Scholaren in Krakau* . . . (Breslau, 1901), p. 30. M. I. Shchelkunov, *Istoria, tekhnika, isskustvo knigo pechataniia* (The History, Technique, Art of Printing) (Moscow-Leningrad, 1920), p. 292. Waldensian theories in Fiol's statements were underscored by Rev. J. Fijalek in "Początki cenzury prewencyjnej w Kościele rzymskokatolickim i w Polsce" (The Beginnings of Preventive Censorship in the Roman Catholic Church and in Poland) *Studia Staropolskie* (Studies of Old Poland) (Cracow, 1928), p. 142.

However, Nemirovskiĭ entertains the notion that Fiol was on trial for Hussite heresy and not for printing Cyrillic books. But no evidence that Fiol was a follower of Jan Hus exists. On the contrary, we know that Fiol remained a devout Catholic to the end of his life. Nemirovskiĭ, while lacking documents to support his theory, offers the argument that if Fiol had been on trial for printing Cyrillic books, Turzo would not have had the courage to ask the Primate of Poland for permission to continue printing and selling them, and he would rather try to conceal his participation in this business.[11]

Nemirovskiĭ fails to consider that in the conditions prevailing in Poland at the time Turzo had no reason to fear the ecclesiastic tribunals. He was a devout Catholic who had taken lawful means to ask the authorities for a license, and his son was a member of that very Roman Catholic Chapter. Turzo had very powerful friends at the King's court, too.

Nemirovskiĭ suggests that Fiol was not more severely punished because he was not on trial for printing Cyrillic books but for being a Hussite. First, that theory is questionable as no such accusation against Fiol is recorded. Since the Hussite heresy was considered one of the greatest transgressions against the Catholic faith in Poland (as well as in Germany), Fiol would never have received such light treatment had that been the case. Catholic authorities did not recognize the Eastern rite, but they were obliged to tolerate it since approximately half of the Polish-Lithuanian Commonwealth's population was Eastern Orthodox.

The simple fact is Fiol could not lawfully be punished for printing Cyrillic books as there was no law forbidding it; furthermore, powerful and influential people were behind the enterprise. However, once the ecclesiastic tribunal did forbid the printing, neither Fiol nor Turzo could disregard the other. As for Nemirovskiĭ's supposition that after the death of Archbishop Oleśnicki the printing of Cyrillic books was resumed by Fiol in 1493–96 (more or less in secret), there is not an iota of substantiation in the existing documents.

Our primary interest is in Fiol as a printer and publisher of Cyrillic books. Therefore, we will not discuss his possible heresies or inclinations in that direction, if he had any at all, but will leave the matter to theologians and religious historians. From Fiol's confession of faith it is easy to deduce that two canons of the Catholic faith were at stake, both strongly stressed in the wording of the confession: "That only in the Catholic Christian Holy Church and in the Catholic Christian faith there is the sole salvation of the soul, and not in any sect; and that only in the Holy Sacrament of the Eucharist is the true God present, and Communion in but one substance, bread, is sufficient to the Christian people for salvation."

The accusation was not really against Fiol but against the Orthodox Church, which was, in the opinion of the Roman Catholics, only a sect, and was also

[11] E. L. Nemirovskiĭ, *Nachalo slavianskogo knigopechataniia*, p. 203.

against the Orthodox usage of communion *sub utraque specie,* partaking of both bread and wine. Communion *sub utraque specie* (in both kinds) is not a dogma in the Orthodox Rite, only a church custom. The Roman Catholic Church, however, has made a great issue of it. Naturally, Orthodox liturgical books would also fall into this category, and therefore printing them would be deemed anti-Catholic by overly zealous conservatives.

Discontinuation of printing Cyrillic books automatically removed Fiol from further harassment. Bound by his oath and apparently convinced that the ecclesiastic authorities were serious, he was never again involved in printing, certainly not in Poland, and we have no indication of subsequent contacts with other printers. Here is further indication of his caution: when the famous humanist Conrad Celtes, whom Fiol knew when Celtes studied at Cracow University, asked the printer about Cyrillic books, the printer sent word through a mutual friend, Jan Sommerfeld, Sr., that he had none and failed to answer Celtes's two letters. The correspondence of Sommerfeld to Celtes on May 15, 1498 refers to this matter as follows:

> Approached Sveypold in your behalf twice; I strove to get from him by entreaty those things which you ordered: He asserts that he has none of the Ruthenian books in his possession and adds that he had written to you.[12]

While advisable for Fiol not to have Cyrillic books around, it was discourteous of him not to answer Celtes's letters. However, after his experience with the Inquisition, his actions are excusable. Interestingly, only the documents pertaining to Fiol's trial give his occupation as "printer," and stress it clearly. Later documents never mention that trade in connection with him again.

Fiol's unquestionable accomplishment in printing the first Cyrillic books has given some Eastern scholars impetus to take advantage of his place in history and misuse his name for religious, political, national and chauvinistic purposes.

Although the colophon[13] of both *Osmoglasnik* and *Chasoslovec* state: "This book was executed by a Cracovian citizen, Szwajpolt Feol, of German extraction, Frank," some scholars have changed the name in an effort to support a variety of theories as to his origin. Several variant spellings of the name exist in the respective documents, but unstable spelling was usual at the time. However, the name Feol

[12] Stanisław Tomkowicz, "Drukarnia kirylicka Świętopełka Fiola w Krakowie . . . ," (Świętopełk Fiol's Cyrillic Printing Press in Cracow . . .), *Przewodnik Bibliograficzny* (Bibliographical Guide), Vol. VII, No. 8. (Cracow, 1884) 166. "Sveypoldum tuo nomine bis adi; quae jussisti, ab eo precario exegi: Nullum apud se ruthenae literae librum habere affirmat, et scripsisse se tibi ajebat."

[13] "Colophon" is from the Greek word "summit, finishing touch"; the concluding paragraph of a special note at the close of the book indicating the title, author, and information about the printer, place and date of printing. Used in the fifteenth and sixteenth centuries, the colophon was later replaced by the title page.

prevails and was used twice in the colophons printed in Cyrillic and in other documents written in Latin; Feyol appears eight times; Feyel six; Feyl four; Fail three; Veyhell once; Feyhell once; Fleyel once and Fyol once. Nevertheless, scholars following the foremost Polish bibliographer Karol Estreicher use the form Fiol instead of Feol, although the correct form according to the documents and the colophons is Feol.

Karol Estreicher tried to Polonize the printer, deeply convinced that he was a native Cracovian whose family had lived there for generations and that his real name was not Szwajpolt Feol or Vieol, but Świętopełk Fiol.[14] Indeed, many Russian scholars take for granted, without an iota of proof, that Fiol was a Slav.

Most of the theories regarding Fiol's nationality were advanced approximately a hundred years ago. After the publication of about sixty documents at the beginning of this century by the Polish scholars Kaczmarczyk and Ptaśnik, Polish, Belorussian and Russian scholars are now in agreement as to Fiol's German nationality. Nevertheless, Ukrainian scholars are still trying to adopt him. In 1967, P. Iur'ev endeavored to make the printer a Ukrainian by birth and changed his name to Swiatopolk Fiola, and in 1969, O. Hubko also concurred.[15] They came to the conclusion that he was a Lemko because Fiol lived for some time in the Carpathian Mountains populated mostly by Ruthenians. The Lemkos were a Ruthenian mountain tribe settled between the Poprad River and the town of Ivonich in the northern lowlands of the Beskid Mountains. Fiol, had he actually been a Lemko, could be called a Ukrainian, but the supposition by Iur'ev and Hubko has no foundation in the documents.

Hubko has also come to the conclusion that Fiol was an Eastern Orthodox Christian: "Fiol was a Lemko, descendant of the White-Croatian Ruthenian Eastern denomination."[16] However, Fiol's Confession of Faith in 1492 is purely Catholic. It might be said it was obtained under pressure of the Inquisition, but Fiol remained a Catholic the rest of his life. He did not waver even after Luther's appearance when many in Poland (especially those of German origin) left the Catholic Church. In his last will and testament the printer made a bequest to a Franciscan monastery stressing his devotion to Catholicism.

However, Fiol's most fantastic genealogy has been created by M. Bošnjak. Following the assumption of Zeno Kuziela, the Ukrainian scholar, Bošnjak proceeded to make the printer a Ukrainian-German celebrity. He selected a Gregorius Fiol from Lublin as Szwajpolt's father and claimed Szwajpolt was born in that city in

[14] Karol Estreicher, "Günter Zainer i Świętopełk Fiol," *Biblioteka Warszawska* (The Warsaw Library), (Warsaw, 1867), III: 202–203.

[15] P. Iur'ev, *Pervopechatnik v Krakove. Iz istorii pervopechatnykh sviazeĭ slaviano-russkikh* (First Printer in Cracow. History of Early Slavic-Russian Printing Relations), (Warsaw, 1967), p. 17.

[16] O. Hubko, "Do pochatkiv ukraïns'koho drukarstva" (Beginning of Ukrainian Printing), *Arkhivy Ukraïny*, (Kiev, 1969), No. 3, 12–28.

1460. According to Bošnjak, Fiol's own statements pertaining to his German origin were made merely to indicate his family's early origin. Bošnjak's fabricated theory is without documentation. He writes:

> The founder of Ukrainian printing and first printer of Cyrillic books, Svietpolt Fiol (Schwaitpold, Szwajpolt, Sweyboldus, Svaipolt, Veyel, Veyl, Feyel, Fail, Feiol, Fyol) was by descent a German from the South German town of Neustadt on the Esch, in a region that in his time was called Franconia. In the colophon of *Octoechos* [Osmoglasnik] and of *Chasoslovec,* he is called Svaipolt Feol, "iz nemec nemeckogo rodu frank" and in the last will dated May 7, 1525, are stated his name and origin as Schwaitpold Fail, "de Nova Civitate apud Esch oriundus." His father, Gregorius Fiol, is cited in 1452 in a census of the citizens of Lublin in Poland, a town that at that time was inhabited by a large population of Ukrainians, as stated by J. F. Golowatzkij, so that Sveitpolt could have been born at Lublin in 1460. In the colophon he indicated his family origins. As far as we know of his family there lived at Neustadt his elder brother Euchacius. Fiol entertained close family connections with Euchacius, and the daughters of this brother are mentioned in the last will as his prospective heiresses.[17]

Contrary to Bošnjak's and others' supposition, numerous documents state that in 1479, a German, Szwajpolt Fiol, who had immigrated to Poland some time before, became a citizen of Cracow. *Libri iuris civilis civitatis Cracoviensis* from 1479 notes: "Schweipolt Fyol von der Newnstad an der Eysch perlenhaftir i-(us) h-(abet), et l-(itteras), dedit III fert -(ones)."[18] Fiol, May 7, 1525, placed his signature in Latin on his last will: "Schwaipoldt Fail *de Nova civitate apud Esch oriundus.*"[19]

Some Eastern scholars would also have us believe Fiol became a martyr and a victim of the Inquisition in Poland. They stress his spirit was broken and his life's impetus destroyed, that because of persecution he was obliged to leave Cracow and Poland. They say he settled in Hungary, in Levoča, the birthplace of Turzo, and in 1511 acquired citizenship. There he supposedly died in poverty, having been forced to give up his occupation as a printer. Characteristically, no one took care of him in his duress except the benevolent Germans who gave him their support and affection.

J. F. Golowatzkij was the first to tell the sad tale:

> Viol, deprived of all his possessions, felt obliged to leave the Polish capital, and thus retired beyond the Carpathian Mountains, in Leutschau [Levoča][20] in the Zips, where in

[17] Mladen Bošnjak, *A Study of Slavic Incunabula,* translated by F. Dobrovolsky (Leyden, 1968), p. 77.

[18] K. Kaczmarczyk, *Księgi przyjęć do prawa miejskiego w Krakowie 1392–1506* (Libri iuris civilis civitatis Cracoviensis, (Cracow, 1913), Nr. 7812, p. 283. (Municipal record book of Cracow's citizens).

[19] Ptaśnik, "Cracovia impressorum . . . ," No. 267, pp. 111–112, quoted from *Scabinalia Cracoviensia,* 10, p. 634.

[20] Levoča is a town in Slovakia. Until 1918 it belonged to Hungary.

the Hungarian mountain town he found amongst Germans more sympathy and favor than he had amongst the Poles. Nonetheless, he had neither the courage nor the means to continue his printing endeavors.[21]

Kuziela saw Fiol's trial as a religious and national affair. Not only did he decide the Cracow Cyrillic incunabula were actually Ukrainian, he also concluded that Fiol was a representative of the Germans who started cultural cooperation between Germany and the Ukraine. In addition he implied that the Catholic action against was in reality a step toward aborting a Ukrainian independence movement, despite historical fact that Ruthenia looked voluntarily to Poland from the beginning of the fourteenth century for protection from Tartar and Muscovite suppression. Nevertheless, he wrote:

> Fiol's whole program of independent Ukrainian action in Cyrillic printing became a wreck, not because of a lack of money as some thought, but due to local political and religious opposition, as well as a hostile attitude from the Polish Catholic Church. Fiol had to fight with these difficulties constantly . . . Fiol's prints were destined for the Ukrainians who held them in great esteem for a long time in spite of new and better prints which followed. We hope that more attention will be paid to them and their printer, as they deserve it for being the first Ukrainian and Cyrillic prints, and the first visible example of German-Ukrainian cultural cooperation.[22]

The truth of this matter can be found in documents cited by Ptaśnik and Kaczmarczyk which ascertain that following his trial Fiol lived a normal life as a businessman of many interests and many disputes in court.[23] He lived tranquilly with his wife in both Cracow and Levoča and was never again persecuted by anyone, especially not the Catholic Church.

Quite the opposite occurred. Recently discovered documents indicate that Fiol, who according to Golowatzkij was a victim of the Roman Catholic Church and

[21] Jakov Fiodorowitsch Golowatzkij, "Sweipolt Fiol und seine Kirillische Buchdruckerei in Krakau vom Jahre 1491," *Berichte der Kaiserlichen Akademie der Wissenschaften zu Wien. Phil.-hist. Klasse,* 83 (1876), p. 437.

[22] Kuziela, "Der Deutsche Schweitpold Fiol . . . ," pp. 78, 79 and 81. "Die Durchführung des ganzen fiolschen Planes scheiterte nicht so sehr an Geldmangel, wie manchmal angenommen wurde, sondern an localen kirchenpolitischen Widerständen und an der feindseligen Haltung der polnisch-lateinischen Kirche. Fiol musste ständig mit diesen Schwierigkeiten kämpfen. . . . Die fiolschen Drucke waren daher für die Ukrainer bestimmt und wurden von ihnen trotz neuerer besserer Drucke noch lange in grossen Ehren gehalten. Es ist nur zu wünschen, dass man ihnen wie auch ihrem Drucker die Beachtung widmet, die sie in jener Hinsicht als erste ukrainische und zyrillische Drucke überhaupt und als erste sichtbare Beispiele deutsch-ukrainischer kultureller Mitarbeit verdienen."

[23] J. Ptaśnik. "Monumenta Poloniae Typographica." Various selected documents cited on pp. 24–116, from the years 1492 to 1525 pertaining to Fiol and his family. K. Kaczmarczyk, *Księgi przyjęć do prawa miejskiego w Krakowie, 1392 do 1506* (Libri iuris civilis civitatis Cracoviensis). Town Hall records regarding Fiol between 1490 and 1506.

who according to Kuziela became a martyr to the cause of Ukrainian independence, actually went to work for the Church. Ten years after his trial Fiol was put in charge of mining affairs for an estate belonging to the Church, the Cistercian monastery in Kamieniec Ząbkowicki (Kamenz) in Silesia. When the mines in Reichenstein became the property of Prince Charles of Ziębice, Fiol was named Court Mining Supervisor. He was so harsh and ruthless in his new position that the miners revolted and the entire affair was actually reported in the Silesian chronicles.

Codex Diplomaticus Silesiae, edited by Konrad Wutke and published in 1900, is comprised of documents from 1136 to 1528 pertaining to mining and foundries in Silesia. The document for August 26, 1502, relating to the transferral of Złoty Stok (Reichenstein) from the estate of the monastery in Kamieniec Ząbkowicki to the estate of Prince Charles of Ziębice, confirmed the charter given to "Schweipolt Veyhell [Fiol], Cracow citizen," and gave him the right to drill shafts on the cloister property. The Prince was even more benevolent. When confirming these privileges, he also extended them to Fiol's successors and heirs.[24]

This evidence not only indicates that the Cracow trial failed to have any subsequent detrimental influence on Fiol's life, but astonishingly he was granted important mining privileges by the Catholic authorities. The long history of persecution by the Poles and tales of Fiol's nervous and moral breakdown are purely Kuziela's invention. The only cause Fiol ever embraced was his personal one; he always worked for strong, wealthy and influential Polish lords or in cooperation with rich businessmen such as Jan Turzo. The printing of the Orthodox Cyrillic books was purely a business venture for Fiol and indicates no interest in the Eastern Orthodox Church or Ukrainian independence movement.

A document dated July 2, 1503, and entitled "Revolt of the Miners' Association in Złoty Stok (Reichenstein)" is most interesting and revealing but far too lengthy to be cited here. If there was ever any real doubt regarding Fiol's true character, this document explains the full extent of Kuziela's error. It reveals Fiol was not the oppressed, but rather the oppressor—harsh and unscrupulous to the miners in his employ.

The Polish scholar Karol Maleczyński considers this event to be the first revolutionary movement of Polish miners in the history of Silesia. He writes:

[24] Konrad Wutke, "Schlesiens Bergbau und Huttenwesen. Urkunden 1136–1528," *Codex diplomaticus Silesiae,* Bd. XX. Herausgegeben vom Vereine für Geschichte und Altertum Schlesiens. Breslau 1900. "Wo auch der gnante her Jacobus abbte und die gancze szammelunge des offtegemelten closters Camentez dem ersamen weysen Schweipold Veyhell, burger von Crocaw, uf des gedochten closters herrschaft und eygenthum zu Meyffersdorff etliche beue zu thun vergunst, im auch ein privilegium dorober gegeben haben, wollen wir, das gnanter Schweipolt seyne erben und nachkommen sich desselbigen halden und das in Keinem wege obirgreyffen sollen. . . ."

The oldest known insurrection of the Silesian Miners' Association took place in 1503 in Złoty Stok. The direct cause of the unrest was, as is stated by the official documents and declarations of the accused, the sentencing to death of one poor fellow laborer and the violation of the old laborer's privileges by the Prince's Marshal [Fiol]. No details of the nature of this violation and no data as to whether it was the first such case could be obtained from the protocol of the commission which investigated the case in the name of Charles, Prince of Ziębice. From further investigation, we can assume that the indignant miners, whose claims were not given any attention, went in a group before the house of the Prince's prefect of the district of Złoty Stok. What happened later, whether there were any further disturbances cr demonstrations, etc., the protocol does not reveal, except that both sides acknowledged guilt and the miners' association promised that such demonstrations would not occur again.[25]

The fact that both sides admitted guilt may have burdened Fiol, but to what extent cannot be determined. Documents of the *Codex Diplomaticus Silesiae* up to 1528 do not mention Fiol's name again. Probably, after the riot and court process, he left Silesia. While the riots, as far as we can determine, were a direct result of Fiol's high-handed tactics, he again was not adversely affected.

Thus, in light of documented facts the Ukrainian scholars were a bit hasty with Fiol's canonization. His qualifications for martyrdom are lacking. Often in trouble, Fiol always managed to find a way out. Since Kuziela and others have stated that Fiol lost everything and died a pauper as a result of his troubles in Poland with the Catholic Church, a brief consideration of his financial status seems to be in order here.

After Fiol's move to Levoča, under the protection of the powerful Turzos, he operated a profitable wine business. Documents reveal his wife inherited 200 złotys while he was living there in 1511.

Fiol's last will does not indicate he was a rich man but he was far from poor. It is documented that he received a yearly stipend of 62 złotys and 12 groschen from Turzo until the end of his life, in addition to the annual grant from King Casimir for his invention of the mine draining system. This income alone was sufficient for an opulent life without considering the income from his own business ventures. Fiol did not die in poverty, nor did he ever break his relations with Poland. Cracow was his place of residence to which he returned periodically from his numerous business trips and ventures abroad. He prepared his last will and testament in Cracow, died and was buried there.

Nemirovskiĭ (we must return to the Russian scholar again) gives Fiol more than his due. The printer, in his opinion, was not only a very industrious man but also an intellectual and humanist whose interest in Cyrillic printing stemmed from a

[25] Karol Maleczyński, "Z dziejów gornictwa śląskiego w epoce feudalnej," *Szkice z dziejów Śląska.* Edited by Ewa Maleczyńska (From the History of Silesian Mining during the Feudal Period. Essays in the History of Silesia), (Warsaw, 1953), pp. 216–217.

The "Jagellonian" Earth Globe (ca. 1510), showing the newly-discovered land, America.

desire for cultural achievement. Despite a lack of documented supporting evidence, Nemirovskiĭ tries to convince us that Fiol was a close friend of Callimachus and Celtes and was also a member of the literary organization *Sodalitas Litteraria Vistulana.* According to him this society inspired and promoted Cyrillic printing. He states: "Slavic printing was the realization of humanistic ideals toward universal enlightenment. Without doubt if Celtes would have stayed in Cracow for a longer period of time, he, with other members of the humanistic circle, would also have strived to organize the printing of books in Latin and Polish."[26]

The Russian critic A. C. Mylnikov supports this conjecture rather punctiliously though unenthusiastically: "Certainly all these hypotheses are more or less plausible conjectures and logical assumptions. They must be put to the test of time in order to obtain confirmation."[27]

We might reiterate here that printing in Latin had begun in Cracow in 1473–74 and in Wrocław in 1474 some twenty years before Celtes arrived in Cracow. Also no documents support Nemirovskiĭ's statement regarding the participation of *Sodalitas Litteraria Vistulana* in Fiol's Cyrillic enterprise.

We also have enough information about Callimachus to know that it would have been impossible to overlook his interest in Cyrillic printing if he had had one. The same conclusion for that matter applies to Celtes. If Celtes had been a close friend of Fiol and had encouraged him to begin the Cyrillic printing press, certainly he would have received copies of the Cyrillic books immediately after they were printed; he would not have had to make inquiries about them some years later.

Fiol never attended a university, and we have absolutely no proof that he was ever a member of any humanistic circle which numbered the highly educated among its members. No doubt he was intelligent, inventive and industrious; nonetheless, we have no evidence of broad intellectual interests. If he were friendly with Callimachus and Celtes and a member of the literary society, why then, after their departure from Cracow, did he show no interest in any intellectual activity in the following thirty-five years of his life?

Those years were the most significant in Cracow's history, during which great masterpieces of sculpture by the famous master of woodcarving, Wit Stwosz, were executed. His glorious altarpiece for the Church of Saint Mary was endowed by Cracow citizens with Fiol's friend Turzo lending his sponsorship, but the printer was not listed among the donors. Then too, in the first quarter of the sixteenth century Polish printing in the vernacular flourished with such prominent printers as Haller, Ungler, Wietor and Scharffenberg showing the way.[28] However, Fiol

[26] E. L. Nemirovskiĭ, *Nachalo slavianskogo knigopechataniia,* p. 30.

[27] A. C. Myl'nikov, "Na puti k resheniiu 'krakovskoĭ zagadki'" (On the Way to Solving "The Cracow Riddle"), *Kniga; Issledovaniia i materialy,* (Moscow, 1973), XXVI, 224.

[28] Jan Haller, 1467–1525; Florian Ungler, 1536; Hieronim Wietor, 1480–1546; and Mark Scharffenberg, 1545.

did not participate in this great humanistic endeavor, nor is there any indication of activity on his part in other intellectual fields.

Fiol's biography is yet to be written. With new documents and information, perhaps, it will be possible to obtain more details and a better insight into this active, industrious man who was neither a martyr nor a hero. Most of his troubles were not due to persecutions but to his own uneven and impetuous character. Fiol was like so many men of that fascinating era of the Renaissance who, despite all their faults and shortcomings, brought a stimulating ferment which resulted in tremendous progress in all fields of human endeavor. Despite not being a member of the *Sodalitas Litteraria Vistulana,* he earned his place in history by developing Cyrillic printing.

3
The Dissemination of Cyrillic Printing

Fiol's trial by the Holy Inquisition naturally brought an abrupt end to the production of Cyrillic books in Cracow. Under the threat of punishment, and the evidence is indisputable, the printer washed his hands of the entire matter and turned his attention to more profitable and less troublesome ventures. For as long as he remained in Cracow following his trial and during his sporadic stays there afterwards, Fiol had absolutely nothing to do with either the production or the distribution of Cyrillic books, at least not in Poland, as his attitude toward Celtes indicates.

With Fiol's enterprise curtailed by the Inquisition, what happened to the printing shop and the books that had already been produced? J. F. Golowatzkij, among others, has stated that Fiol in reality was persecuted for printing Orthodox ecclesiastical books which were condemned by the Roman Catholic Church as being heretical, consequently he was not only disarmed, but his stock of books and printing press were also liquidated: "Under such auspices there is no doubt that Fiol's printing shop was confiscated by the Cracow Holy Inquisition and that the publications in store were destroyed."[1]

We recall that in January 1492 while Fiol was awaiting trial, Jan Turzo asked the Primate Archbishop for permission to print Cyrillic books. At this point Turzo had already paid the first bond for Fiol, whereupon he had been released from prison. Turzo later established a lifetime annuity for the printer and gave him full protection. The evidence that Turzo financed and promoted the printing enterprise from the beginning is overwhelming. In the period from the date of Fiol's imprisonment in November, 1491, until January 13, 1492, when the Bishop refused his petition, Turzo had ample time, money and the safeguard of influence in high places to secure his investment. Given his position, Turzo was not easily intimidated and under Polish conditions had little to fear even from the Inquisition.

Neither the books nor the press was destroyed. The convincing proof of this

[1] J. F. Golovatzkij, "Sweipolt Fiol . . . ," p. 437.

statement lies in the fact that the Inquisition did not issue an order pertaining to the fate of Fiol's shop and product. That fearsome body, invariably, not only publicized its verdicts, particularly those pertaining to heresy, but also made a public spectacle of burning books to teach heretics a lesson and to discourage others from committing such sins. At this point to determine exactly what happened to the printing shop is impossible. More than likely Turzo had it dismantled. But, we do know what happened to the Cyrillic books already printed; they were distributed far and wide in the Polish-Lithuanian Commonwealth and particularly in its eastern regions. Zakhariĭ Kopystenskiĭ's *Palinodia* of November 21, 1621, enumerates many locations throughout Belorussia and Ukraine where he actually saw those books.

In the early days of printing Roman Catholics burned books, but Protestants too very quickly took up the habit, as did the Russian Orthodox Church which not only burned the books, but occasionally threw the people that produced them on the same pyre. The pioneer of East Slavic printing, Dr. Francišak Skaryna, no doubt considered himself fortunate when about 1530 only his Bible was publicly burned on the order of the Grand Duke of Muscovy, Vasily III Ivanovich. Dr. Skaryna had taken the book to Moscow to acquaint Muscovite Russia with printing and to promote the enlightenment of the people. Vasily, the father of Ivan IV, had the torch put to men for much lesser crimes than disturbing the populace with newfangled things like books.

But in Renaissance Poland of the late fifteenth and sixteenth centuries human rights were more respected because Poland's kings were rather sophisticated humanists. Besides, about half the population over which they ruled were followers of the Eastern Orthodox rite.

But what Fiol and Turzo had given birth to in Cracow, the printing of books for the first time in a language known and understood in most of Eastern Europe, could not and would not die by the whim of the Inquisition. Only a year later Makarios opened his great Cyrillic printing shop with four presses in the Balkan Peninsula in Cetinje, Montenegro, and the following year, 1494, printed *Osmoglasnik,* Part One, containing the first four odes.

Even if we entertain Golowatzkiĭ's supposition that Fiol's books and printing shop were destroyed, and we are convinced that they were not, the particulars of Cyrillic printing and the methods of its production were known by men who had worked for Fiol in Cracow. We know that none of his employees was harmed or detained; thus, it is not unreasonable to suppose that they, at least some of them, left Cracow. And with them the concept of printing books in Cyrillic was spread throughout all of the Orthodox territories.

While Fiol never again occupied himself directly with printing, possibly he aided at least one of the later efforts. Turzo was always busy with more profitable ventures. But one other person whose role in the Cracow printing venture was of such importance that subsequently he was capable of aiding the establishment of Cyrillic presses elsewhere, and that was Fiol's type engraver, Rudolf Borsdorf.

Unfortunately historical documents reveal very little pertaining to Borsdorf. Born in Braunschweig, Germany, the son of a doctor who had studied medicine in Padua, Rudolph, as stated previously, enrolled at the University of Cracow in 1485 and studied astronomy. The University of Cracow *Album Studiosorum* for the year 1485 notes:

> In the fifth Rectorate of the honorable lord Mathie de Costhen, doctor of decrees, [law] parish priest of St. Anne, to which he was canonically elected, at the change of season of the year of the Lord 1485 on the day of Mercury the XXVIth of the month of April the hereunder mentioned enrolled (—Positio 333a—) Ludolfus Ludolfi de Brunszwyczk s. [solvit—paid] 3 latos gr. [groschen].[2]

However, some interesting data not used to date associate Borsdorf's family closely with Poland. For instance, from the *Polski słownik biograficzny* (Polish Biographical Dictionary) we learn that Leonard Vitreatoris de Dobczyce (ca. 1470–1508), a professor at Cracow University, was "a friend of the son of the well-known mathematician and astronomer, Ludolf Borchtorp of Brunszwik [Braunschweig] from whom he received the *Codex of Euclid* (Elements), and perhaps also one of the astrolabes preserved in the [Jagellonian] University collections."[3]

Leonard de Dobczyce was the dean of the philosophy faculty in 1506 when the later pioneer of East Slavic printing, Francis of Polotsk [Francišak Skaryna], was awarded a Bachelor's degree. *Liber promotionum* under the date of December 14, 1506, states:

> In the year of the Lord 1506 in the deanship of the same Master Leonard of Dopschyce.... The same year, under the deanship of the same Master Leonard, etc., at the fasting days of Saint Lucy, were awarded the degree of bachelor... Francis of Poloczko, Litphanus.[4]

Therefore, Borsdorf's friend, Leonard de Dobczyce, was one of Skaryna's

[2] Adam Chmiel, ed., *Album Studiosorum Universitatis Cracoviensis* (Cracoviae, 1887) Tomus I Ab anno 1400 ad annum 1489, p. 269, col. 1, line 3. In Rectoratu quinto venerabilis domini Mathie de Costhen decretorum doctoris, ad sanctam Annam plebani, ad quem fuit canonice electus, commutatione estiuali de anno domini 1485 die Mercury XXVI mensis Aprilis infrascripti sunt intitulati. (—Position 333a—) Ludolfus Ludolfi de Brunszwyczk s. [—solvit] 3 latos gr. [—groshen].

[3] Helena Friedberg, "Leonard Vitreatoris z Dobczyc," *Polski słownik biograficzny* (Polish Biographical Dictionary), (Wrocław, 1972), XVIII/1, pp. 71–72.

[4] Josephus Muczkowski, *Statuta nec non liber promotionum philosophorum ordinis in Universitate studiorum Jagellonica ab anno 1402 ad annum 1849* (Cracoviae, 1849) p. 144. "Anno Domini 1506 in decanatu Magistri Leonardi de Dopschyce . . . Anno eodem, sub decanatu eiusdem Mgri Leonardi, etc., ad quatuor tempora Sancte Lucie, ad gradum bacalariatus promoti, . . . Franciscus de Poloczko, Litphanus . . ."

teachers. Considering the very close relationship then existing between professors and students there are unlimited possibilities for speculation and supposition. Most probably Professor Leonard introduced his student, Skaryna, to his friend Borsdorf given their mutual interest in typography. Also a meeting between Skaryna and Fiol is not out of the question, although the latter was, for the most part, occupied in Silesia at the time. Even if Borsdorf had already left Cracow (we have no way of determining whether he had), it is reasonable to suppose that at some time or another the professor told Skaryna, a Belorussian, of the accomplishments of his friend who had produced the first Cyrillic type that was used in Fiol's shop. In the unlikely event that Skaryna did not associate with either Borsdorf or Fiol, Cracow's tradition of having once had a Cyrillic printing shop, together with the Cyrillic inscription in the Wawel Cathedral "Ruthenian" chapel, could well have inspired him to create and build his own printing shop for the purpose of producing Cyrillic books.

The years during which Skaryna was in Cracow were decisive in the history of Polish printing. In September 1505, King Alexander, son of Casimir IV, bestowed upon Jan Haller the first privileges given any printer. Alexander also established the first protective law which pertained to Haller's publications and named him the "founder" of Polish printing. Ptaśnik cited the complete document in Latin in his source materials.[5]

The king stipulated that the privileges granted Haller by the court were to be in effect as long as he was in the business of printing, an indication of the king's efforts to retain Haller in printing endeavors in which he showed such great achievements. Haller was at that time a noted wine merchant, the proprietor of a fine wine shop, and also dealt in copper and other metals.

Jan Haller (1467–1525) from Ruthenberg, Franconia, had enrolled at Cracow University in 1482 and nine years later became a citizen of the City of Cracow. At approximately the time Fiol was ordered to close his shop, Haller entered the book business starting with a small printing shop in 1492. On a larger scale, he ordered books from the best printing presses in Europe, such as Georg Stuchs of Nuremberg, W. Stoeckel of Leipzig, Aldus Manutius of Venice, and others. Mostly they were liturgical books for the church (to go along with the church wine he would deliver for years) and textbooks for the University. The wine shop was still his main business.

A sociable host, from discussions with his educated patrons, Haller learned books were needed at least as much as his wine. He soon concluded it would be simpler and more economical to enlarge his own printing shop. Probably such men as Skaryna's professor led to Haller's interest in books in the first place. The clients of his wineshop were members of the University and literary circles. Pro-

[5]Joannes Ptaśnik, "Cracovia impressorum," pp. 46–47, citing *Matriculae Regni Poloniae* 21, f. 293.

fessors and students in those days tended to celebrate all occasions with wine. Newly awarded bachelors, masters and doctors were obliged to treat the faculty to banquets where wine flowed freely. Thanks to such customs, Haller's wineshop flourished and the Hungarian wine especially beloved in Poland was extolled in song and poetry: *nullum vinum nisi Hungaricum, Hungariae natum, Cracoviae educatum* (it is not wine if not Hungarian, in Hungary grown, in Cracow educated).

Until that time most of the presses in Cracow had a transient character, such as "The Printer of *Turrecremata*" and a few jobwork printers between 1473 and 1476. Fiol's shop intended to be permanent, of course, but had been established for the purpose of printing in Cyrillic. Haller's shop, established on a secure foundation with adequate financial support, was for the purpose of printing any books for which there was a demand.

Haller entered into a partnership with Georg Stuchs, the famous Nuremberg printer, in 1499. Four years later, in 1503, he became partners with Caspar Hochfeder. Each trained the personnel for his specialty: Stuchs's was the printing of liturgical books, while that of Hochfeder was the publication of textbooks. Haller's shop soon became famous country-wide, praised by artistic, intellectual and university circles. Altogether his press produced 230 books. One of the most famous books produced was *Commune Regni Poloniae Privilegium* (Compendium of Polish Statutes) edited by the Crown Chancellor Jan Łaski and published in 1505–1506. The celebrated "Bogurodzica" (Mother of Christ), a twelfth-century religious hymn which later became the national anthem and battle song of the knights, was published in the Polish language for the first time at the beginning of this richly illustrated book.[6]

Young Skaryna could not have been unaware of all this and indifferent to Haller's achievements. Not only is it inconceivable that Skaryna did not discuss the accomplishments of Fiol and Borsdorf with his professor, it is just as unlikely to suppose he was not interested in the career of Jan Haller. Skaryna himself was from a prominent Polotsk merchant family. The Grand Duchy of Lithuania was his country and King Alexander was the Grand Duke of Lithuania and Belorussia his motherland. Skaryna, a lover of books, was in Cracow studying at the University at a time when the achievements of Fiol were still being discussed and those of Haller were amply in evidence. Little wonder that Skaryna was inspired to become the founder of Belorussian printing.

The lack of knowledge pertaining to Borsdorf's whereabouts and activities following the closing of Fiol's printing shop is unfortunate for several reasons. First of all, the designer and molder of the first Cyrillic type deserved a more prominent position in history than he has been dealt. More important, it is both possible and

[6] Józef Seruga, *Jan Haller, wydawca i drukarz krakowski (1467–1525)*. (Jan Haller, Cracow Publisher and Printer, 1467–1525), (Cracow, 1933).

ribus: qui bases estis Reipublice ⁊ item patritijs alijsq; proceribus
Regni vniuersis committam reliquum tutele excusationisq; mee:
ac vti in prefatiuncula voluminis: sic etiam in isto eius complemẽ-
to meipsum familiamq; meã iterum atq; iterum vobis recommen-
do felicibusq; vobis optimi poetarum verbis salue dicã. Valete fe-
lices quibus ẽ fortuna peracta iam sua: quibus parta quies. Nos
alia ex alijs in fata vocamur. ¶ Finis

¶ Explicit dextro sidere: Cõmune incliti Regni Polonie priuile
gium: omni studio ac diligentia Cracouie in edibus Johãnis
Haller ad cõmissionẽ Reuerendi pr̃is dñi Johãnis de Las-
ko: eiusdẽ Regni Cãcellarij impssuz. Quẽquidẽ librũ ⁊
alios quoscunq; p prefatum Haller. ea lege impressos quisq; nosse debet: vt nemo illos alibi genti-
um exaratos: Regno introducat Eosq; vena-
les habeat graui sub pena: ac eorundẽ libro
rum ammissione vigore priuilegij: ipsi
Haller per sacram domini Regis Po
lonie Maiestatẽ desuper gratiose
ex Consilio sue Serenitatis Cõ-
siliariorum concessi: prout
hocidem priuilegium la
tius continet

Anno domini M.CCCCC.vi.
xxvij. Januarij

Jan Łaski: *Commune Regni Poloniae Privilegium*. Cracow, 1506. 2°. Colophon with printer's mark. Printer: Jan Haller.

probable that Borsdorf, with or without Turzo's consent and protection, helped to establish Cyrillic printing shops elsewhere in Italy, Montenegro and, most likely, in Tărgovište, Wallachia, then a neighboring country of Hungary.[7] Fiol had ordered new type from Borsdorf which he was subsequently forbidden to use. Borsdorf might very well have sold the type and delivered Fiol's *Osmoglasnik* to be reprinted or, just as likely, he could have produced a new set of type for the monk Makarios. In any event, it is extremely difficult to accept the notion that the first designer of Cyrillic type discontinued his work after showing such remarkable talent while working for Fiol. Even given the scanty historical evidence it seems likely it was none other than Borsdorf who spread the knowledge of Cyrillic printing from Cracow and Poland into other Slavic countries. However, no conclusions can be definitely drawn until history reveals where he was after 1491 and a comparative study of all the prints can be undertaken.

Indeed a large gap in the research of Cyrillic incunabula persists—to date no serious study of the Rumanian Cyrillic incunabula has been made. Between the years 1508 and 1512 three books were produced in Tărgovište, Ugrowallachia (now Rumania). These three books together amounted to not less than the number of pages produced in Cracow or Cetinje. The people of these lands accepted Christianity of the Eastern Rite quite early and, surrounded by Slavic nations as they were, used the Old Slavonic in the liturgy. The native language began to be used in books by laymen during the Renaissance, but for three centuries ecclesiastical books were printed in Old Church Slavonic, with Rumania, Belorussia and Ruthenia using the same books for church services.

When the first prints from the Tárgovište printing came to light, scholars were amazed to find they carried the name of the printer Makarios. Makarios was also the name of the monk who established the press at Cetinje, in Montenegro, under the auspices of George the Black in 1493. Even more amazing, the Tárgovište Makarios was also a monk. Many authorities are of the opinion the Tárgovište Makarios and the Cetinje Makarios were one and the same—leading to the assumption the Tărgovište press was a continuation of the Cetinje shop after the latter was closed by Turkish occupation in 1499.

This theory was expressed most explicitly by Bošnjak:

> After the fall of Durad Crnojević, Makarije [Makarios] changed his abode for Tárgovišti in Rumania, where he founded the first Wallachian printing-shop and was its manager from 1507 to 1512. He was the first to publish Rumanian works printed in the Cyrillic types from the Montenegrin establishment. At the close of his life Makarije withdrew to the Holy Mountain, joined the Brotherhood of Hilandar Monastery, and became its prior. This monastery harbors certain data from the period 1526–1528 on Makarije, when he reputedly composed some geographic document, to die soon thereafter.[8]

[7] Turzo delivered copper to both countries and especially to Venice, his depot in Italy.
[8] Bošnjak, *A Study of Slavic Incunabula,* p. 95.

Subsequently Bošnjak discovered that the type used in Tărgovište had much more in common with the Cracow prints than those produced in Montenegro, and changed his mind. Later he began to suspect that the Tărgovište type had originated in Rumania. At any rate this printing venture certainly influenced all Rumanian and, in many respects, Russian printing in the sixteenth century. Sidorov stresses this clearly: "The closest to the Moscow prints are the Rumanian editions of Makarios: 1508–1512 in Tărgovište."[9] But, of course, it should be stated in reverse; the Moscow editions resemble the Tărgovište prints more than any other.

We cannot, of course, discount the possibility of two men named Makarios—a very common name among Orthodox people—both monks, who became printers. If so, they were both acquainted with Fiol's prints, and Makarios of Tărgovište was also familiar with his technique. At that time, printers with pioneering spirit were constantly changing their place of residence and work. Clearly a marked similarity between Fiol's Cracow prints and those produced in Tărgovište exists, and all the Cyrillic prints first produced in the Balkans constantly repeated the same content: *Chasoslovec, Osmoglasnik* and the *Triods*. The printing technique is quite similar in all the prints; the type characteristics are similar and all are printed in the same Old Church Slavonic language with only a sprinkling of local elements as opposed to the purely vernacular. Insufficient evidence prevents identifying Makarios of Tărgovište with Makarios of Cetinje, although a strong similarity between the product of the Tărgovište and Cracow shops can be seen by studying the prints.

Present day Rumanian authorities, on the author's request, forwarded a set of photographs of Makarios's Tărgovište prints which will be analyzed more thoroughly later. The similarity of the prints is striking.

The similarity of type with difference in size only allows us to make some supposition as to the fate of Fiol's shop after his trial and leads us to believe that Turzo transferred the Cyrillic press from Cracow to one of his estates in Hungary. At about the same time L. Bassarab, an ambitious Voivod of Ugrowallachia (then enjoying favored status with Hungary), was attempting to start a printing press in Rumania. The Voivod's coat of arms is imprinted on all the Tărgovište prints. It is not outside the realm of probability that Turzo sent Fiol to Tărgovište, and perhaps Borsdorf as well, to set up the shop. This would, at least, account for part of the time between Fiol's 1505 troubles in Silesia and 1512 when he accepted Levoča citizenship. He could very well have spent some months or even years in Tărgovište, joined there by Makarios who had become the official printer. There is also the possibility that after Montenegro fell to the Turks, the Cetinje Makarios

[9] A. A. Sidorov, "Khudozhestvenno-tekhnicheskie osobennosti slavianskogo pervopechataniia" (Artistic and Technical Peculiarities of Early Slavic Printing). In: *U istokov russkogo knigopechataniia* (At the Beginning of Russian Book Printing), (Moscow, 1959), p. 59.

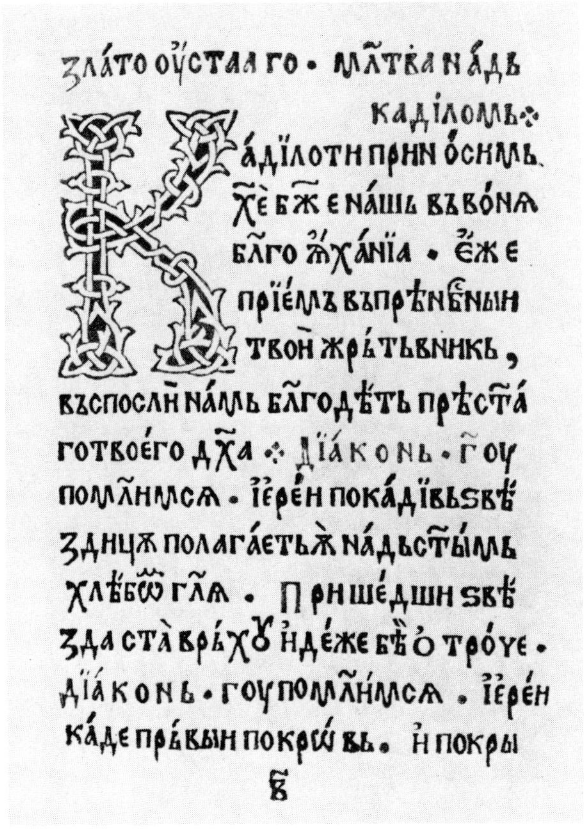
златоѹстаго · мл҃тва надь
каділомь ⁘
Кадїло ти приносимь
х҃е б҃же нашь вь вонѫ
бл҃го ѹханїа · еже
прїемь вь прѣнб҃ныи
твои жрьтьвникь,
вьспосли намь бл҃годѣть прѣс҃та
го твоего дх҃а ⁘ дїаконь · г҃оу
помл҃нимсѧ · ієреи покадївь ѕвѣ
здицѫ полагаеть ѭ надь ст҃ыимь
хлѣбомь гл҃ѧ · Пришедши ѕвѣ
зда ста врьхѹ идеже бѣ о троуе ·
дїаконь · гоу помл҃нимсѧ · ієреи
каде прьвыи покровь · и покры
в

Makarije (Makarios). Târgovişte 1508. *Sluzhebnik* (Missal).

contacted Turzo and was placed in Tărgovište where he continued his Cyrillic printing venture.

In summary, it seems that the fate of Fiol's enterprise becomes clear; the Inquisition closed the printing press in Cracow but was unable to stop the spread of Cyrillic printing. Within three years a new center was created in Cetinje but was closed when that city fell to the Turks. Cyrillic printing then temporarily retreated to Venice only to return and spread over the West Balkans. Ten years later it reached the areas east of the Balkans and a new center was established at Tărgovište. A few years later Skaryna established his great printing enterprise in Prague and Wilno, and Cyrillic printing became entrenched forever.

Obviously the exact fate of Fiol's physical plant cannot be determined with certainty at this late date. However, no evidence supports Golowatzkij's contention that it was demolished; and we know for certain (contrary to Golowatzkij) that the books were not destroyed. Seventy-nine copies of Fiol's prints are still in existence today, almost five centuries later, and according to Zakhariĭ Kopystenskiĭ copies of all four prints could be found soon after they were printed by Fiol in "many locations," where the Eastern Orthodox rite was practiced. They were there in the seventeenth century.[10]

Zakhariĭ Kopystenskiĭ (1550–1627) was the Archimandrite of the Kievo-Pechersk Cave Monastery. A learned man, he traveled extensively, and in 1621 published his religious polemical book *Palinodia,* written the year before, in which he stated:

> The books of both *Triods,* named from the Greek language, were printed in Cracow. They can be found in many churches and monasteries of the Lwów area, also in places such as the monastery of Dorohobuzh, the Horodok estate of the Pechersk monastery, the Botki in the Bielsk area of Podlasie, the estate of his Highness Prince Bohdan Sapieha, Voivode [Palatine] of Minsk . . . in Volhynia, and in many other locations. There is another liturgical book, named *Oktoikh* or *Okhtai* from the Greek, printed in Cracow, which can be found in Smiedyn near Turzysk in Volhynia,[11] in Lithuanian Kamienica, in the church of Saint Simeon, and in other places. There is also a third book, which is called *Horologion* from the Greek and *Chasoslov* in Slavic, and was printed in Cracow in the year 1491 by one Szwajpolt Fiol, during the reign of King Casimir Jagellonian, father of the Polish kings Olbracht, Alexander, and Sigismund the First . . . This book is located in the monastery of Pecherskaia Lavra in Kiev, in the Orthodox church in Lublin, and Lwów in the Holy Cross Church of Łyczaków, a main street of a suburb called Halicz; also in the Great Brest Litovsk in Lithuania where a remarkable council took place in 1596, and in other places.[12]

[10] Karol Heintsch, "Ze studiów nad Szwajpoltem Fiolem, I. Materiały do życiorysu i działalności Fiola" *Rocznik Zakładu Narodowego imienia Ossolińskich* (Wrocław, 1957), Tom. V, 233–342. (From Studies Regarding Szwajpolt Fiol. I. Materials for Fiol's Biography and Activities, Annals of the Ossoliński National Institute. Vol. V. Wrocław, 1957).

[11] Turzysk is ten kilometers south of Kowel.

[12] Zakhariĭ Kopystenskiĭ, *Palinodiia,* November 21, 1621. Printed for the first time in *Pamiatniki polemicheskoĭ literatury v Zapadnoĭ Rusi,* Book I, (St. Petersburg, 1878). Cited from "Ze studiów nad Szwajpoltem Fiolem" by Heintsch, pp. 234–235.

All the places in which Kopystenskiĭ said the Cracow Cyrillic incunabula could be found about 1620 were located in Belorussian and Ukrainian territories, which were then politically associated with the Polish-Lithuanian Commonwealth. The "remarkable council" to which Kopystenskiĭ referred was held in 1596 in Brest-Litovsk, capital of the Polish province of Polesie, which established the Uniat Catholic Church. Kopystenskiĭ quotes only four books and does not ever mention the *Psalter*. The statement by Bošnjak "That the *Psalter* was actually printed is borne out also by Z. Kopystenskiĭ, who has annotated this in his manuscript from the year 1621," has no substantiation in *Palinodia.* [13]

Three years after writing his *Palinodia,* Kopystenskiĭ published his *Besedy Ioanna Zlatoustego na poslanie apostola Pavla* (The Sermons of St. John Chrysostom, concerning the Epistles of St. Paul). In the dedication to Prince Stefan Swiętopelk-Czetwertyński he repeated what he said about the Cyrillic incunabula, adding: "During the reign of King Casimir, there were printed in the Slavonic language books according to the denomination and rites which we observe today, conforming with the creed of the Eastern Church." [14]

Archimandrite Kopystenskiĭ's statements in *Palinodia* and in the dedication to Prince Swiętopelk-Czetwertyński reveal indisputably that he was familiar with all four Orthodox Cyrillic books printed in Cracow by 1491, and was aware the printer was Szwajpolt Fiol. He based his conclusion regarding the time and place of publication and the identity of the printer on information contained in the colophons of *Osmoglasnik* and *Chasoslovec*: "This book was accomplished in the famous city of Cracow during the reign of the great Polish King Casimir, And was executed by a Cracow citizen, Szwajpolt Fieol, of German extraction, a Frank. The book was completed in the year of Christ's nativity of fourteen hundred ninety and one."

Not only was Kopystenskiĭ familiar with the particulars of the production of Fiol's books and their distribution after printing, he also knew their value to the people of Eastern Europe. There, Cyrillic books were in very great demand indeed because of the devastation of those territories by the Tartars beginning in 1241, and throughout the whole of the thirteenth and fourteenth centuries resulting in the destruction of many religious manuscripts. Since the Orthodox clergy was often singled out for the special wrath of the Tatars, few new manuscripts were copied and those that were contained numerous errors and colloquial additions. As Kopystenskiĭ relates, Fiol's books, therefore, were held in great esteem for their relative accuracy and uniformity. Kopystenskiĭ himself was a staunch critic of Roman Catholicism but believed that the kings and queens of the Polish-Lithuan-

[13] Bošnjak, *A Study of Slavic Incunabula,* p. 84.

[14] Zakhariĭ Kopystenskiĭ, *Besedy Ioanna Zlatoustogo na poslanie apostola Pavla* (Sermons of St. John Chrysostom Concerning the Epistles of the Apostle Paul) (Kiev, 1623). Cited from Heintsch "Ze studiów nad Szwajpoltem Fiolem," p. 235.

ian Commonwealth (which encompassed Orthodox Belorussia and Ukraine) were sincere protectors of the Orthodox Church and promoters of the Cyrillic press.

Characteristically, of all the scholars studying incunabula, the only one who disregards Kopystenskiĭ's valuable information regarding the dissemination and location of Fiol's books is E. L. Nemirovskiĭ. The attached sketch illustrates the dissemination of Fiol's prints in the fifteenth and sixteenth centuries taking into account the information provided in *Palinodia.*

In spite of all arguments and documents with material proof of seventy-nine books and fragments of Fiol's books preserved up to date, some Russian scholars are still insisting that Archbishop Oleśnicki issued the order for their destruction. The only proof Isaevich could present is that in the binding of two contemporary printed books pages from Fiol's prints were used as wastepaper: "The recurring findings of separate leaves from Fiol's first Slavic printings in the lining of the binding of printed contemporary books confirm the supposition that immediately after the ban of printing 'heretical' Orthodox books by the Primate of Poland, Zbigniew Oleśnicki (January, 1492), a considerable part of Fiol's editions was destroyed and what was left was used as wastepaper."[15] It is hardly correct to refer to "recurring findings of separate leaves from Fiol's first Slavic prints" when Isaevich's diligent search has only found two.

[15] Ia. D. Isaevich, "Kirillovskie staropechatnye knigi v kollektsiiakh Pol'skoĭ Narodnoĭ Respubliki—Varshava, Krakov, Vrotslav" (Early Cyrillic Printed Books in the Collections of the Polish People's Republic), *Kniga,* VIII (Moscow, 1963).

4
Habent Sua Fata Libelli—Fiol's Prints: From Cracow to the U.S.S.R.

Considering that the eastern part of the Polish-Lithuanian Commonwealth and approximately half of its total population subscribed to the Eastern Orthodox rite, it would seem logical to conclude that Fiol and Turzo printed the Cracow Cyrillic books for that ready market. This would especially appear to be true since Kopystenskiĭ found the books still in use throughout Belorussia and Ukraine over a hundred years after their publication. Personal opinion often triumphs over logic. For instance, the Russian scholar O. Sobolevskiĭ has stated that Fiol's Cyrillic books were published primarily for the use of the South Slavic countries and Moldavia. Despite the strong influence that Cracow's Cyrillic printing eventually exerted on South Slavic incunabula, Sobolevskiĭ's statement has no foundation in fact; no evidence of the wide use of Fiol's books in Moldavia and the South Slavic countries in the sixteenth century can be shown.

In his latest work E. L. Nemirovskiĭ unexpectedly introduced a new theory as to the intended destination of Fiol's books. Apparently basing his argument on the old saw that possession is nine-tenths of the law (sixty-eight of the seventy-nine copies and fragments of Fiol's prints known to exist are now in U.S.S.R. libraries), Nemirovskiĭ blithely concludes Fiol's books were printed for distribution in Russia in the first place. By "Russia" Nemirovskiĭ means the Grand Duchy of Muscovy.

The Belorussian scholar Symon Braha has replied to that assumption: "Because the British Museum today has in its possession an enormous collection of ancient Egyptian scrolls, does not prove that they were written especially for England. This was only the result of the fact that Egypt for a long period of time has been a colony of the British Empire."[1] To avoid any misunderstanding Nemirovskiĭ's Table V is reproduced:

[1] Symon Braha, review of E. L. Nemirovskiĭ, *Nachalo slavianskogo knigopechataniia,* 1971. *Zapisy,* New York, Byelorussian Institute of Arts and Sciences, No. 12, 1974, p. 121.

Preserved Copies of Fiol's Prints,
Including Data of Their Provenance

	Oktoikh	Chasoslovec	Triod Postnaja	Triod Cvetnaja	TOTAL
U.S.S.R. Holdings:	6	24	24	14	63
Including:					
Those with notes of Great Russian provenance	5	15	14	10	44
In this number with notes of the XVI–XVII centuries	2	12	11	5	30
Those with notes of Ukrainian, Belorussian and Polish provenance	-	5	4	3	12
In this number with notes of the XVI–XVII centuries	-	1	2	2	5
Holdings outside of the U.S.S.R.	-	1	3	6	10
TOTAL	6	25	27	20	78

Nemirovskiĭ states:

> The majority of the copies now located in the U.S.S.R. have provenance notes of Great Russian origin (44 of 68). A considerable amount of those books (30) have notes of the sixteenth and seventeenth centuries. There are twelve with Ukrainian, Belorussian and Polish provenance notes. Only five of them are with comparatively early dates. In our opinion, all this proves that Fiol and Turzo printed their books if not on a direct order from Moscow, then at least calculating mainly on Moscow. A lesser part of the edition was destined for dissemination throughout the eastern territories of the Polish-Lithuanian empire, populated by Ukrainians and Belorussians.[2]

[2]Nemirovskiĭ, *Nachalo slavianskogo knigopechataniia,* p. 208. Henceforth cited as *Nachalo.* Russian text follows:

Большинство экземпляров, находящихся ныне в СССР, имеет записи великорусского происхождения (44 из 68), при этом значительное количество книг (30) имеет записи XVI–XVII вв. Записей украинского, белорусского и польского происхождения меньше (12). Лишь пять из них еравнительно ранние.

To support this weak speculation Nemirovskiĭ introduces in the closing chapter of his book another hypothesis that Turzo had trade connections with Moscow and was selling copper there. His agent, we are told, brought samples of manuscripts to Cracow from Moscow to be printed by Fiol. This might seem feasible except that at the time Fiol was printing his books, Turzo was not yet in the copper business on a large scale. Not until 1495 did he and Jacob Fugger become partners, dividing their sphere of interest for the disposal of the copper ore from the mines in Possony, Hungary. Under the agreement Fugger sold copper in Western Europe, while the territories of Central and eventually Eastern Europe were Turzo's. Not until the following year were Turzo's agents (they could buy and sell other merchandise, including ecclesiastical books) assigned territories and penetrated the vast lands of the Polish Crown, Prussia, the Grand Duchy of Lithuania, Ruthenia, Hungary and the Balkans. That was five years after Fiol's printing shop was closed. For that matter, no document exists proving that Turzo's agents reached Moscow until the end of the century. So much for the idea that Turzo's salesmen secured prototypes for Fiol's books, from Muscovy or anywhere else. Fiol's books were printed in the fifteenth century. Whatever happened in the sixteenth century is immaterial to the issue at hand.

Thus, it is unconvincing of Nemirovskiĭ to apply data from the second half of the sixteenth century to prove that Muscovite Russia participated in some manner in developing the Cracow Cyrillic prints. Those provenance notes supposedly supporting his hypothesis are useless for that purpose.

However, the importance of provenance notes in early written and printed books cannot be stressed enough. The handwritten provenance notes form a pedigree of each book and from them it can often be determined where, when and to whom it was sold or given. The notes also often contain valuable information pertaining to the environment and other cultural features, and, in addition may reveal the names of persons, libraries, schools, book collectors, and sometimes mention historical events.

Incunabula in Polish and Western libraries containing notes from the fifteenth and sixteenth centuries are intimately related to their original sources and have their own history. They are, in fact, historical and cultural monuments. Russia, on the other hand, is one of the few European countries which has no incunabula of her own since the first Russian printing press was built in Moscow only in 1562, i.e. long after the incunabular period ended. Nemirovskiĭ's frantic efforts to provide Russia with a cultural interest she did not have historically come to naught.

Все это, на наш взгляд, доказывает, что Фиоль, и Турзо печатали свои издания если не по прямому заказу из Москвы, то, по крайней мере. рассчитывая преимущественно на Москву. Меньшая часть тиража предназначалась ими для распространения на восточных землях Польско-Литовского государства, заселенных украинцами и белорусами.

Getting access to the provenance notes in Fiol's books presents a drastic problem for the student of Cyrillic incunabula. Sixty-eight of the known seventy-eight existing copies are now in Soviet institutions, but none was there in the fifteenth century and precious few a hundred years later—a time which counts decisively in tracing the travels of the Cyrillic incunabula. They were during that crucial time frame for the most part in Belorussia and Ukraine. During the wars with Russia in the seventeenth century and partition of Poland in the eighteenth century (when the vast territories of Ukraine, Belorussia and Lithuania were annexed and half of Poland was occupied by the Russian empire), many book collections were taken to Russia. Included in the collections removed by the Russians was the famous Załuski Library in Warsaw, which became the nucleus of the Imperial Libraries in St. Petersburg and Moscow. Thereafter very few of the Cyrillic incunabula printed in Cracow were to be found in Poland or in Belorussia or Ukrainian territories.

During these wars, and with the subsequent eighteenth century annexation by Russia, Belorussia was stripped of all her cultural wealth, as Braha has emphasized. One of the most precious booties during these wars was always books, merchandise of exceptional value. On many of these books presently in Russian libraries, especially in the capital, there may be found annotations which denote that the books were taken during the war on the territories of Belorussia, Ukraine, Poland and other countries.

> Whole libraries such as monastic, church, private and governmental were taken and transferred to Russia. It is in this manner that in the archives of the Russian Empire "settled" about 600 volumes of the famous *Lithuanian Metrica*. . . . In addition to this in the XIX century on those territories old and rare books were bought up by rich Russian booksellers and booklovers.
>
> Not "orders" from Moscow but the above mentioned methods were the grounds for "settling" books from Belorussia, Ukraine, Poland and other conquered nations, in the libraries of the capitals of the empire and private collections. Of the famous editions of Dr. Skaryna, the Belorussian printer of Prague and Wilno, the greatest and most complete set can be found in the libraries of Moscow and Leningrad. On one of these books (Skaryna's Bible) "acquired" during the invasion by Tsar Alekseĭ Mikhailovich appears . . . an eloquent and forceful note: "This book belongs to Alekseĭ of Petrovich Gladkov—this book was taken in Grodno, Lithuania, in the year 7163 (1655) on August 27th."[3]

Before turning our attention to the provenance notes contained in the preserved copies of Fiol's prints, using the material collected in Russia by Nemirovskiĭ, we will let the Russian scholar give the reason one encounters such difficulty in their

[3]Braha, review of *Beginning of Slavic Printing*, pp. 120–121.

study: "Regrettably, early notes of the fifteenth century do not exist. Early notes often were destroyed by subsequent owners. They were cut off, erased, black patched."[4]

Nemirovskiĭ's statement speaks for itself. Considering the manner in which they were acquired by their new owners during the seventeenth and eighteenth centuries there is little reason to speculate as to why traces of their origins were obliterated. All of Fiol's prints contained blank leaves when they came off the press, and most of the provenance notes would have been made on these pages. The sixty-eight copies now in various Russian collections—and Nemirovskiĭ concurs—have only a few of the original blank leaves intact.

Concealing all traces of affiliation with Poland was systematic, deliberate and thorough. In all seven copies of *Osmoglasnik* currently in U.S.S.R. libraries, each copy, even those well preserved, has leaves 1 and 169 missing. To quote Nemirovskiĭ: "In any preserved copy leaf 1 and 169 do not exist. This is especially regrettable because verso of leaf 1 had a woodcut and leaf 169 had the colophon with Fiol's printer's device. Those leaves are known only from a facsimile."[5]

The absence of leaf 1 might occur because the woodcut illustration was desirable to have as a holy picture among other icons. Systematic elimination, however, of leaf 169 is undeniable proof of a cover-up of the origin of the book. The colophon praises the Polish king, and the Cracow coat of arms indicates the first printing center. The only copy in the West, the Wrocław City Library copy, had both leaves, from which the facsimiles were made. Unfortunately this copy disappeared during World War II.

The same tendency of concealment applies to *Chasoslovec*. Some copies preserved in excellent condition do not have the leaf with the colophon. Characteristic is the copy in the Kiev State Public Library with many missing leaves (37 at the beginning, with many more in the balance of the book); however, it does have the leaf with the colophon. Nemirovskiĭ notices this finding with astonishment: "Strange to say, that the leaf with the colophon was preserved."[6] No wonder the Ukrainians were proud of Fiol's achievement. They were part of the whole project and they made an effort to preserve the colophon as a document of their glory. In the twenty-three copies of *Chasoslovec* preserved to the present some retain leaves with the colophon and this is of great value for the study of Fiol's incunabula.

OSMOGLASNIK PROVENANCE NOTES

We can only conclude from Nemirovskiĭ's chapter entitled "Provenance and

[4] E. L. Nemirovskiĭ, *Nachalo,* p. 125.
[5] E. L. Nemirovskiĭ, "Slavische Inkunabeln in kyrillischer Schrift . . . " p. 87.
[6] *Ibid.,* p. 97.

Ownership Notes" that none of the six copies of *Osmoglasnik* now in U.S.S.R. libraries contain Muscovite Russian provenance notes from the sixteenth and seventeenth centuries. Nemirovskiĭ himself states: "The preserved copies of the 1491 *Octoikh Osmoglasnik* in respect to provenance notes give little information."[7]

Copy 1: According to Nemirovskiĭ this copy, from the famous book collection of Ivan Nikitich Carskiĭ, was in Russia very early. It once contained many notes from an early date, but the first section was destroyed in the sixteenth century and was replaced by handwritten sections. Notes located in the lower part of those pages from the seventeenth century were blotted out in the following century and now the only notes are from the year 1717. Perhaps Nemirovskiĭ possesses other information which allows him to conclude this copy has been in Russia since the sixteenth century. Essentially we must abide by the given facts; statements regarding lost notes, destroyed leaves and blotted out parts cannot be accepted as proof of Russian ownership. The date 1717 is the only one which can be verified.

Copy 2: M. P. Pogodin's copy, according to Nemirovskiĭ, once contained a few early notes, but they were partially cut off. A portion of these cut-off notes can be found in Undolskiĭ's copy. A thorough study of the combined parts establishes the handwriting as Russian from the early part of the eighteenth century.

Copy 3: V. M. Undolskiĭ's copy contains a note dated August 8, 1769, on leaves partially cut off from the Pogodin copy.

Copies 4, 5, and 6: Nemirovskiĭ does not refer to any provenance notes in these copies; therefore if they do exist, we do not know about them. Thus, no opinion can be formed regarding their early locations.

CHASOSLOVEC PROVENANCE NOTES

Copy 1: This is apparently the second copy of Fiol's prints to be uncovered in Russia. It was located at a monastery not far from Rostov by the Iartsov brothers not later than 1525.

Copy 2: This very interesting copy contains notes regarding the Bukhvostov family under dates 1517, 1560, and 1570, which reveal the birth of boys in two generations, followed by notes pertaining to a famine which lasted three years, and high prices. The next note deals with the ownership of the book by a monastery and others. There is also a note from about 1677. It was located at a monastery on one of the Lake Onega islands. There is no doubt this book was in Russia in the sixteenth and seventeenth centuries, and was the first of those surviving to reach Russia.

Copy 3: This copy contains a note in Rumanian Cyrillic cursive made in 1558. It

[7] Nemirovskiĭ, *Nachalo*, p. 80.

was found in the nineteenth century in Rumania near the Hungarian border. There were no prior connections with Russia. Reported for the first time by I. S. Svencickij in 1908:

> The copy was found in a church located in the [Carpathian] mountains close to the Hungarian border. On the verso of leaf 272 and on leaf 273 r. in Rumanian half uncial cursive handwriting a note dated 1558 [concerning the gift]: "'Papa' [priest] Timofeĭ Fedorov son's—to my son Peter." On the lower board [of the binding] note in cursive: "Mr. Theodore Gurianskiĭ for the binding of this half uncial paid 8 golden pieces. . . ." Binding—lindenwood boards covered with leather."[8]

Copy 4: This book was in Russian possession at least from the beginning of the seventeenth century; the proof of which is in notes concerning contemporary events—the first from 1601 recording the harsh winter and famine. Many pages contain numerous notes regarding historical events in Moscow from 1380 to 1626 copied from some chronicle. Another person continued the entries until 1676.

Copy 5: This print contains a note with the date 1641 but without reference to a location. Inscription partially preserved: ". . . da Elia Prophet. Priest Ageishche Ermolaev bound this book in the year 1641."[9] There is no way to verify Nemirovskiĭ's claim that the character of the handwriting is Muscovite half uncial cursive.

Copy 6: This book contains a date only—1650. Nemirovskiĭ claims it is Russian because of some handwritten additions pertaining to Muscovite saints in the calendar. No data given as to when these additions were made.

Copy 7: This copy contains a note with the date 1658 by the famous Muscovite patriarch Nikon.

Copy 8: Contains a note with the date 1677 which Nemirovskiĭ claims is Muscovite Russian although he offers no proof. Also, according to his equivocal statement it contains a Russian note from the eighteenth century.

Copies 9, 10, and 11: Nemirovskiĭ states: "Notes were made in Belorussia and Lithuania," but gives no further details.

Copy 12: Now in the Moscow University Library, this copy has numerous inscriptions in Polish; also a note in Belorussian cursive of the eighteenth century and additional notes in the binding paper.

Copy 13: This copy has many notes stating that it was in Lithuania from an early date and contains many inscriptions of new saints in the calendar. This copy is currently in the Library of the Lithuanian Academy of Sciences in Wilno (Vilnius).

Copy 14: Notes indicate this copy was the property of Professor M. K. Bobrov-

[8] I. S. Sventsitskiĭ, *Kataloh knih tserkovno-slavianskoĭ pechaty* (Catalogue of Church Slavonic Printing), (Zhovkva, 1908), p. 46.

[9] Nemirovskiĭ, *Nachalo*, p. 127.

skij (1784–1848) of Wilno University, with his own note "*Zapiska v exemplaru Zyrowickom.*" There are also early inscriptions in the calendar written in Cyrillic.

Copies 15–24: Nemirovskiĭ mentions no notes in these copies.

Nemirovskiĭ is very conscientious in presenting all the information possible regarding Russian notes in the incunabula, but he neglects those in other languages. Nevertheless we will utilize his fragmentary remarks to analyze his hypothesis that Fiol's prints were produced on order from Moscow.

After citing all provenance notes in Russian, Nemirovskiĭ states:

> We have proved the number of copies of the 1491 *Chasoslovec* in Russia in the sixteenth century to be two; in addition there was one (containing Russian notes) in the seventeenth century. Grand total: eight copies with Great Russian notes of the sixteenth and seventeenth centuries and only one copy containing South Slavic notes.[10]

Nemirovskiĭ's arithmetic is suspect; if two copies of *Chasoslovec* contain notes from the sixteenth century and one copy contains notes from the seventeenth century, how then can he later state that the grand total is eight copies with Great Russian notes of the sixteenth and seventeenth centuries with only one copy containing South Slavic notes? The latter pertains to the copy found in Rumania and was already counted in his total of eight copies containing notes. Nemirovskiĭ should have stated that seven copies contain Russian notes from the sixteenth, seventeenth and also eighteenth centuries, and one copy contains South Slavic notes. The entire summary is misleading and incomplete for the obvious reason: the Russian scholar omits mention of the Belorussian, Lithuanian and Polish notes *in extenso.*

Therefore, we will complete the summary for him: two copies (Nos. 1 and 2) of *Chasoslovec* now in the U.S.S.R. contain Russian notes from the sixteenth century; two copies (Nos. 4 and 7) contain Russian notes from the seventeenth century; three copies (Nos. 5, 6 and 8) have notes which Nemirovskiĭ claims to be Russian, of which one is actually from the eighteenth century; one copy (No. 3—Rumanian) contains notes in South Slavic from the sixteenth century; Belorussian, Lithuanian and Polish notes, presumably from the fifteenth up to the eighteenth centuries, can be found in six copies (Nos. 9, 10, 11, 12, 13 and 14). No information is given relative to the provenance notes which may be in the remaining ten copies of *Chasoslovec* now owned by the U.S.S.R.

TRIOD POSTNAJA PROVENANCE NOTES

Copy 1: This copy contains a 1536 note in Muscovite handwriting and was the property of Prince Belskiĭ, diplomat and warrior during the reigns of Tsars

[10] *Ibid.*, p. 128.

Vasiliĭ III and Ivan IV. Another note, made in 1649, states the book was then in the village of Kitovo near Suzdal', northeast of Moscow.

Copy 2: A note from 1592 and others from 1613 and 1653 were, according to Nemirovskiĭ, written in Muscovite Russian. The book is now in the Museum of Ukrainian Art in Lwiw (Lwów) which, until 1944, belonged to Poland. This copy was purchased from a Moscow bookseller named Shybanov.

Copy 3: A note from 1598 pertaining to ownership is not clear. A second note dated 1629 mentions another owner and indicates a location far east of Moscow.

Copy 4: Notes from 1604 and 1620 indicate this copy was in Moscow and owned by the Tsar's family. Later, and for many generations, it was in the possession of the family of a priest named Vasiliĭ Ivanov in the Riazan district. The very interesting note reveals how books were preserved from one generation to the next.

Copy 5: This one contains notes without dates. Nemirovskiĭ claims this copy to be Russian basing his theory on the appearance of the half uncial handwriting. Without verification he states the notes were made on the brink of the seventeenth century. An *ex libris* reveals the "Kozelsk wilderness." There is a Kozelsk near Smolensk, Belorussia. Perhaps the name also appears in Russia, although we have been unable to discover it there.

Copy 6: Contains only the date 1632.

Copy 7: This copy contains a note from 1657 in Belorussian handwriting. Nemirovskiĭ stresses that the Russian notes in the previously discussed copies are from a much earlier period than this one with the Belorussian note. He disregards Kopystenskiĭ's statement that there were many copies of Fiol's books in Belorussia and Ukraine in the fifteenth and sixteenth centuries when but a few copies existed in Russia.

Copy 8: A note on this copy indicates it was the property of the fourth wife of Tsar Ivan IV, the Terrible. The note is in Russian handwriting and done no later than 1626. This copy is now in Kiev.

Copy 9: This copy contains many notes which, according to Nemirovskiĭ, are of Russian origin. A notation dated 1704 places this copy at Velizh, northeast of Vitebsk, a town that was historically in Belorussian territory.

Copy 10: Contains notes from the end of the seventeenth and the beginning of the eighteenth centuries locating this copy at Toropets, near Smolensk, in Belorussia.

Copy 11: Contains notes from the end of the seventeenth and beginning of the eighteenth centuries. No other details given by Nemirovskiĭ.

Copy 12: This copy contains many Polish and Ukrainian notes, one of which is dated 1707. Fragmentary notes on the binding paper are in Polish on one side and in Ukrainian on the other. The date February 17, 1663 is on wastepaper (a fragment from the Episcopal Court deed) used to glue together the loose leaf 54.

Copy 13: This is Pogodin's copy which contains many notes in Ukrainian and Polish which are not dated but are from the seventeenth and eighteenth centuries.

The last page of this copy is completely covered with notes. Nemirovskiĭ does not cite them.

Copy 14: This copy contains many notes from the eighteenth century giving no location. Nemirovskiĭ does not claim the notes of 1734 and 1785 as being written in Russian.

Copy 15: Contains a note from the seventeenth century which locates this copy in Krevo, Lithuania. There is also a note in Latin-Polish: "*hic liber viri Kreve eglesiae nativitatis.*"

According to Nemirovskiĭ:

> In eleven copies of *Triod Postnaja* there are notes preserved from the sixteenth and seventeenth centuries. Only three notes are dated in the sixteenth century and all [three] were made in Muscovite Russia. Among the notes dated in the seventeenth century only one is of West Russian [Belorussian] origin. Therefore, confirming our previous statement that the evidence is overwhelming that the [original] destination of Fiol's editions was the territory of Muscovite Russia.[11]

Again the evidence, under close scrutiny, does not support Nemirovskiĭ's contention. In our analysis three copies have Russian notes from the sixteenth century; of the seven copies with notes dated in the seventeenth century, at least three can be traced to Ukraine. Six of the copies contain Belorussian, Polish or Ukrainian notes. Those copies were, up until the eighteenth century, located in Polish, Belorussian, or Ukrainian territory to which they had been sent, in all likelihood, directly from Fiol's printing shop in the fifteenth century. Nemirovskiĭ does not mention notes in the eight remaining copies of *Triod Postnaja* now in Russia. Consequently the ratio is eight copies with Russian notes to sixteen copies with other or none at all.

TRIOD CVETNAJA PROVENANCE NOTES

Fourteen copies of *Triod Cvetnaja* are preserved in the U.S.S.R. and six elsewhere. No doubt his perusal of the Russian copies was most disappointing to Nemirovskiĭ as he found not a note from the sixteenth century to support his theory that Fiol's books were produced on order from Muscovy. "Unfortunately," he wrote, "there are no early provenance and ownership notes on the preserved copies of *Triod Cvetnaja*. The earliest are from the beginning of the seventeenth century."[12]

Copy 1: This copy has the date 1600, but the location is not legible. It was located in "the Church of the Blessed Mother's Nativity" and according to Nemirovskiĭ was donated by one Ivan Ramejkov. He claims this copy was in

[11] *Ibid.*, p. 149.
[12] *Ibid.*, p. 164.

Muscovy at an early date because of the Russian cursive character of the notes. Braha does not agree with the theory that the character of the script is sufficient to accept the note and copy as "Great Russian." Braha has also pointed out that the name Ramejka is typically Belorussian.[13]

Copy 2: A note on one of the Saltykov-Shchedrin Library *Triods* dated 1660 indicates that this copy belonged to the family of Prince Drutskoi. No location is given. Notes on the first page have been partially removed. What remains is a note of ownership: "To the Prince Vasiliĭ Iurevich Drutskoĭ with his own hand subscribed." On other pages are dates: "Summer 1675" and "year 1652, 3rd May." Nemirovskiĭ remarks: "Prince Drutskoĭ's old Lithuanian-Belorussian family together with the Glinskiĭ family settled in Moscow, Russia, at the beginning of the seventeenth century. It is not unlikely that this copy of *Triod* was brought from Lithuania."[14] Thus, the note may be in Russian handwriting, but the book was brought from Lithuania where it had been from at least the sixteenth century.

Copy 3: Nemirovskiĭ finds this is a very interesting copy but fails to explain why. The earliest note, dated 1703, indicates this book was given as a present to the prominent scholar Stefan Jaworski (1658–1722), a professor at Kiev Academy. Following this inscription are numerous notes referring to its various owners. This copy was uncovered in Ukraine and from there was taken to Russia.

Copy 4: This copy contains a note dated 1740 by the Catholic priest Danilevich; the location given is the village of Pareduby in Volhynia, Poland. This copy was transferred by bibliophile Olchowskiĭ in Lwów, Poland in 1932, and given to Archbishop A. Szeptyckiĭ. It was in the "Studion" collection of the archiepiscopal library until World War II. At present it is in the University Library, Lwów, U.S.S.R.

Copy 5: According to Nemirovskiĭ this copy contains many notes from the eighteenth century written in both Polish and Belorussian.

Copy 6: This copy contains notes handwritten in Russian from the eighteenth century.

Copies 7–14: Nemirovskiĭ gave no information on these.

Nemirovskiĭ concludes: "In six of eight copies of *Triod Cvetnaja,* notes of the seventeenth and eighteenth centuries were made in Russia. Thus . . . our previous opinion regarding the geographical destination [Muscovy] of Shvaĭpolt Fiol editions is also fully acceptable in this case."[15]

The provenance notes, in our analysis, strongly indicate that five of the six books Nemirovskiĭ says are "Russian" were actually from Belorussian, Polish and Ukrainian territories. Notes in Russian handwriting from the eighteenth and nineteenth centuries simply do not change the fact. Copy No. 1 was taken to Russia

[13] Braha, review of *Beginning of Slavic Printing*, p. 120.
[14] Nemirovskiĭ, *Nachalo*, p. 165.
[15] *Ibid.*, p. 165.

from Belorussia; Copy No. 2 was from Lithuania; Copy No. 3 was still in Ukraine at least at the beginning of the eighteenth century; Copy No. 4 was taken to Russia from Poland and Copy No. 5 was in the hands of both Polish and Belorussian owners before it was taken to Russia during or after the eighteenth century. Copy No. 6 contains only Russian notes, but they were not made until the eighteenth century, which in no way indicates, or should be interpreted as indicating, this copy was sent directly to Russia from Fiol's shop two centuries earlier—nor that *Triod Cvetnaja* or any of the other Cracow Cyrillic incunabula were printed on order from Muscovy.

A thorough investigation and analysis of the notes contained in the editions of all four of Fiol's books now preserved in Russia indicate that Nemirovskiĭ's Table V (see above) is incorrect. Based on Nemirovskiĭ's own description of the notes in the Cracow Cyrillic incunabula now in Russia, we offer a revised and corrected table:

	Oktoikh	Chasoslovec	Triod Postnaja	Triod Cvetnaja	TOTAL	Percentages
U.S.S.R. Holdings	6	24	24	14	68	87%
Outside of U.S.S.R.	-	1	3	6	10	13%
Total	6	25	27	20	78	100%
Nemirovskiĭ's claims to Russian notes for the XVI and XVII centuries	2	12	11	5	30	38%
Our findings from Nemirovskiĭ's description—						
XVI century	0	2	3	-	5	6%
XVII century	0	5	4	1	10	13%
TOTAL	0	7	7	1	15	19%

Notes made in Fiol's editions in Russian handwriting in the centuries after their publication proves only that the books got to Russia one way or another. Giving Nemirovskiĭ the benefit of the doubt and allowing his claim that thirty-eight percent of the existing notes are in Russian is nonetheless not convincing evidence the books were published on order from Muscovy. Furthermore, in our revised analysis based on the descriptions of the notes, we have determined a maximum of only twenty percent of the existing notes are of Russian origin. We must also take into consideration that many of the earlier, sixteenth and seventeenth century, notes were cut off, patched over or otherwise destroyed, and these certainly were notes pertaining to ownership, etc., *before* the books were taken to Russia. Until the U.S.S.R. government allows non-Russian scholars the privilege of examining all their copies of Fiol's books *in situ,* or at least making microfilms or microfiches of them, Nemirovskiĭ's conclusions must remain suspect.

It is apparent, as supported by Kopystenskiĭ's observations, that Fiol's books were published chiefly for the Belorussians and Ukrainians. Obviously the other Orthodox nations acquired copies of the books; proof exists in the few copies found in Rumania and Russia which contain sixteenth century notes from those countries. Too, we must consider that Turzo and Fiol were businessmen. Pioneers they may have been, but they also established the Cyrillic press with an eye toward profit. They would have sold the books wherever there was a market, even China.

Braha in his review of Nemirovskiĭ's *The Beginning of Slavic Printing* stresses important facts which further undermine Nemirovskiĭ's supposition that the books were ordered by Muscovy. Pointing out the first Moscow date—1517—appearing in any of the books, he logically asks why "the first book of this 'order' reached Moscow twenty-five years after it was printed?"[16] According to Braha the timing of the order and delivery is not only dubious but next to impossible. When Fiol's books were being printed, relations between Muscovy and the Grand Duchy of Lithuania were very strained. As a matter of record the two countries were at war in 1492–1493, at exactly the time Nemirovskiĭ would have us believe Fiol was clandestinely printing books on order from Moscow![17]

Moscow, in Fiol's time, was neither ready to accept new ideas nor inclined to become a market for printed books. We know only too well what happened to Dr. Skaryna forty years later when he took his Bible to Moscow. And forty years after that when the pioneers of Muscovite printing, Ivan Fedorov and Piotr Mstislavets, opened a shop there, they were able to print only two books before the mob (instigated by the clergy and not without government consent) destroyed their press. The printers managed to save their lives by escaping abroad. Fedorov later fully documents this mood of Moscow toward printing in *Apostol* which he printed in Lwów, Poland, in 1574, ten years after he fled from Moscow:

> I have not begun to set all this forth to you without reason, but because of the great persecutions which we often experienced not from the ruler himself but from many government officials and spiritual leaders and teachers who because of envy brought many accusations of heresy against us wishing to turn good into evil and finally to destroy God's work, as is usual for immoral, ignorant and backward people neither accustomed to grammatical[18] skills nor filled with spiritual wisdom, but who basely and vainly spread the evil word. For such is envy and hatred that they fabricate slander uncomprehending

[16] Braha, review of *The Beginning of Slavic Printing,* pp. 119–120.

[17] *Ibid.,* p. 120.

[18] The meaning here is rather "writing," "literary." See also Lubomyr R. Wynar, "History of Early Ukrainian Printing 1491–1600," *Studies in Librarianship.* University of Denver, Vol. 1, No. 2, 1962, 54–55.

where it leads to and on what it is based. These circumstances have exiled us from our country and native land.[19]

Fedorov's complaints were substantiated by Queen Elizabeth's ambassador Giles Fletcher in his work *Of the Russe Common Wealth* (London, 1591). Fletcher was in Moscow from 1588 to 1589, and the burning of Fedorov's printing press was reported to him by an eyewitness. Incidentally he also mentioned that the art of printing came to Moscow from Poland.

> Some yeres past in the other Emporers time, there came a Presse and Letters out of *Polonia,* to the citie of *Mosco,* where a printing house was set up, with great liking & allowance of the Emperour himselfe. But not long after, the house was set on fire in the night time, and the presse and letters quite burnt up, as was thought by the procurement of the Clergy men.[20]

Humanism never reached Moscow and thus the idea of printing, as a free enterprise in the vernacular, was not only strange but totally unacceptable to some church and government authorities. Not until more than a hundred years after the development of typography were printing presses allowed in Moscow, and these were exclusively for the purpose of printing ecclesiastical books in Old Church Slavonic under conditions of very tight scrutiny and censorship.

In the opinion of the most prominent men of sixteenth century Muscovite Russia (men such as Prince Andreĭ Kurbskiĭ, a representative of the aristocracy, and Artemius, a representative of the clergy) the Russian people did not need printed books in the vernacular language since they might foster ideas dangerous to the church and religion. As a result of such attitudes Russia never went through the stimulating trends of Humanism and did not participate in the spectacular achievements of the Renaissance.

In closing the discussion concerning the fate of Fiol's books we must refer to a historical document confirming the seizure of books and art objects during the time of the partition of Poland. The Polish-Soviet peace treaty concluded on March 18, 1921 at Riga, contains articles in which the Soviet Union accepts the obligation to return all cultural objects, books, etc., taken by tsarist Russia. Some were returned but not all, especially thousands of manuscripts and books printed in Cyrillic. To date they are in libraries and museums all over the U.S.S.R. According to Chwalewik many of Fiol's incunabula currently in the Soviet Union are those that have not been returned to Poland.[21]

[19] M. V. Shchepkina, "Perevody predisloviĭ i posleslovĭi pervopechatnykh knig," in *U istokov russkogo knigopechataniia* (Moscow, 1959), p. 235.

[20] Giles Fletcher, *Of The Russe Common Wealth, or Manner of Gouernement by the Russe Emperour (commonly called the Emperour of Moscovia) the Manners and Fashions of the People of that Country* (London, 1591), p. 85. (Cited by Wynar, *op. cit.* p. 56.)

[21] Edward Chwalewik, *Zbiory polskie, archiwa, biblioteki, gabinety, galerie, muzea i inne zbiory pamiątek przeszłości w ojczyźnie i na obczyźnie* (Polish Collections, Archives, Libraries, Study Rooms, Galleries, Museums and Other Collections of Memorabilia of the Past in Poland and Abroad). (2 vols., 2nd ed.; Warsaw-Cracow, 1926), pp. 277–377.

5
The Manuscript Prototypes and Language of Fiol's Books

While the evidence indicates it took some three decades for the first of Fiol's prints to reach Muscovy Russia, Archimandrite Zakharii Kopystenskii's books reveal that the Cracow Cyrillic incunabula reached the Orthodox Christians in the Polish-Lithuanian Commonwealth immediately after they were published. The prints were sent from Cracow north-east into Belorussia and south into Ukraine. The books were also sent into Rumania and Hungary and in the far north they early reached the Russian territories of Pskov and Novgorod. There were no more copies of Fiol's Cyrillic books to be found in Catholic Cracow by 1498.

The Orthodox people sought and valued Fiol's editions. The paper, printing and type were all of high quality; the texts were well selected, and best of all they were printed in the Old Church Slavonic common to all followers of the Eastern Orthodox rite and used as the liturgical language in the same manner Roman Catholics used Latin. The printed books, unlike the earlier manuscripts, were uniform in content.

The perplexing problem—which manuscripts were used as models for Fiol's four books—has been the subject of long and continued debate, especially among East European scholars.

There have, of course, been many theories as to the origin of the prototypes for Fiol's prints. A. I. Sobolevskii, a Russian scholar of the old regime, was convinced that Fiol's books were based on texts of Southern Slavic or Moldavian origin. The language of the texts, Sobolevskii said, was the so-called "Middle Bulgarian,"[1] which was predominant in the Moldavian Orthodox Church from the tenth to the seventeenth century. Sobolevskii concluded that the books had been ordered by the Moldavian princes (voivods) who furnished the prototype manuscripts to Fiol.

Sobolevskii was a linguist and his statement was based on the phonetical and morphological characteristics of the language, as well as on some characteristics of South Slavic orthography which, incidentally, appear especially in the colophon

[1] A. I. Sobolevskii, "Zametka o iazyke pechatnykh izdanii Shvaipol'ta Fiolia i Skoriny" (Note on the Language of Fiol's and Skaryna's Prints), *Chteniia v istoricheskom obshchestve Nestora-letopistsa,* (Kiev, 1888), II, 192–193.

in which words end with the soft "jer" instead of the hard "jer." This is ably explained by Lunt.[2]

A few years later a second Russian scholar, P. V. Vladimirov, announced that his findings differed from those of his countryman. Vladimirov theorized that the original texts were set from East Slavic copy, but contained some new South Slavic linguistic and orthographic changes as a result of what became known as the "Second South Slavic influence" on the language of the north.[3] This came about as a result of the migration of a great many clergy from the South after the fall of Byzantium in the middle of the fifteenth century.

About a half a century before the fall of Constantinople and the Turkish conquest of the Balkans, two great Lithuanian (Belorussian) Metropolitans, Kiprian and Camblak of Bulgarian origin, prepared the renewal of Old Church Bulgarian through their numerous publications in the Middle Bulgarian language. The writings and language of Kiprian and Camblak influenced Belorussian and Ukrainian Cyrillic works. From the end of the fourteenth century this started the so-called "Second South Slavic Influence" in the above mentioned territories.

The latest findings by Ilya Talev, although not too accurate in placing historical events, substantiate the above mentioned facts of a much older existence of the "second influence":

> . . . the authority of the Russian (Ruthenian) Metropolitans of Bulgarian origin, Kiprian and Camblak, doubtlessly regarded the Middle Bulgarian language of the second half of the 14th century as the best, most truly supranational Church Slavic, and the prestige of the 14th century Bulgarian revised editions in the monasteries of Constantinople and Mt. Athos.[3a]

Vladimirov also emphasized the presence of some Eastern Slavic insets in the texts. As an example he mentioned that *Chasoslovec* printed by Fiol quotes Saint Peter of Moscow, an Orthodox Metropolitan of the fourteenth century, who was not then known in the South. Saint Peter of Moscow was not a Russian, he was born in Volhynia, educated there and was also a founder of an Orthodox monastery in Volhynia. He was a Ruthenian — Ukrainian.

Vladimirov's theory was accepted with the general conviction that the texts were either of Belorussian or Ukrainian provenance where the second Slavic influence was very strong. The influence of the clergy from the south resulted in the Belorussian and Ukrainian copyists' irregular use of soft "jer's," as well as the correct use of symbols for nasal vowels so typical of South Slavic orthography which, in those days, however, had only traditional values. Belorussian and

[2] Horace G. Lunt, *Old Church Slavonic Grammar* (2nd ed.; The Hague, 1959), §1.23 and 2.520, p. 19.

[3] P. V. Vladimirov, "Nachalo slavianskogo i russkogo knigopechataniia v XV i XVI vekakh" (Beginning of Slavic and Russian Printing in the 15th and 16th Centuries), *Chteniia v istoricheskom obshchestve Nestora-letopistsa,* (Kiev, 1894), VIII, p. 24–29.

[3a] Ilya Talev, *Some Problems of the Second South Slavic Influence in Russia* (Munich, 1973), p. 365.

Ukrainian copyists followed the use of the symbols for nasal vowels meticulously, while in Russian manuscripts the confusion of nasal and non-nasal vowels reached a point of complete bewilderment after the eleventh century. This was for a period of time the reason Russian manuscripts were not on the list of canonical texts.[4]

There were other less important reasons, but this is basically why either Belorussian or Ukrainian manuscripts were used in choosing texts for the Orthodox rite in the extended territories of the Polish-Lithuanian Commonwealth.

The Rumanian scholar and historian P. P. Panaitescu revived the Sobolevskiĭ theory in 1961 and stated that Fiol's prints were ordered by the Moldavian Prince Stefan the Great.[5] Panaitescu was supported by the Bulgarian historian Peter Atanasov who then claimed that the prototypes for Fiol's prints were of Bulgarian origin and that Bulgarians were employed in Fiol's shop as specialists in the Old Church Slavonic language and Church literature.[6]

The view that the manuscripts which Fiol used as original texts for his prints, as offered by Sobolevskiĭ and Panaitescu, was censured by Nemirovskiĭ. He insists that Fiol's original texts were of Russian, or rather Muscovite, origin. Nemirovskiĭ bases his theory on the fact that Saint Peter is mentioned in Fiol's *Chasoslovec.* On this single disclosure the Russian scholar hangs his theory that all four books printed by Fiol were based on Muscovite manuscripts. Nemirovskiĭ paraphrased Panaitescu's statement that Fiol's books were ordered by Prince Stefan of Moldavia and announced that Muscovy was the initiator of Cyrillic printing in Cracow, that the whole enterprise was under Moscow's protection and Moscow's order. Why then, we might ask, were the books printed in Catholic Cracow and not in Moscow? Fiol, given the opportunity, would not have hesitated in accepting an invitation to Russia.

On the surface, the theory of a South Slavic origin of the prototype manuscripts seems more plausible than does Nemirovskiĭ's hypothesis of a Muscovite origin if we allow ourselves seriously to entertain either of them. Moscow was far from Cracow and cultural relations between Poland and Ivan III's court were all but nonexistent. Besides, it must be pointed out there was no interest in the art of printing in Moscow for another fifty years, while in Moldavia in 1508, an ecclesiastical book called *Sluzhebnik* (Missal) was printed followed by two others. This was the beginning of Rumanian typography in Cyrillic on a reasonably high level. Nevertheless, Panaitescu's and Antanasov's statements remain only a hypothesis, and a rather weak one at that, because no documents exist to support it and only a few of Fiol's books were found in the South.

Nemirovskiĭ gathered considerable material in an effort to destroy Sobolevskiĭ's

[4] Lunt, *Old Church Slavonic Grammar,* §2.6 and 2.61, p. 34.

[5] P. P. Panaitescu, *Liturghierul lui Macarie* (Bucureşti, 1961), pp. 38–39.

[6] Petŭr Atanasov, "Bŭlgarski tekstove v pŭrvite slavianski kirilski inkunabuli" (Bulgarian Texts at the Outset of Slavic Cyrillic Incunabula), *Ezik i literatura* (Language and Literature) (Sofia, 1966), 21, no. 5, pp. 30–31.

notion that Fiol's books were based on texts of Moldavian origin and, on the other hand, to support Vladimirov's suggestion that the prototypes were of East Slavic provenance. That part of *Chasoslovec* called "Mesatseslov" (Church calendar) enumerates saints who were unknown in the South and also lists the names of those saints known to the entire Orthodox Church but in the East Slavic manner which, of course, is different from the form of their names in South Slavic. Basing his argument on that alone, Nemirovskiĭ eliminated the possibility of a southern origin for the prototype of all four of Fiol's prints quite convincingly. He fails, nonetheless, to offer proof of any Muscovite contribution.

Vladimirov's discovery that Fiol's *Chasosolvec* quotes St. Peter of Moscow does not indicate any affiliation between the prototext for that print and the Muscovite Orthodox Church. The influence of the Russian Orthodox Church was widespread in the fifteenth century over all Russian territories including the northern states independent of Muscovy such as the city-state of Pskov and the republic of Novgorod, both closer culturally to Lithuania than to Moscow. The influence of these highly cultural and commercial centers and other northern principalities was not taken into consideration by Nemirovskiĭ who, in this case, narrows Russia only to Muscovy which in those days was only one of several Russian principalities.

Theoretically accepting the single clue, a mention of Saint Peter of Moscow, as sufficient to prove the original text of *Chasoslovec* came from Russia, or even Moscow, does not by any means indicate that the prototype texts for the other three books were also of Muscovite origin. Nemirovskiĭ thoroughly studied Moscow church texts but has paid only partial attention to the church literature of other Russian territories. Moreover, his study of Ukrainian texts has been superficial and he has completely ignored those of Belorussia.

This is stressed most strongly by Braha:

> E. L. Nemirovskiĭ is not looking for national insets in Fiol's editions on the territories of the Grand Duchy of Lithuania. He is seeking them within his own Russian national boundaries, in the territories of the Grand Duchy of Moscow. He tries to associate the beginnings of Cyrillic printing with Muscovy and make it dependent on Muscovite manuscripts and on the "official circles of the Moscow government. . . ." In line with Vladimirov Nemirovskiĭ repudiates the hypothesis of the Moldavian South Slavic origin of Fiol's publications and searches for it still farther away, over fifteen hundred kilometers from Cracow, in Moscow. In addition he ignores the rich old tradition of Cyrillic manuscripts on the vast territories that extend between Cracow and Moscow, including the Orthodox territories of the Grand Duchy of Lithuania.[7]

While basing his theory of a Muscovite origin for the prototype manuscript of *Chasoslovec* on the single mention of Saint Peter of Moscow, Nemirovskiĭ ignores

[7] Braha, review of *The Beginning of Slavic Printing,* pp. 118–119.

the saints from Ukraine and Belorussia mentioned in Fiol's books, such as Theodosius Pecherskiĭ, Vladimir Velikiĭ, Hlib (Gleb), Boris and others. This is emphasized by Sokolyshyn.[8]

Eventually even Nemirovskiĭ must admit no original text, Muscovite or any other, of Fiol's prints has been found to date. As long as the originals remain unknown the mystery of the prototexts used by Fiol's printers is open to discussion. It is possible that a thorough study of Belorussian and Ukrainian ecclesiastical manuscripts of the fifteenth century could solve the question once and for all.

The language of the books printed in Cracow was Old Church Slavonic. It is the language used by Saints Cyril and Methodius when, with their followers, they translated the Holy Scriptures from Greek into the Slavic dialect of their place of origin, Salonika. This language, after the separation of the Christian churches in 1054, developed as the Slavonic Orthodox Church liturgical language and for centuries dominated the Orthodox ecclesiastical books and Church literature.

Old Church Slavonic, the oldest written Slavic language, is used by linguists as the main source of information concerning the lexicography and grammar for all Slavic languages. It is also helpful in the reconstruction of the proto-Slavic language, the so-called Common Slavonic from which all Slavic languages were derived. Old Church Slavonic is basically Old Bulgarian and Macedonian. It was used in Church literature as the primary language over vast territories in Eastern and Southern Europe; understandably, however, over the centuries local dialects penetrated Church Slavonic manuscripts to one degree or another when new copies were produced. Some words of the fifteenth century native languages were introduced in all four editions printed by Fiol. They either originated through errors or were the result of vernacular insertions by individuals who found the text of the master copy difficult to read or understand. Most of the loanwords contained in Fiol's books are in the colophons which were not copied from a prototype text but were newly created. As a result the colophons became the source of many misinterpretations in the matter of language as well as on the subject of dates.

Some Ukrainians, Kuziela for instance, insist that the language of the colophons and words not of Church Slavonic origin which were introduced in the books printed by Fiol are "Ukrainian." Kuziela has pointed out six instances of "Ukrainianisms" (Ukrainian deviations from Old Church Slavonic) in Fiol's books, and on this basis makes the following statement: "All texts of Fiol's prints are of East Slavic provenance and indicate distinct marks of Ukrainian dialect."[9]

Kuziela's examples are as follows: *у городѣ* (u gorodie); *у Краковѣ* (u Krakovie); *живь буде у вѣкы* (zhyv bude u vieky); *усплачюся* (usplachyusya); *пов-*

[8] Aleksander Sokolyszyn, "Sweipolt Fiol: The First Slavic Printer of Cyrillic Characters," *American Slavic and East European Review,* 18 (1959), 88–94.

[9] Kuziela, "Der Deutsche Schweitpold Fiol . . . ," p. 81a.

читься (povchytsya); *окрывавив* (okryvaviv). Only the first two are from Fiol's colophons; obviously Kuziela could not find any more "Ukrainianisms" in them. In addition, the first "u gorodie" is distorted; in fact it appears in the colophons as the Church Slavonic "gradie." Deviations from the Church Slavonic language in these two cases depend on a change of the preposition въ (v) to "у" (u) or "оу" (ou). This is a constant characteristic of the Belorussian language in which, then and today, a "u" would be used in such cases and never "v." Therefore, the change of "v" to "u" is a common rule in Belorussian; in Ukrainian they are sometimes interchangeable but not in the two cases under discussion here. As early as the year 1229 in the treaty between Smolensk and Riga we have *оу ризѣ* (u rizie); *оусхочеть* (ushochet); *оуздумал* (uzdumal). And in the *Hramota* (Charter) issued by the Grand Duke Vitold in Polotsk in 1399 the "u" appears three times in one sentence: "u Polotsku, u chetver, u 6-yj den." This "u" is purely and typically Belorussian. This matter is discussed in detail by E. F. Karskiĭ.[10]

In three other instances, taken from the text of the books, Kuziela's "Ukrainianisms" are not valid because they are forms which are common to both languages. The last example, "okryvaviv," is a Belorussian word also in usage today.

Kuziela has taken all of his arguments from M. Hrushevskyĭ's *History of Ukrainian Literature.*[11] Hrushevskyĭ is an authority on Ukrainian history but not on linguistics. Actually he mentioned five examples more than those cited by Kuziela.

The first two of these are again the exchange of "v" and "u" in Belorussian; the next two are common to both languages and therefore cannot be considered as "Ukrainianisms," and the fifth, *съгреческое* (s grecheskoe), cannot by any means be called so either, as it is exclusively Belorussian.

In Church Slavonic the final syllable "yia" changed to "oi" in Ukrainian and to "oe" in Belorussian. On the whole none of the examples of "Ukrainianisms" cited by Hrushevskyĭ is solely Ukrainian and one has no validity at all. Therefore Kuziela's belief cannot be supported.

There are, notwithstanding, many examples that are exclusively Belorussian in Fiol's prints. Slavic comparative grammar accepts the rule that one of the basic measures for the differentiation between the Belorussian and Ukrainian language is the changing of the old "jat" into "e" in Belorussian, and to "i" in Ukrainian. *хлеб* (khleb), *хліб* (khlib); *лес* (les), *ліс* (lis), *бес* (bes), *біс* (bis). Even Hrushevskyĭ admits that "most characteristic of Belorussian phonetics was the exchange of "гъ" (jat) for "e" and these frequent exchanges in orthography were shown by "e"

[10] E. F. Karskiĭ, *Belorussy. Iazyk belorusskogo naroda* (The Belorussians: The Language of the Belorussian People), (Moscow, 1955) I, 330 et seq.

[11] M. Hrushevs'kyĭ, *Istoriia ukraïns'koï literatury* (History of Ukrainian Literature), (Kiev, 1927), Vol. 5, passim.

while in the Ukrainian language "jat" was changed into "i" and in its orthography those two letters—"jat" and "i"—intermingle."[12]

But returning to Fiol, the passage in the colophon "из *нѣмецъ*" (iz nyemets); *немецкого родоу* (nemetskogo rodu), "nemets" is written once with "jat" and again by "e." This is proof that the author of the colophon pronounced "jat" in the Belorussian manner as "e" and not in Ukrainian articulation as "i," and did not articulate "nimets" but as the Belorussian always does as "nyemets." This also applies to the name of the printer written in both colophons with the use of the "jat." Therefore his name should be pronounced Feol or Fieol and not Fiol.

Braha, in his review of Nemirovskiĭ's book, gives the best explanation as to the accurate pronunciation of the printer's name based on the linguistic rule concerning the phonetic exchange of Old Slavonic "jat" in Belorussian for "e" and in Ukrainian for "i":

> In both colophons in which the name Feol was written by "jat" there is revealed the pronunciation of this name which should be with an "e" and not an "i." It is necessary to pay attention to the spelling of the words "nemets nemetskogo." In these words following the letter "n" in the first word is "jat" and in the second "e." This appears, identically, in the colophons of both *Oktoikh* and *Chasoslovec.* It is proof that the author of the colophons pronounced them with an "e" and not with an "i"; therefore the spelling of Feol's name by "jat" should be pronounced Feol. . . . Of all the above deliberations the conclusion is that the correct spelling is with an "e"—Feol or Fieol—and erroneously as Fiol or Fijol.[13]

There are other examples of similar exchange in Fiol's books besides "s grecheskoe," as mentioned previously. We also find the Belorussian *змеа* (zmeya); *Андрея* (Andreya) which in Ukrainian could only be pronounced *змія* (zmiya), *Андрія* (Andriya).

Not only do we find elements of the Belorussian literary language in Fiol's books, but also traces of a Belorussian dialect which could not have been introduced by a Ukrainian. One dialectal feature in Belorussian is the interchange of "ch" and "ts," which is characteristic of the Polotsk and Smolensk areas of northeast Belorussia. Similar interchanges can be found in some Polish dialects but never in Ukraine or southern Russia. In Vitold's *Hramota* of 1399, for example, *Полоцаном* (Polotsanom) is used instead of *Полочаном* (Polochanom). Examples of the interchange of "ch" and "ts" in Fiol's books—*оуценици* (utsenitsi) instead of "uchenitsi," *вйнченосицю* (vunchenositsu and vuntsenositiu) are the best proof of their Belorussian origin. U. V. Anichenka has discussed the differentiation of Old Belorussian from Old Ukrainian in detail in his *Belaruska-*

[12] *Ibid.*, p. 95.
[13] Braha, review of *The Beginning of Slavic Printing,* pp. 122–123.

Ukrainskiĭa piśmova-mounia suviazi (Interrelations between Written and Spoken Belorussian and Ukrainian).[14]

The exchange is also characteristic of the Pskov and Novgorod regions of North Russia, but not of Moscow. Such interchanges appear consistently in the Mazovian region of the northeastern part of Poland which borders on Belorussia. It is so prevalent in this area that it is referred to in Polish grammar as "mazurzenie." This linguistic phenomenon occurs from Mazowsze-Poland through northeastern Belorussia and northern Russia up into Finland, where it is believed it originated.

Not much attention has been paid until now to the "Polonisms" in Fiol's prints, although Nemirovskiĭ mentioned them in his last book. The colophons contain three words of Polish origin, he tells us: "*dokonchana*" from the Polish "*dokończyć*" (to finish): "*gradie*" from the Polish "*gród*" (fortified town or city, also castle): and "*meshchaninom*" from the Polish "*mieszczanin*" (townsman). In *Osmoglasnik* on the page containing the Table of Signatures, the printer used the word "*lichba*" from the Polish "*liczba*" (number) in instructing the use of numbers in folding sections. Based on these four examples, Nemirovskiĭ concluded:

> Linguistic peculiarities of the text of *Oktoikh* demonstrate that in compiling and editing the book people were engaged whose native language was Ukrainian or Polish and who, naturally, were knowledgeable in the Old Slavonic language of the ecclesiastical books and perhaps also in the colloquial language of Muscovite Russia.[15]

The Russian scholar failed to take into consideration that the word "liczba" is common in Czech, Polish and Belorussian and cannot really be called a "Polonism." The word was noted in the Ukrainian language for the first time only in the sixteenth century. Braha supports this view and also introduces some interesting new material:

> Being unaware that the language of the colophons and a notation in Fiol's books is old literary Belorussian, Nemirovskiĭ found only "Polish" and "Ukrainian" words, failing to notice that they are actually Belorussian. For instance he writes that the word "*lichba*" (number) is of Polish origin . . . from the word "*lichyts*" (to count). Author Nemirovskiĭ does not know that in Fiol's time (as well as today) the Belorussians use the word "*liczyć*" and not the word "*shchytat*" used by the Russians. The word "*lichba*" always appears in ancient monuments of the Belorussian language, for instance in the *Hramota* (Charter) of Duke Vitaut [Vitold] of 1427 "*po etoj lichbie.*" This word is not a "Polonism" because up until the fifteenth century Poles used the word "*chyslo*" instead of "*lichba*" in both speech and writing.[16]

[14] U. V. Anichenka, *Belaruska-urkainskiia pis'mova-moŭnyia suviazi* (The Interrelations between Written and Spoken Belorussian and Ukrainian) (Minsk, 1969), *passim.*

[15] Nemirovskiĭ, *Nachalo,* p. 91.

[16] Braha, review of *The Beginning of Slavic Printing,* pp. 123–124.

A lesser "Polonism" is the word "dokonchana" (finish). In the Smolensk *Hramota* of 1230 there is the word "*доконьчил*" (dokonchil), in the Riga *Hramota* of 1300 it appears as "*мир доконьцан*" (dokońtsan) with the interchange of "ch" and "ts" typical of this region. The Polish language in the thirteenth century had not yet influenced the Belorussian, but the word "dokonchyats" and derivatives of it were being used all over Belorussia. As to the last "Polonism," Duke Vitold's *Hramota* of 1388 used the word *meshchan* and from that time it can be found in numerous documents. The Belorussians used the word *miesto* (town) as early as the twelfth century so they could easily have created the word *meshchanin* for townsman without assistance from the Poles. The word *grad* (gród) for castle was known to all Western Slavs; the Belorussians, located just to the east, used it very early and could claim it, as well as the other cases cited, as their own. In conclusion, obviously the "Polonisms" were in reality words common to both Polish and Belorussian.

These few "Polonisms" found in Fiol's books, added to the morphological changes stated previously, support our theory that Belorussians were the editors and compositors of the prints. It is well known that during the sixteenth century many Polish words were accepted into the Belorussian language; Polish and Belorussian words used together could sometimes appear like literary Latin-vernacular macaronicisms in those days. Professor Czesław Miłosz accentuates this distinctly, although with some exaggeration: "The linguistic situation was very fluid. . . . Some texts sound practically like Polish texts written in Cyrillic with Eastern Slavic case endings added."[17]

Educated Belorussians were well acquainted with the Polish language. Therefore, when the professional printer, a Pole or Polonized German, gave instructions as to the arrangement of the Table of Signatures and used the word "lichba," it was very easy for the Belorussian helper to accept and subsequently introduce it into the text. We know from history that all these words were used by Belorussians for centuries before any Polish influence began, but none was adopted into the Russian language. Not until the sixteenth century did the Ukrainians, and not until the seventeenth century did the Russians, accept some "Polonisms," and never in the manner or to the extent as the Belorussians.

In his last book Nemirovskiĭ made a claim reminiscent of that expounded earlier by Kuziela in its homage to nationalism: that all texts of Fiol's prints are of Great Russian provenance and indicate distinct marks of the Russian language. Again he offered no documentation of his claim. If there were any deviations from the Old Church Slavonic in Fiol's books typical of the Russian language, surely Russian scholars before Nemirovskiĭ would have found them.

The Ukrainians are justified to some extent in claiming credit for helping to pro-

[17]Czesław Miłosz, *The History of Polish Literature* (London, 1969), p. 106.

duce Fiol's prints as they, like the Belorussians, were part of the Polish-Lithuanian Commonwealth and their cooperation with the printer was possible. But, we have proof the Belorussian influences were much stronger by thousands of documents written in that language. Not only was it the official language of the Grand Duchy of Lithuania Chancellery, but the codes of laws written from the fifteenth century, and printed in the sixteenth century, were executed exclusively in Belorussian. Moreover, the Belorussians were the first to establish printing presses among the Eastern Slavs about fifty years earlier than Moscow.

Nemirovskiĭ finally came to the same conclusion but belittled the significance of the contribution of the Belorussians:

> Dialectal peculiarities of the language which, however, are not distinctly exposed, let us accept that the compositor or typesetter of the 1491 *Oktoikh* was connected with a Belorussian, or rather with a Ukrainian environment.[18]

We know from many sources that the Belorussian culture was dominant among the Eastern Slavs in the Polish-Lithuanian Commonwealth, and that up until the eighteenth century no linguistic or cultural infiltration coming from Moscow can be established. In the fifteenth century, the Polish kings as well as the whole of the upper class in Lithuania were using Belorussian as the literary language. Naturally when Fiol was looking for Old Church Slavonic editors he may have turned to Wilno rather than to Lwów, and for certain, not to Moscow. Moreover, many Belorussians were in the King's court in Cracow, having been brought there by the kings and magnates of the Grand Duchy of Lithuania. With them came their Orthodox priests, secretaries, courtiers and other officials, some of them highly educated. Culturally the Ukrainians and the Belorussians were equal partners, but as contributors to Fiol's printing enterprise the latter had the potential to make the greater contribution.

Belorussians are inclined to conclude that Fiol's prints were prepared by his Belorussian workers, and destined primarily for Belorussia and the territories under the sphere of her cultural influence. The acceptance of Belorussian language characteristics in Fiol's prints does not exclude the possibility that some Ukrainians were on his staff. However, if they existed, they may have known and used Belorussian because it was the literary language of the whole of the Grand Duchy of Lithuania. Accepting the supposition that Fiol also employed Ukrainian workers, it is quite possible some traces of the Ukrainian language were accidentally left in the prints. The conclusion that Fiol's books were published primarily for the benefit of the Belorussians cannot be verified. In the sixteenth century, as Kopistenskiĭ stated, Fiol's books could be found more or less equally dispersed throughout Belorussian and Ukrainian territories.

[18]Nemirovskiĭ, *Nachalo*, p. 97.

In conclusion, what Karataev said approximately one hundred years ago on this subject appears as most appropriate and accurate. Referring to the language used by Fiol in colophons and registers, Karataev stated:

> Fiol was expressing himself in contemporary literary language, used in those days by educated and literary people in writing. This language was based on national dialects, Little Russian [Ukrainian] and Belorussian, not without Church Slavonic influences.[19]

One misconception with reference to Belorussia and its language is constantly repeated, i.e., that its literary language is currently in its formative period. Even the prominent scholar Horace Lunt, when discussing the Eastern group of Slavic languages, states:

> The Eastern group comprises Great Russian, commonly known simply as Russian; Little Russian, now generally known as Ukrainian, and also formerly known as Ruthenian in those parts of former Austro-Hungary where it was spoken; and White Russian [Belorussian], only recently elevated to the dignity of a literary language.[20]

The valid facts in relation to Belorussian are: (1) The Belorussian language is as old as Great Russian and Little Russian (Ruthenian or Ukrainian); (2) From the thirteenth century through the sixteenth Belorussian was used as the official language at the Chancellery of the Grand Duchy of Lithuania and consequently developed its own literary form; (3) The first Bible in the Eastern Slavic group was translated into Belorussian by Dr. Francišak Skaryna in 1517; (4) The Lithuanian Codes of Law were written and printed in Belorussian in the sixteenth century; (5) A huge polemical political and religious literature of the Reformation period from the sixteenth and seventeenth centuries is written in Belorussian; and (6) The first printing press among the Eastern Slavic nations was founded by a Belorussian. Dr. Francišak Skaryna, working in Prague during 1517–1519 and in Wilno during 1520–1525.

After the partition of Poland in the eighteenth century Belorussia was subjected to political, religious and cultural oppression by Russia for over a period of two centuries. That which happened to the language was similar to the fate of the Bohemian language after the Thirty Years' War (1618–1648).

Recent archaeological and historical findings reveal distinct differences between Ukrainians, Belorussians, and Russians. When the Eastern Slavic tribes settled in Europe they occupied territories with different ethnic groups: on the southwest the Iranian population of the Steppes of Scythia, to the north the

[19] Ivan Karataev, *Opisanie slaviano-russkikh knig napechatannykh kirillovskimi bukvami, 1491–1730* (Description of Slavic-Russian Books Printed in Cyrillic), (St. Petersburg, 1878). I from 1491 to 1600, p. 7.

[20] Lunt, *Old Slavonic Grammar,* p. 7.

ancestors of the Baltic tribes — Lithuanian and Letts, to the east Ugro-Finns. In time they were assimilated by the invaders, who exerted certain influences in many ways. These various linguistic and ethnic substrata created basic differences among eastern Slavs; the Ukrainian nation with its Iranian, Belorussian with Baltic and Russia with Ugro-Finn residues. These findings are the results of the latest research conducted in the East by numerous scholars. V. V. Sedov in his final analysis states:

> Deriving from various dialectic pre-Slavic groups, arriving from various regions and in various times, the Slavic tribes of the Upper Dnieper and Dvina in the thirteenth and fourteenth centuries, blend into a homogeneous Slavic nation — Belorussian. The reason for this was the uniformity of the Baltic substratum in the whole Belorussian territory. The local Baltic population gradually blended into the Slavic. . . . Certain language peculiarities lead to the conjecture that the formation of the Belorussian language came about in conjunction with the Baltic substratum.
>
> The Baltic substratum elements appear not only on the Belorussian ethnic territories but also in other separate regions of the Russian settlement. However the uniqueness of the Belorussian territory depends on the Balts being the only ethnic and linguistic substratum in this region and have been there for at least 2000 years. . . . The southern territories between the two rivers Volga and Oka, inhabited by the Ugro-Finnic population, were penetrated by the Balts only in the first millennium of our era. The Balts here were under the influence of the Ugro-Finnic substratum. The dialects throughout the whole southern Great Russian territories have unquestionably an Ugro-Finnic substratum. . . .[21]

[21] Valentin V. Sedov, *Slaviane verkhnego Podneprovia i Podvinia* (Slavs of the Upper Dnieper and Dvina). Moscow, 1970.

6
Dating Fiol's Prints by Paper and Watermarks

It has been accepted for several decades that Fiol's printing shop was definitely closed at the beginning of 1492, and there has never been any question as to the identity of the printer—Fiol printed all four books. Although all data concerning the time and place of publication and the name of the printer are contained in the colophons of Fiol's books, some controversy has been created by scholars who differ in opinion as to the sequence in which the books were printed.

The colophons of both *Osmoglasnik* and *Chasoslovec* mention Cracow as the place of printing and the year 1491 as the date of publication. Scholarly investigations have revealed beyond a doubt that both *Triods* were printed in the same printing shop. This fact was substantiated by the identity of type used in both, by the paper used in printing and by characteristics of the set and proof sheets presently located in the Jagellonian Library in Cracow (Incunabulum No. 1136). On one side of *Triod Postnaja*'s sheet sixty-nine are parts of leaves 32^r, 39^v, 134^r, and 137^v.[1] On the other side is a proof sheet of the letters which, in the final printing, were to be printed in red on leaves 267^r, 268^v, 269^v, and 270^v of *Chasoslovec*.[2]

Some researchers have concluded that *Triod Postnaja* and *Chasoslovec* were printed simultaneously in 1491 since the proof sheets were printed on the same paper. This is not a valid conclusion. Proof sheets used to line other books during the binding process could only be proof that both books were printed in the same printing shop. On the other hand Fiol's use of the paper for both does support the author's theory that *Chasoslovec* was printed shortly after *Triod Postnaja*.

It is important to establish the sequence in which Fiol's books were printed. In our studies we have considered the view offered by various scholars, including the ridiculous one that all four books were printed simultaneously in one year. Our

[1] r = recto, a right hand page; v = verso, a left-hand page.

[2] Aleksander Birkenmajer and Kazimierz Piekarski, "Korektowe arkusze druków Szwajpolta Fiola" (Proofsheets of Szwajpolt Fiol's Prints), *Congrès International de Bibliothecaires et des Amis du Livre tenu à Prague du 29 juin au 3 juillet, 1926. Procès-Verbaux et Mémoires* (Prague, 1928), II: 57–58.

conclusion is based on known historical facts and a thorough study of the paper used by Fiol.

The colophons of *Osmoglasnik* and *Chasoslovec* state: "The book was completed after Christ's nativity, one thousand four hundred ninety and one." In the past the wording of this last part of the colophon has been endlessly disputed and completely misinterpreted by Polish scholars because of the misunderstanding of three words: "*po božijem naroženijem.*" Poles under the spell of their own language interpreted the passage as "after Christmas" instead of "*anno a nativitate Dei,*" shortened to "*anno Domini*" and meaning "in the year"—not "after Christmas." Ukrainian scholars committed the same error.[3] The facts are, as pointed out by the Belorussian scholar Dr. Vitaut Tumash, in correspondence with the author:

> The documents in the Belorussian language issued by the Polish kings of the Jagellonian dynasty (1384–1572), who were also the Grand Dukes of Lithuania, usually contained such sentences as "w leto po božijem naroženija, pod leto božieho naroženija, leto božieho naroženija"—translated as *anno a nativitate Dei,* in that sense, it means in the year of God's nativity but never "after Christmas."

The so-called *Hramota* or charter issued by Lithuanian Grand Duke Vitold in Polotsk in 1399 for the merchants of Riga granting them trading privileges with Polotsk is dated as follows: "Written in Polotsk on Thursday of the fourth week of Lent, on March 6th *po božemu naroženij,* of the year 1000 and 400 less one [1399]." Here, without a doubt, *po božemu naroženij* can only mean *anno Domini*; in the year after God's nativity.

Correction of this misinterpretation aids invaluably in answering long standing questions relative to the wording in the colophons, a subject of long, fruitless discussions and erroneous conclusions. In the first place it would not have been possible for Fiol to print two books in the few days, or at most three weeks, between Christmas 1491 and January 1492, when the shop was closed and ceased to function.

A proper understanding of the colophon language indicates that *Chasoslovec* could very well have been printed at the beginning of 1491 and *Osmoglasnik* at the end of the same year; hence both would carry the same date, 1491. Some scholars suspected that the wording of the colophon (interpreted as "after Christmas, 1491") was meant to cover some clandestine activity of Fiol's printing shop or that the printing press was an underground activity but have been unable to explain what or why. It was not possible in 1491 to conceal a large enterprise such as Fiol's Cyrillic press. While Fiol's books were not advertised in Cracow, they were well

[3]Szczepan Zimmer, "Polskie druki cyrylickie" (Polish Cyrillic Prints), *Wiadomości* (News), London, Nr. 1232 (November 9, 1969), 4–6. The author must admit that in the past he has committed the same error as all other Poles in writing on the subject of Fiol's incunabula.

known in Orthodox Church circles and were widely distributed in the Belorussian and Ukrainian territories, then politically closely associated with Poland.

The proper interpretation of the colophon date also allows a meaningful discussion of the span of time needed for printing Fiol's four books. The total presswork for Fiol's prints comprised 519.5 sheets in 1234 leaves. The average output of a fifteenth century printing shop was about 100 sheets per year per press. With one press it would have taken four to five years to produce Fiol's four large books in the great quantity which, judging by the number still in existence, we know had to be published. With two presses it would have taken him a minimum of three years to produce the four books.

E. L. Nemirovskiĭ has offered the theory that Fiol had at least two presses working simultaneously with a great number of typesetters, pressmen, proofreaders, etc.—employees of Belorussian and Ruthenian extraction whom he recruited from among Cracow University professors and students. According to Nemirovskiĭ's theory 400 working days were needed to print all four books; 250 for type composition, 150 for impressions, in all approximately one to one and a half years.[4] Theoretically, Fiol could have owned two presses, or even four for that matter, the same number Makarios had later in Cetinje. But there is no proof he had more than one; and there are strong indications he had but one. The uniformity of impress argues for one press only.

In addition, a list of student names enrolled at Cracow University does not reveal any abundance of professors and students of Ruthenian origin in Fiol's time.[5] If a large number of Ruthenians were available to help out in Fiol's enterprise then we must ask why the most prominent person connected with the press, Borsdorf, the engraver, was a student of German extraction.

In his *Nachalo slavianskogo knigopechataniia* (The Beginning of Slavonic Printing) Nemirovskiĭ revised his earlier theory and came up with an entirely new hypothesis. *Osmoglasnik,* he stated, was published in 1491. *Chasoslovec* was partly printed with *Osmoglasnik* in 1491 and partly with the *Triods* in 1493; *Triods,* he maintains, then, were printed after *Osmoglasnik* and *Chasoslovec*! Furthermore the shop was reopened between 1493 and 1496 and the printer could have been someone else altogether. Nemirovskiĭ's statement is as follows:

> We indicate that *Chasoslovec, Triod Postnaja* and *Triod Cvetnaja* were printed and came out about 1493. How does this agree with the date 1491 on the imprint page of *Chasoslovec*? The date could have been put there deliberately to conceal the continued activity of the printing shop after 1491, which had no approval by proper authorities. For the same reason the *Triods* could have been stripped of the printer's imprints. How long did the printing shop operate? Obviously not more than two or three years. Calli-

[4] Nemirovskiĭ, *Nachalo,* pp. 195–196.
[5] *Album studiosorum Universitatis Cracoviensis,* vols. I–IV.

machus died in 1496 and a new wave of reaction commenced. Nonetheless in 1498, when Celtes asked for the Slavic books printed by Fiol, the latter answered he had none in his possession.[6]

By no stretch of the imagination can this interpretation be considered accurate. Nemirovskiĭ's inconsistencies and contradictions are obvious; he states that both *Triods* and part of *Chasoslovec* were printed and published in 1493; a few lines later he states that the printing shop operated "obviously not more than two or three years." In the very next sentence he suggests that Fiol's shop closed in 1496 as a result of the reactionary wave of Catholicism following the death of Callimachus. He offers no explanation for the 1493 date when he suggests that Fiol or someone else finished the prints.

This complex set of speculations is purely a figment of Nemirovskiĭ's imagination, through which he desperately tries to support his statement that *Osmoglasnik* was printed first, followed by *Chasoslovec,* although only partially executed in 1491. By accepting the year 1491 as the year in which Fiol began his printing activities and being, understandably, unable to substantiate the notion that all four books could have been printed in one year (we have already seen the inaccuracy of this theory), Nemirovskiĭ created the reinstallation of the printing shop in 1493. He tells us the other books were executed following that date.

For the sake of clarity, let us examine Nemirovskiĭ's hypothesis that the books were printed in the following sequence: *Osmoglasnik* in 1491; *Chasoslovec* was begun in 1491 and completed in 1493; *Triod Postnaja* and *Triod Cvetnaja* in 1493, or possibly later, but not after 1496. He supports this supposition with other arguments: (1) Printers usually start with smaller print runs (there were 86 sheets of paper used for *Osmoglasnik,* 95.5 for *Chasoslovec* and 157 for *Triod Postnaja* and 183 for *Triod Cvetnaja,* and (2) Printers successively increase, not decrease, type ornaments (*Osmoglasnik* has one woodcut ornamental initial; *Chasoslovec* has two; *Triod Postnaja* has three of two woodblocks; *Triod Cvetnaja* has 63 of 13 woodblocks). Thus the sequence established by Nemirovskiĭ is, in his opinion, again supported by the increased use of ornaments. Finally, he states, since the paper used in both *Triods* is the same as in the last sections, or quires, of *Chasoslovec,* they must have been printed simultaneously. Proofreading sheets, now in the Jagellonian University Library, are printed on one side of the sheet with part of *Triod Postnaja* and on the other with part of *Chasoslovec.* According to Nemirovskiĭ this is proof that *Chasoslovec* was printed first and *Triod Postnaja* later.

In analyzing Nemirovskiĭ's hypothesis we will begin with the last of his suppositions: the proof sheets have documentary value in that they prove that *Triod Postnaja* and *Chasoslovec* were printed in the same printing shop, also about the same time or period. *Chasoslovec* for the most part was printed on a different

[6]Nemirovskiĭ, *Nachalo,* p. 205.

paper, although some remnants left over from the *Triods* were used. The use of the paper remnants from the *Triods* in the last sections (quires) of *Chasoslovec* has no significance and is of no value in the attempt to reconstruct Fiol's printing timetable. Applying Nemirovskiĭ's theory to a modern analogy: Suppose someone owned a printing shop which printed a new version of the Bible in 1971, using a part of a stock of paper he had on hand. Three years later he prints the proof sheets for a novel and the last section of the novel on the same paper. Would that in any manner suggest, much less prove, that he printed the Bible and the novel in the same year? It would if we applied Nemirovskiĭ's logic to Fiol's timetable.

Nor is the increased use of ornamentation a basic sign of better and improved printing. While *Triod Cvetnaja* contains the most decorative elements, it is the most primitive and inefficient work done by Fiol. Woodblock initials are not a sign of quality in typography now nor were they in Fiol's time. The initials and other illuminative elements in *Triod Cvetnaja* resemble the technique and style used in contemporary manuscripts; later typography indicates that efforts were made to break away from this tradition. Woodblocks often crack in the drying process that follows printing and are not reusable. Skaryna's portrait, for example, has been printed in three different books of the Bible: *Joshua Sirach* (1517), *Kings* (1518), and *Genesis* (1519), and all three printings were from new woodblocks.[7] The same design depicting the coat of arms of the city of Cracow as printed in *Osmoglasnik* and *Chasoslovec* are from different woodblocks. Therefore, Nemirovskiĭ's argument is, in reality, counter to his theory. As he improved his printing technique, Fiol decreased the number of woodblocks and increased the use of initials cut in metal. Thus, the last book printed, *Osmoglasnik,* hardly resembles a medieval manuscript while *Triod Cvetnaja* does very much.

Nemirovskiĭ's suggestion that the size of the print runs indicates a basis for the determination of the chronology of the books cannot be taken seriously either. Fiol did not initiate the printing of Cyrillic books haphazardly. Not only was he given the money by Turzo to do so and probably instructed by him, but he was also given sample manuscripts by some competent person with directions as to the sequence in which they were to be printed. The schedule of printing was well planned and executed accordingly.

Thus it is most likely that *Triod Cvetnaja* was printed first, then *Triod Postnaja.* These books covered the two most important periods of the Christian religion, Lent and the time from Easter to Pentecost. The third book printed was *Chasoslovec,* containing portions of the ecclesiastical office extending throughout the entire year. *Osmoglasnik,* containing variable parts of the service from the first Sunday after Whitsun until the tenth Sunday before Easter, was printed last.

[7] Symon Braha, "Partrety doktara Skaryny" (Dr. Skaryna's Portraits), *Konadni* (New York and München), 1963, No. 7, p. 146.

In short, Nemirovskiĭ's theory as to the sequence in which the books were printed has no documentary basis; nor does his statement that the printing shop was reestablished after the death of Archbishop Oleśnicki. The death of the Archbishop could not affect the law one way or the other. It is inconceivable that Fiol or anyone else would, or could, have reinstated Cyrillic printing in Cracow only two years after the Chapter's interdict forbidding the printing and distribution of Eastern Orthodox books.

Little attention has been paid to the paper used in Fiol's books although the Russian scholar N. P. Likhachev researched the subject thoroughly and offered an excellent analysis in his *Paleograficheskoe znachenie bumazhnykh vodnykh znakov* (The Paleographic Significance of Paper Watermarks).[8] In the third volume of Likhachev's work reproductions of watermarks from Fiol's prints offer valuable insights into many basic questions still disputed by incunabulists.[9]

There is a continuity of watermarks on the paper used in three of the books. *Triod Cvetnaja* and most of *Triod Postnaja* were printed on paper with three identical watermarks. As the printing of *Triod Postnaja* progressed, new paper was used that contained a new, fourth watermark. *Chasoslovec* was printed partially on paper with a new watermark and partially on paper used for both *Triods,* probably remnants. To date we have not been able to find a continuation of the paper used in the printing of *Osmoglasnik,* where sixteen different watermarks were used.

The lack of a direct link between the paper used in *Osmoglasnik* and in *Triods* could be used as argument that *Osmoglasnik* was printed later. If *Osmoglasnik* had been printed first, some of its remnants would have been used for printing subsequent books. The great variety of paper with differing watermarks probably indicates that paper stock had been gathered for new books that Fiol was planning to print in the future. We know from other sources that Fiol had ordered a new set of type from Borsdorf which he never received, or at any rate had no chance to use.

A description of watermarks collected by Likhachev, including modifiers and completions from the works of C. M. Briquet and Eduard Bodeman, follows and is arranged in chronological order according to the sequence in which the books were printed.[10] The numbers are from Likhachev, *Paleograficheskoe . . . ,* I. Symbols are given from volume III, Tables CCCCXLV–CCCCXLVIII. To date, twenty-one different watermarks have been found in the four books.[11]

[8] N. P. Likhachev, *Paleograficheskoe znachenie bumazhnykh vodnykh znakov* (Paleographic Significance of Paper Watermarks), (St. Petersburg, 1899), 3 vols.

[9] *Ibid.,* Vol. III, 445–448.

[10] C. M. Briquet, *Les filigranes. Dictionnaire historique des marques de papier. Des Leur apparition vers 1282 jusqu'en 1600.* (The New Briquet—Jubilee edition.) General editors: J.S.G. Simmons (Amsterdam, 1968); Eduard Bodeman, *Xylographische und typographische Inkunabeln der Königlichen öffentlichen Bibliothek zu Hannover.* (Hannover, 1866), No. 54.

[11] Numbers are from Likhachev, *Paleograficheskoe. . . , I,* 397–399. Symbols are from volume II, Tables CCCCXLV–CCCCXLVIII.

TRIOD CVETNAJA

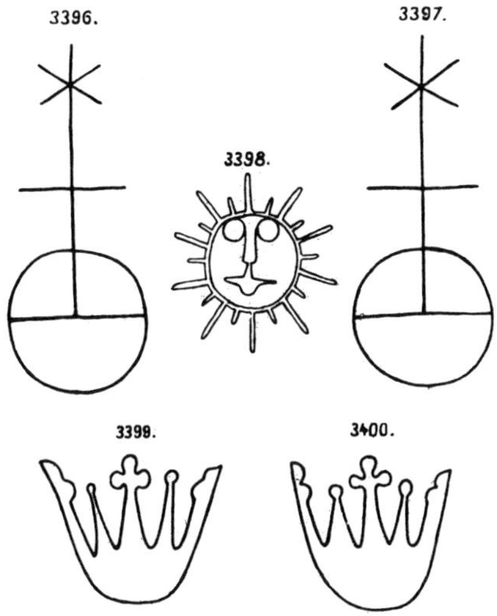

Likhachev No.'s

No. 3396 & No. 3397: A circle from the diameter of which a perpendicular line is drawn, ending in a small star through the crossing of three lines. (Briquet, No. 3056–3068).

No. 3398: The sun, with a human face; a watermark identical with No. 3393 and No. 3394. (Briquet, No. 13944).

No. 3399 & No. 3400: A crown with five prongs. (Briquet, No. 4778, No. 4798).

Watermarks No.'s 3396–3400 are taken from *Triod Cvetnaja* in the collection of W. M. Undolski, Copy No. 5.

TRIPESNEC — TRIOD POSTNAJA

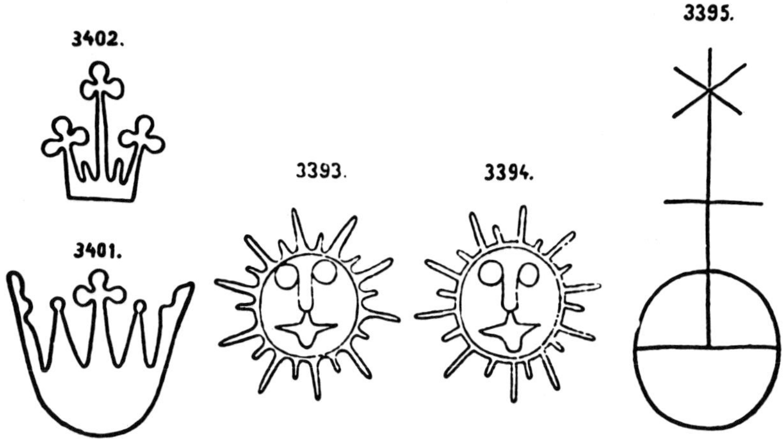

Likhachev No.'s

No. 3401:	A crown with five prongs identical with No. 3398 and No. 3400 of *Triod Cvetnaja.* (Briquet No. 4798).
No. 3402:	Small crown with three prongs each crowned with three leaves. (Briquet No. 4799).
No.'s 3393 & 3394:	The sun with a human face. Two variants almost identical with No. 3398. (Briquet, No. 13944).
No. 3395:	A circle from the diameter of which a perpendicular line is drawn, ending in a small star through the crossing of three lines, identical with No. 3396 and No. 3397 of *Triod Cvetnaja.* (Briquet, No.'s 3056–3068).

Watermarks Nos. 3393, 3394, 3395, 3401, and 3402 are taken from the *Triod Postnaja,* a copy at the Imperial Public Library, St. Petersburg.

There are three basic watermarks contained in both *Triodions*: circle, sun and crown, with small variations and only in *Triod Postnaja* does a new watermark appear—small crown with three prongs.

The watermarks, in addition to the type, prove that both *Triodions* were printed in the same printing shop and at about the same time; first, *Triod Cvetnaja* and second, *Triod Postnaja.*

CHASOSLOVEC

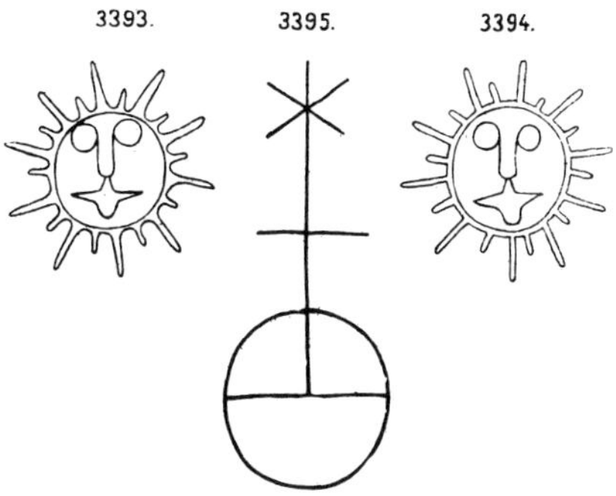

Likhachev No.'s

No. 3393 & No. 3394: The sun with a human face. The watermarks are identical with those in *Triod Cvetnaja* and *Triod Postnaja.* (Briquet, No. 13944).

No. 3395: Circle with the diameter. The watermark is identical with those in both *Triodions.* (Briquet, No.'s 3056–3068).

The above watermarks were taken from *Chasoslovec* printed in Cracow by Szwajpolt Fiol in 1491; now Copy No. 2 of the Rumiantsev Museum in Moscow.

The fact that both watermarks—the sun with the human face and the circle with the diameter, etc.—are identical with those found in the *Triodions* prompted Likhachev to state that all three prints are of the same origin: "There cannot be another deduction; according to the watermarks (identical in both *Triodions*) with the dated editions by Szwajpolt Feol, that the origin is common."[12]

Thanks to the watermarks, the common origin of the dated editions is obvious. Naturally, the similarity of type is the first proof, now well supported by paper watermarks.

Briquet No.
No. 6503

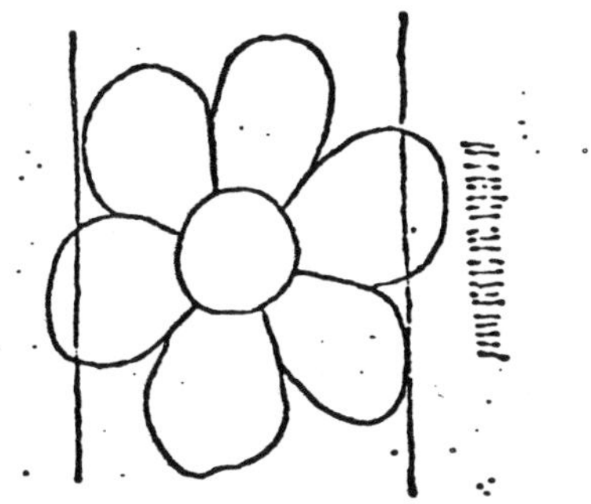

The third watermark not mentioned by Likhachev is a flower. It is found in the Briquet collection as No. 6503. This symbol does not appear in any other book. It probably indicates a supplementary paper.

[12] Likhachev, *Paleograficheskoe . . . ,* III: 396.

OSMOGLASNIK — OCTOECHOS

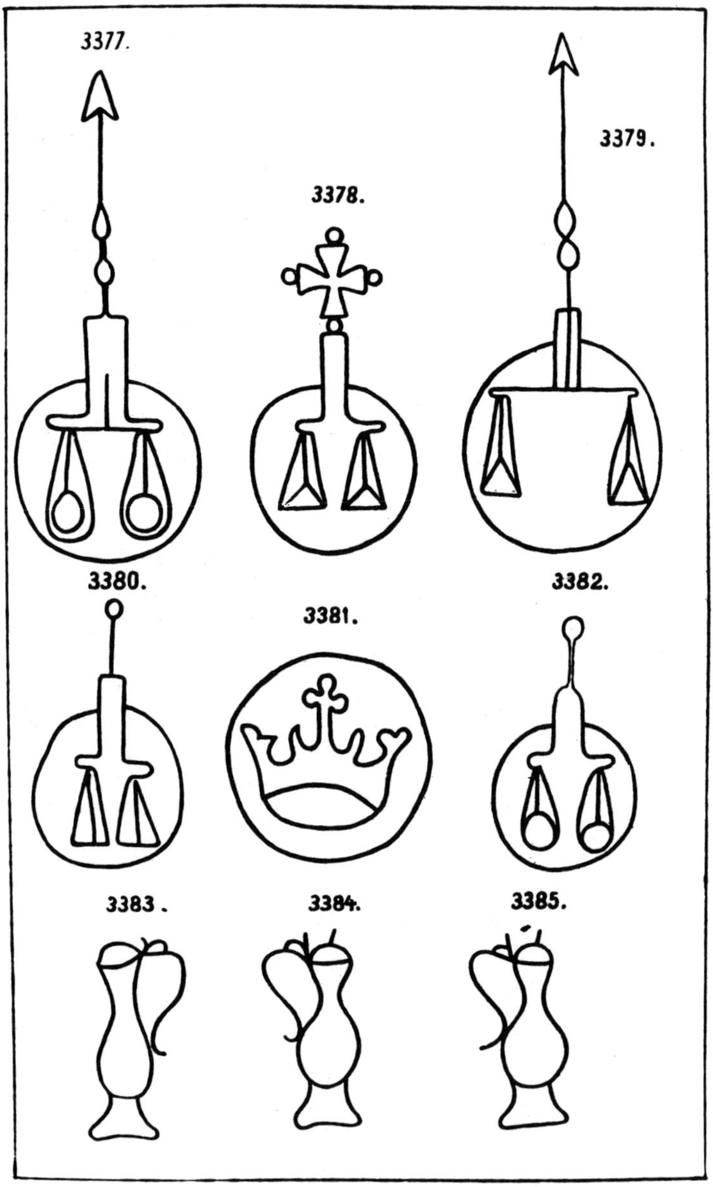

OSMOGLASNIK

Likhachev No.'s

No. 3377:	Scales in a circle; the plates of the scales are round; there is an ornament above the scales, ending in an arrow. (Briquet, No. 2547).
No. 3378:	Scales in a circle in the form of a triangle; a cross above the scales adorned by small balls. (Briquet, No. 2565). (Mošin, No. 7).[13]
No. 3379:	Scales in a circle; the plates of the scales in the form of a triangle; an ornament above the scales, ending in an arrow. (Briquet, No. 2468).
No. 3380:	Tiny scales in a circle; the plates of the scales in the form of triangles; a line above the scales, ending in a small circle.
No. 3381:	A crown in a circle. (Briquet, No.'s 4862, 4864).
No. 3382:	Tiny scales in a circle; a line above the scales, ending in a circle; the plates on the scales are round.

Watermarks No.'s 3377–3382 are taken from the *Osmoglasnik* printed by Szwajpolt Fiol in 1491, a copy in the Public Library in St. Petersburg.

No.'s 3383–3385:	A small, smooth pitcher with one handle: three variants.

Watermarks are taken from Fiol's *Osmoglasnik,* a copy at the Rumiantsev Museum in Moscow. Most of the book was printed on paper with this watermark. (Briquet, No.'s 12544–12547).

[13] V. Mošin, "Vodeni znaci najstarijih srpskih štampanih knjiga" (Watermarks of the Oldest Printed Serbian Books), *Zbornik, Muzej primenjene umetnosti* (Beograd, 1967), II, 7–24.

OSMOGLASNIK (Cont'd)

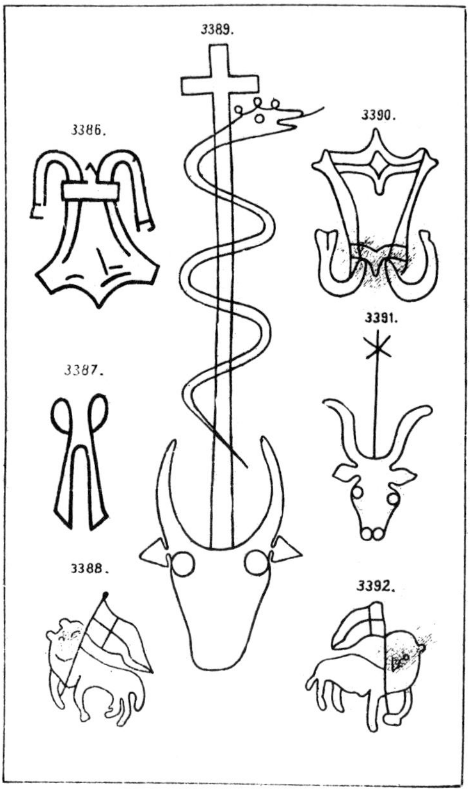

Likhachev No.'s

No. 3386:	A symbol representing an unidentified object. (Briquet, No.'s 16061–16063).
No. 3387:	Tiny scissors in the form of pliers.
No. 3388:	A lamb with a flag. (Briquet, No.'s 23–25). Identical with No. 3392.
No. 3389:	The head of a bull with a large cross between the horns. A snake is entwined around the cross. Usually this kind of watermark is a very correct drawing. This symbol was found on two leaves only, used perhaps when replacing some errors. (Briquet, No.'s 15366–15381).
No. 3390:	Watermark, representing an unidentified object, similar to No. 3386. (Briquet, No. 15364).

No. 3391: The head of a bull, small; a small line between the horns, the line ending in a small star formed by the crossing of three lines; the nostrils are two circles. (Briquet No. 15054, No. 15061, No. 15064, No. 15063, No. 15089). F. Piekosiński found this paper in manuscripts of 1390–1450.[14]

No. 3392: A lamb with a flag. (Briquet, No.'s 23–25). Identical with No. 3388. The lamb with a flag—Likhachev No. 3388 and No. 3392.

The watermarks No.'s 3388–3392 are taken from Fiol's *Osmoglasnik* copy which was in the Public Library in St. Petersburg.

Another watermark was found by Likhachev, described as a salamander in a circle. Because it was not distinct enough it was not photocopied by Likhachev. No one else mentioned this watermark. It would be advisable to check more carefully on this symbol.

Two watermarks mentioned by Nemirovskiĭ[15] under his No. 2 and No. 3, which Briquet lists as No. 15364 and No. 15365 are not to be found in Likhachev's work and should be added to the list.

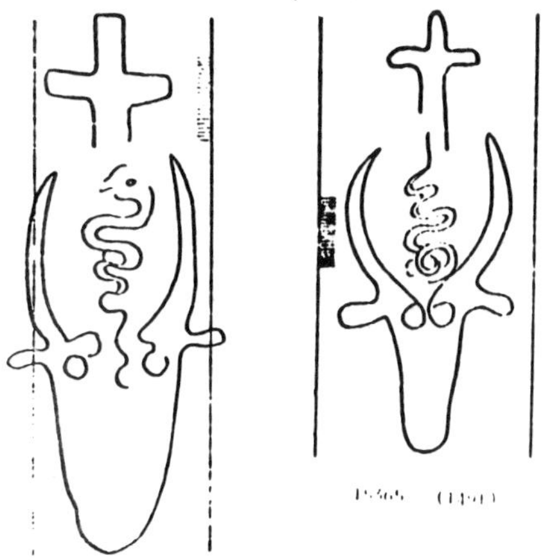

Briquet No.'s

No. 15364: The head of a bull with a snake between the horns; above the head a cross. Nemirovskiĭ does not describe the position of the snake. In Briquet No. 15364 drawing we find that the position of the snake is upright.

No. 15365: The head of a bull with a snake between the horns; above the head a cross with prolonged vertical stem. Again

[14] Franciszek Piekosiński, *Średniowieczne znaki wodne, Wiek XIV.* (Watermarks of the Middle Ages, XIV Century), (Cracow, 1893), see also: *Wybór znaków wodnych z XV stulecia* (Selected Watermarks of the XVth Century), (Cracow, 1896).

[15] Nemirovskiĭ, *Nachalo,* p. 98.

Nemirovskiĭ does not describe the position of the snake. In Briquet, No. 15365 drawing the position of the snake is with the head downward, the tail up. Both watermarks are rare. They were found in the archives of Wrocław, the capital of Silesia.

In all there are sixteen watermarks in *Osmoglasnik,* none of which is identical with those found in the other three books. Therefore without the colophon, Fiol's printing shop would not have been identified by examining the paper alone. But we cannot exclude the fact that in other copies we can find common watermarks for all four prints. Unknown to us some remnants could have been used for those copies, or for those that have not yet been studied for watermarks.

In studying Bodeman's description of the six watermarks listed under No. 54, we find that two of them are mentioned by Likhachev as appearing on paper used in Fiol's *Osmoglasnik*—namely No. 3386 and No. 3387. Francisco Del Tuppo's *Aesopi Vita et Fabulae* was printed on this same paper in 1585 in Naples. It was a large book in folio opulently illustrated. Bodeman stated: It is "a very rare and beautiful edition with many interesting and good woodcuts, which were attributed to Matheus Moravus."[16]

We found that watermark No. 3405, on Likhachev's Table CCCCXLVIII (tiny scissors, a variant of symbol No. 3387), appears on paper on which *Osmoglasnik* was printed in Cetinje, Montenegro, in 1494. It is entirely possible that both printers obtained their paper independently from Naples; but it is also possible that the paper used to print the Cetinje book came from Cracow with the sample copy of Fiol's *Osmoglasnik*. Because Likhachev did not reproduce watermark No. 3387 himself but took it from Bodeman's drawings, it is necessary to check once more the three prints on which this mark appears: Francisco Del Tuppo's *Aesopi Fabulae* (Naples, 1485); Fiol's *Osmoglasnik* (Cracow, 1491) and Makarios's *Osmoglasnik* (Cetinje, 1494). It is also interesting that Mošin's No. 7 watermark was taken from Cetinje's *Osmoglasnik* (Prvoglasnik, 1494). It is almost identical with the watermark reproduced by N. P. Likhachev under his listing No. 3378 from *Osmoglasnik* printed by Fiol in 1491.

We have taken other factors into consideration in addition to a thorough analysis of the paper used by Fiol: progressive technical improvements such as the alignment of type, margins, modern marking of sections, colophons, decreasing use of woodblocks replaced by a better use of cast metal initials—and have concluded, as stated previously, that Fiol's editions were printed in the following sequence: *Triod Cvetnaja* first, then *Triod Postnaja*; next came *Chasoslovec* and fourth and last, *Osmoglasnik* was printed. All were executed in a span of about three years, between 1488 and 1491, by the master printer Szwajpolt Fiol.

[16] Bodeman, *Xylographische und typographische Inkunabeln . . . ,* No. 54. "Sehr seltene und schöne Ausgabe, mit vielen interessanten und guten Holzschnitten welche dem Math. Moravus zugeschrieben werden."

7
Characteristics of Borsdorf's Type

Fiol had little trouble securing professional printers for his shop. As we have seen men in Cracow and elsewhere in Poland had learned the infant art and were able to aid him in the organization of a printing press according to Western standards. Typesetters, however, were another matter. A knowledge of Cyrillic script was a prerequisite. Fortunately, finding such men was not difficult in Cracow as many members of the King's court were followers of the Orthodox rite.

Fiol was successful in being able to solve quickly what could have been a major problem, finding a type designer with an inventive spirit to produce a set of type of the Cyrillic alphabet. Borsdorf solved this problem splendidly, and a new cultural adventure opened to mankind. His design is a combination of medieval uncial with a touch of classic antiqua, shaped in the form of majuscule—straight, rounded, clean, readable, but nonetheless, certain letters taking a cursive form. Borsdorf's type is a kind of amalgam of uncial and half uncial; basically it is South Slavic *ustav* (uncial) with some elements of Belorussian *polustav* (half uncial). Even though written at the turn of this century, Evfemiĭ Fedorovich Karskij's book *Byelorusy, Jazyk byeloruskago naroda* (The Belorussians: The Language of the Belorussian People) presents the best study to date of *ustav* and *polustav* with many examples and details, and special attention paid to Belorussian *polustav*. There is a noticeable difference between the Belorussian, the Ukrainian and Russian *polustav*. *Ustav* or Cyrillic uncial is the oldest form of Cyrillic character, used between the eleventh and fifteenth centuries. Influenced by the Greek majuscule, this penmanship was artistic, readable, clean, straight and rounded with minimal abbreviations. Beginning in the thirteenth century the *polustav* or half uncial was developed with characteristic smaller size letters, many abbreviations, ligatures (a character consisting of two or more letters joined to avoid awkward spaces and to economize space) and with the letters more elaborated with nooses, prolongations of strokes, flourishes, among others.[1]

Borsdorf followed the Slavonic-Byzantine examples and in designing the type

[1] E. F. Karskiĭ, *Belorussy. Iazyk belorusskogo naroda* (The Belorussians. The Language of the Belorussian People), Akademiia Nauk SSSR (Moscow, 1955), I, 49–76.

he retained purity in the spirit of Cyrillic penmanship. Except for minimal adaptation of Glagolitic handwriting with some difficult letters, no influence of contemporary Western printing—German Gothic or Latin-Italian Antiqua—can be found. Borsdorf designed his type face slightly condensed which, with a tight setting of letters and words, caused the characters to appear much more condensed than they actually were. Readability is fair. The legibility of Fiol's is striking considering there is no spacing between words in the sentences and the type is not perfectly cut with heavy strokes of borderlines on individual type. A. A. Sidorov, sceptical in regard to Fiol's achievements in type design, nevertheless has objectively admitted: "On the whole, the Russian [Cyrillic] type cut by Borsdorf for Feol, while sometimes not good in design, nevertheless is easy to read."[2]

Similarities with manuscripts are to be found in the following: (1) Some letters in the alphabet have several forms; (2) Names were not capitalized; (3) No spacing between words in sentences; (4) Regarding words there were no rules on division of words nor any signs for that purpose; and (5) Sentences were well spaced and marked.

Borsdorf prepared the following sets for Fiol (derived from both *Triods* and *Chasoslovec*):[3]

			Amount
I.	(7)	Caption letters for *Chasoslovec*	29
II.	(8)	Caption letters for *Triods*	49
III.	(9)	Majuscules—big size	24
IV.	(10)	Majuscules—smaller size	30
V.	(11)	Minuscules	47
VI.	(12)	Superscript letters without titlo[4] (abbreviation marks)	6
VII.	(13)	Superscript letters with abbreviation marks	16
VIII.	(14)	Punctuation, aspiration and accentuation marks	12
IX.	(6)	Initials—in *Triods* and *Chasoslovec*	18
		Total	231

The Cyrillic alphabet improved by Cyril's pupils originally contained 44 letters. Glagolitic had only 40. Borsdorf used most of the same letters except for a few that were obsolete; however, he introduced some innovations, especially several variations of the letter "O." Together his set of minuscules contains 47 symbols.

Cyrillic and Glagolitic alphabets do not have special symbols for numbers. The

[2] A. A. Sidorov, "Khudozhestvenno-tekhnicheskie osobennosti slavianskogo pervopechataniia" (Artistic and Technical Peculiarities of Early Slavic Printing) in *U istokov russkogo knigopechataniia* (At the Beginning of Russian Book Printing), Akademiia Nauk USSR (Moscow, 1959), p. 54.

[3] Numbers in parenthesis. See attached tables.

I.

№ 7. *Буквы связныя въ надписяхъ.*

Caption letters — from Chasoslovec.

II.

№ 8. *Буквы связныя въ надписяхъ.*

Caption letters — from Triods.

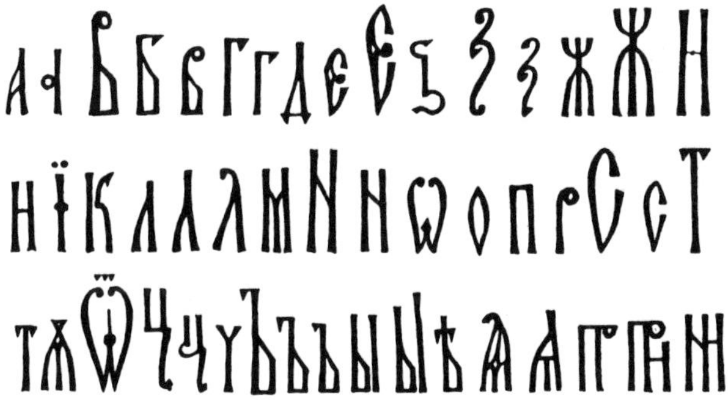

III.

№ 9. *Буквы прописныя большія.*

Capital letters — large.

IV.

Majuscules

№ 10. *Буквы прописныя малыя.*

(Capital letters small.)

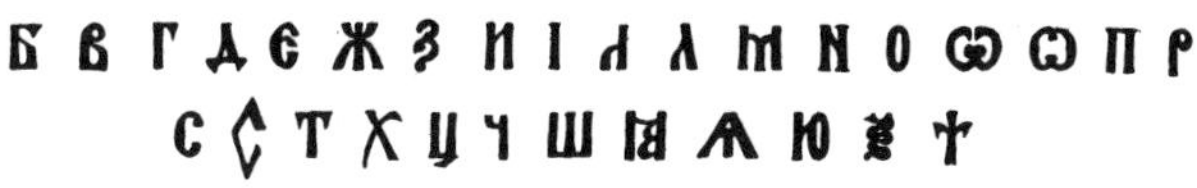

V.
Minuscules

№ 11. Буквы строчныя.

a b v g d e e/ye zh dz z i ï/y k l m n o o o o o p r s

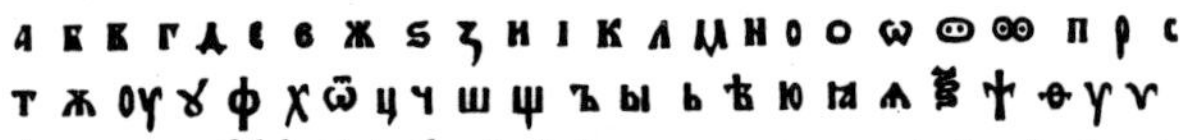

t ą ou ou f kh ot ts ch sh shch y ye yu ya ę ksi psi ph y iu
hard jer soft jer

VI.
Superlinear letters without abbreviation marks.

№ 12. Надстрочныя буквы безъ титлъ.

VII.
Superlinear letters with abbreviation marks.

№ 13. Надстрочныя буквы подъ титлами

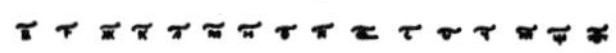

VIII.
Punctuation, aspiration and accentuation marks.

№ 14. Знаки и ударенія.

Initials from *Triod Postnaja* and *Cvetnaja.*

alphabetical letters with the "titlo," [4] a curved horizontal line above each letter, stands for a specific number such as shown on page 96.

To avoid any misunderstanding it must be stressed that in Cyrillic, as well as in the Glagolitic alphabets, majuscules and miniscules differ only in size and not in design. (Compare sets No. III, IV, and V on pages 93 and 94.)

Superscripts demand an explanation—they are anything written above a word or letter as a diacritical mark indicating a special meaning. In medieval Latin superscripts were extensively used, and a whole system of their application developed. According to Bogdan Horodyski, superscript was used sparingly up to the

[4] Titlo: (Greek—τιτλος, Latin—titulus = title). A mark over a letter in the form of a horizontal straight or wavy line used with the half uncial and cursive writing to indicate abbreviation or the use of a letter to represent a number.

Numerals in Cyrillic

sixteenth century in the Cyrillic uncial and half uncial.[5] There was no established system except for a few basic rules. Superscripts were used for the purpose of:

a. Abbreviation—by placing one of the omitted letters in smaller sized character over the word with or without "titlo," when the following were omitted.

b. Assigning numbers—"titlos" were placed above letters which stood for numbers. Before and after the number there is usually placed a full stop. "Titlo" sign used for numbers varied slightly from the others.

Nomina sacra as a rule were written or printed abbreviated by retaining only the first and last letters of the word with "titlo" above, for instance *Christos* ХСЪ. Words often used, for the purpose of economy of space, were also abbreviated by placing one of the omitted letters above the word with or without "titlo," for instance *Konec* — КОЧ (end).

These sets were collected from both *Triods* and *Chasoslovec* by I. P. Sakharov in *Obraztsy slaviano-russkogo knigopechataniia s 1491 goda* (Examples of Slavic-Russian Printing from the Year 1491), printed in St. Petersburg in 1849 but released for distribution in 1891.[6] As far as can be determined, the pictures are accurate reproductions of Borsdorf's type. They are not, however, reproduced photographically.

Altogether there are 231 different types and marks in both *Triods* and *Chasoslovec*. The only woodcut initial—*B* (V)—in *Osmoglasnik* was a new one, and, therefore, was not used in the other books. *Osmoglasnik* also contains several cast iron initials of plain design. These, along with some of the cast iron initials from *Chasoslovec*, were not reproduced by the collector. Therefore, we estimate the total number of Borsdorf's type, diacritical marks, and initials at about 240. Gutenberg had 300.

Technically, Borsdorf's type does not differ from the Latin, Gothic, Greek, Hebrew and others used in Western printing in the fifteenth century or for that matter throughout the entire course of printing. Following Western technique which achieved high standards during the fifty years after Gutenberg, Borsdorf introduced only one innovation, but a very important one for Cyrillic printing. Diacritical and abbreviation marks, the "titlo," were cast separately in Borsdorf's type, while in others, especially in Gothic, they were cast together. In Cyrillic printing it was more convenient and economical to have them separate because of their great use in the Cyrillic alphabet. Makarios of Cetinje, on the other hand, followed the style of the Western printers and was obliged to prepare more type. Separating letters from diacritical marks was however more demanding in ac-

[5] Bogdan Horodyski, *Podręcznik paleografii ruskiej* (Manual of Russian Paleography) (Cracow, 1951), p. 42.

[6] I. P. Sakharov, *Obraztsy slaviano-russkogo knigopechataniia s 1491 goda* (Examples of Slavic-Russian Printing from the Year 1491), (St. Petersburg, 1849) [not distributed then]. Reprint 1891.

curacy and precision work. It was also time consuming and mistakes were unavoidable.

As yet no thorough study has been made of the type used in the entire process of Cyrillic printing as was done for Western printing in Konrad Haebler's *Typenrepertorium der Wiegendrucke.*[7] Some Russian scholars have conducted partial investigations. Not having the opportunity to perform comparative studies on the different copies other than those available in the West, we will attempt to analyze the result of the Russian research. Nemirovskiĭ is of the opinion that only one set of type for all four books was used with no changes or improvements. On the other hand, Antonina Sergeevna Zernova, who conducted a more intensive study, stated that she found differences in the cut of type in all of Fiol's books.[8] Our studies of the type, although incomplete, reveal that the *Triods* were printed with a different set of type than were *Osmoglasnik* and *Chasoslovec.* The types, however, were of the same design. Worn-out characters were not just recast, they were redesigned; new matrices were prepared, and then a set of improved type cast. Our theory that more than one set of types was fashioned by Borsdorf has been supported by the findings of other researchers, especially those of A. A. Sidorov.

Sidorov's studies of artistic and technical peculiarities of the Slavic first printings stress improvements in the typography of Fiol's prints from the *Triods* to *Osmoglasnik.* He determined that the *Triods* are more primitive in execution than the later books. This is especially shown in the proportions of the page column. The *Triods'* proportions are strangely elongated in relation of height to width; averages (as the lines are uneven) are in general, 23.13 cm.[9] Sidorov also stresses technical deficiencies in *Triod Cvetnaja* which, in our opinion, was the first book printed by Fiol. "In *Triod Cvetnaja* the lines are not even; leaf 88 ends on two small red strokes on the following page," he writes. "Some capital letters were broken during the pressing."[10] No mention is made of such deficiencies in the following books. With practice comes mastery. Sidorov stresses that the last page of *Chasoslovec* successfully used two colors for decorative purposes with the wedge shape of the page, and in *Osmoglasnik* proportions of the columns are more harmonious, 19.1 cm. to 12.3 cm. Evolution and improvements are obvious in *Osmoglasnik*; some pages were reworked because of uneven margins.

As Fiol's prints and type have not yet been thoroughly described, the differences in opinion pertaining to the execution of the books are extreme, from Zernova's

[7] Konrad Haebler, *Typenrepertorium der Wiegendrucke* (Leipzig, 1904–1924), vols. 1–6, tables with letters—majuscule *M* for Gothic and *Qu* for Antiqua enabling identification of books and printing shops of the fifteenth century.

[8] A. S. Zernova, "Metodika opisaniia staropechatnykh knig kirillovskoĭ pechati" (Methodology of Describing Old Cyrillic Prints), *Trudy Gosudarstvennoiĭ biblioteki SSSR* (Works of the State Library USSR) (Moscow, 1960), Vol. 4.

[9] A. A. Sidorov, "Khudozhestvenno-tekhnicheskie osobennosti . . . ," p. 54.

[10] *Ibid.,* p. 56.

that all four books were printed with different type to Nemirovskiĭ's that the same type was used for all four prints. All descriptions and dimensions delivered up to the present must be viewed cautiously. On the other hand standards used today are most difficult to apply to fifteenth century printing. Nevertheless some generalities can be used with regard to the forming and designing of Borsdorf's type.

The size of the type face is about ten points, ca. 3.76 mm. (as in contemporary Garamond-korpus).[11] The space between two lines is also about 3.76 mm. so the height of the whole line is almost 7.8 mm. In both *Triods* the type page, containing thirty lines, is about 235 mm. (a little over nine inches); *Chasoslovec* with nineteen lines is about 150 mm. (ca. six inches); and *Osmoglasnik* with its twenty-five lines is approximately 195 mm. or ca. eight inches.

Borsdorf's minuscule alphabet has two ascenders: ligature *ou* ȣ and the latter *jat* ѣ, ten descenders and two letters with ascending and descending parts, ф *f-ert* and ѱ *psi*. Some letters are peculiar, especially the letter *M* м which has a middle part descending below the line. This letter, like the set of *M*'s in *Typenrepertorium der Wiegendrucke,* could aid us in establishing associations with other prints and printing shops. Another letter which could be very helpful is ч (*ch*) which is very asymmetric. These two letters could offer a convenient clue for ascertaining a relationship with subsequent printing establishments. Characteristic of Borsdorf's alphabet is the lack of ligatures which became current in contemporary (the end of the fifteenth century) manuscripts and handwriting. The only one in his alphabet is *oy-y* (read *ou-u*).

Some features of Borsdorf's design differentiate his type from contemporary handwriting found in Cyrillic manuscripts. In contrast to contemporary tendencies toward slanting lines in writing, Borsdorf's type is characterized by perpendicular straight lines in letters, causing his print to appear slightly archaic. Possibly the sample text used by Borsdorf was rather old (in uncial); possibly he designed his type to differentiate print from contemporary writing with its inclination toward cursive lines.

Another very individual trait in Borsdorf's type is the triangular notches of horizontal lines in letters, like т г. Many other letters also have the same more or less triangular notches at the end of extended lines (see b, g, k, l, and others). This was contrary to the handwriting custom of the period. Scribes finished letters with a turned-up rather rounded stroke. Borsdorf found it easy to prepare his type with the finishing stroke turned down and triangular. The inspiration for this, we feel, lies in the old Cyrillic. We find it in many manuscripts of the

[11] Pierre S. Fournier (1712–1768) in his *Manuel typographique* 2 vols.; Paris, 1764, established a unit of typographical measurement of type called "point." It is the vertical thickness of the body. A point is equal to 1/666 of a meter = 0.376 mm. = .013837 inch. There are approximately 72 points to the inch.

thirteenth century. See the following illustration and note the striking resemblance to Fiol's type.

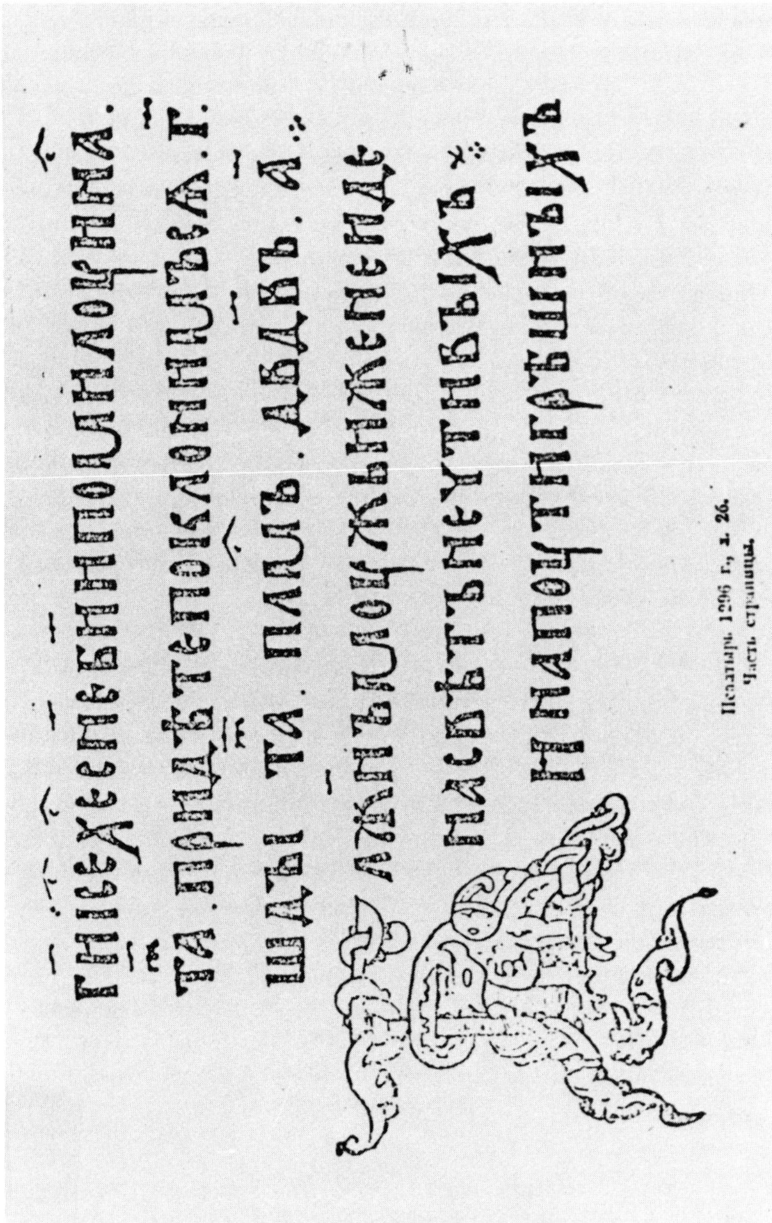

Psalter of 1296. Tetarological Initial and Script in South Slavonic.

Typical features of the Cyrillic script and typography are the caption letters of elaborate design for decorative purposes. Sets No. I and II on page 93 present Borsdorf's characters used in the so-called *vyaz',* that is the joined interlace of adjoining caption letters into one continuous line. *Vyaz'* appears in titles and headings of chapters, also in the first line of Psalms and prayers as parts of special services. Fiol, in accordance with the spirit of Western typography, printed his clichéd line—*vyaz'* from type composition and not from woodblocks. This was contrary to other early Slavic typographers who for a long time stuck to the manuscript tradition in the use of woodcuts; Fiol's second innovation.

Vyaz' is of Byzantine origin. Slavic nations accepted it very early, and through the centuries had developed a few basic forms. Among the South Slavic nations the floral design, which dominated the fourteenth century, was in use. From the fifteenth through the sixteenth and seventeenth centuries, the Belorussian style prevailed, with its distinctive elongated lettering, remarkable in its legibility. The Muscovite style of *vyaz',* difficult to read but exceedingly decorative and elaborate, evolves from the sixteenth century. The use of *vyaz'* in typography continued into the nineteenth century.

To visualize how *vyaz',* the so-called clichéd line, presents itself and its evolution through the centuries, see the following illustration. *Vyaz'* is one of the characteristic features of Cyrillic manuscripts and books. The evolution of this feature has a tendency toward obscuring the legibility in favor of the decorative effect. Fortunately Fiol retained in his books the clear and simple form.

In addition to the sets of the regular alphabet Borsdorf designed two sets of caption letters. The larger one was for the *Triods* printed in folio and the smaller for *Chasoslovec,* printed in quarto. Basically both are in the same style; nevertheless, the set for *Chasoslovec* appears to be more distinct, uniform in design, letters are of the same height (12 mm.), giving the impression of an efficient and able workmanship. Only two letters "O" and "R" have two variants. The set of caption letters for the *Triods* appear to be primitive and the design crude. Practically each letter has its own height and many of the letters have two or three variants.

Comparative study of Borsdorf's caption letters with those in contemporary manuscripts reveals that the readability of both sets was good and in general did not differ in style from the regular alphabet. This would indicate that Fiol placed more emphasis on the legibility rather than on the decorative elements of his prints.

In all four prints Fiol's *vyaz'* is composed in pure Belorussian style, as seen in the samples which follow.

1. в недлю ѡ мытари и фарисеи поѹ[чение]
   v ne(d)[e]lju *o* Mytar*i* *i* *Ph*ar*i*se*i* poo*u*[čenie]

2. часословец имѣꙗ и нощнѹю и дневнѹю слѹжбѹ
   ča(s)[o]slove(c) *i*měja *i* noščn*ou*ju *i* dnevn*ou*ju sl*ou*(ž)b*ou*
   по ѹставѹ иже
   po *ou*stav*ou* *i*že

3. въ стѹꙗ великѹꙗ сѫботоѵ вечрь
   v' s[vja]t*ou*ja velik*ou*ja s*u*botou ve(č)[e]r'

4. глас д пѣснь перваꙗ ирмосъ
   glas(') d̄[4] pěsń pervaja *i*rmos'   (128)

Horodyski, Bogdan. *Op. cit.* Fot. 14. Samples of *"vyaz'"* — "first clichéd lines" — fifteenth to the eighteenth century. Manuscripts in the Warsaw National Library.

1.

V PET' VEČER NAGI V' ZVA

Triod Cvetnaja — according to Karataev, *Opisaniye slavyano-russkikh . . .*, p. 12.

2.

TRPEŚNEC NADÉŽJU

Triod Postnaja — according to Karataev, *Ibid.*, p. 10.

3.

S BGOM POCÍNAE OSMÓ glasnik

Osmoglasnik — according to Karataev, *Ibid.*, p. 2.

Przemyśl Evangeliar. Fourteenth century uncial, Moldavian edition.

Sunday Sermons. Russian half-uncial of the fifteenth century.

The influence of the written sample copies is distinctive in the first incunabula. Some printers even made an effort to imitate handwriting. This manifests itself particularly in illumination, especially and understandably in Cyrillic when, in the case in point, the type designer was of German descent. As long as we are unable to determine which manuscripts were used as sample copies, it is most difficult to appraise the ingenuity of Borsdorf. Indications are that he did not imitate a sample text but was creative enough to design a new type in the old Slavic-Byzantine style and spirit.

Also in doing so, it appears he did not follow all four of the sample texts with which he was supplied. Perhaps he was following the style of only one or perhaps, referring to all four, he created his own design. Manuscripts with original Cyrillic uncial script dominated from the tenth to the thirteenth century. We may, therefore, refer to Borsdorf's type as Cyrillic conservative. He used one ligature, as we have pointed out, and abbreviations in moderation with an effort to avoid the apostrophe. As a result his type caused Fiol's prints to appear more modern than some done later.

It was the custom to use punctuation very rarely but to use it properly. As there was no spacing between words, the only cardinal rule was to stop at the end of a line. Sometimes only one letter of the next word filled leftover space. Sentences, however, were well-scored by punctuation marks.

Borsdorf was successful in creating Cyrillic type. The question of whether he knew any Slavic language is a puzzle that has not been and probably never will be solved. The frequently offered view that he had to know the language in order to produce the excellent type used by Fiol is not entirely convincing. Many printers of the era produced type for printing Greek, Hebrew and other languages without any knowledge of the languages. But Borsdorf's type so well expressed the very essence of the Slavic language that it is hard to believe he did not have some knowledge of it. And Fiol, himself an engraver, was fully satisfied with Borsdorf's work.

On the other hand it is entirely possible that Fiol merely compared the type to the manuscript script from which the patterns had been taken. If we were able to determine which manuscripts were used and had access to them, it would be possible to determine whether Borsdorf's type was a duplication of the script or a printer's free creative composition. A comparison of *Triod Postnaja, Triod Cvetnaja, Osmoglasnik* and *Chasoslovec* manuscripts with Fiol's prints would, at least partially, answer the question. Nemirovskiĭ is the only scholar who has attempted such a comparison, but he studied only Russian manuscripts, omitting the Belorussian and seldom using the Ukrainian. Therefore his studies are incomplete. At any rate he did not find any original texts which could have served as models.

The close contacts with neighboring Moldavia were helpful in providing books for the Ruthenian principalities of Halicz and Vladimir, which were allied with the Polish kingdom in the fourteenth century. Throughout these territories numerous

Cyrillic manuscripts of Moldavian and Bulgarian origin were found in churches and monasteries. The so-called *Przemyśl Evangeliar* is a Moldavian manuscript in uncial of that period. This manuscript found barely a hundred miles from Cracow, as well as others also located close to the printing center, should be taken into consideration in search of the pattern for Borsdorf's type. The striking resemblance of Fiol's prints to the *Przemyśl Evangeliar* type would indicate how little in common it has with the Russian manuscript presented here for comparison.

8
Characteristics of Fiol's Typography

Before we describe the characteristics of Fiol's typography, a recent discovery of new material generally unknown to scholars must be presented. In all the known preserved copies of both *Triods*, the first two and the last two leaves are missing opening the field to various speculations as to what they could have contained. The majority of scholars were inclined to believe they were blank. The absence of any printer's device in both *Triods* was the reason they were, according to bibliographical rules, marked as unidentified and the name Fiol given in brackets as the hypothetical printer.

A complete and well preserved copy of *Triod Cvetnaja* was found in Braşov, Rumania in 1971. The great importance of this discovery, instrumental in solving some basic questions regarding the Cracow Cyrillic printing presently will be discussed in detail. The Braşov copy was unearthed by Prof. Emil Micu, director of the Braşov Museum, in October 1971. Ion-Radu Mircea, a Rumanian scholar, revealed the discovery in his article "From Cracow to Braşov: The Incunabulum from 1491" printed in the *Anul International al Cărţii*, 1972 (International Yearbook of 1972). Prior to this there were two short articles;[1] however their value was only in announcing the discovery.

The *Triod Cvetnaja* as described by Mircea is part of a collection of 1,250 manuscripts and old prints which had belonged to the Church of Saint Nicholas in Şchkeia, located in the vicinity of Braşov (now the capital of the province of Braşov, Rumania). Before World War I this territory belonged to Hungary and in Latin was called Transylvania (Land Beyond the Forest). In Hungarian the territory was known as Erdély and in Rumanian Ardeal; in Fiol's time it was known as Siebenbürgen, and Braşov was then called Kronstadt.

In his studies of this collection Mircea found seven Cyrillic manuscripts from

[1] Ion-Radu Mircea, "De la Cracovia la Braşov: Incunabulul din 1491" (From Cracow to Braşov: The Incunabulum from 1491), *Magazin istoric*, 8/65 (Rumania, 1972): 50–51. Emil Micu and Ion-Radu Mircea. "Un incunabulul unicat in bibliotecile noastre" (A Unique Incunabulum in Our Library). *Scinteia*, [daily paper] February 4, 1972. Catinca Muscan, "Incunabulul de la Scheii Braşovului," (Incunabulum of Scheia-Braşov) *Magazin*, [weekly] (March 4, 1972), p. 5.

the fourteenth and fifteenth centuries (nine after 1424) and twenty-one from the sixteenth century. These were predominantly of Rumanian (Wallachian or Moldavian) origin, but the collection also contained manuscripts of Serbian or Bulgarian, Galician (Polish-Ukrainian), and Muscovy-Russian provenance. In the collection were also the first Cyrillic books of Serbian or Russian provenance printed in the sixteenth century.

As Mircea does not describe any of these manuscripts and old books, we are unable to determine their titles and printers. Furthermore, his terminology is based on generalities: for instance, he refers to Rumania instead of using the proper names for that territory in those centuries, Wallachia and Moldavia. In his references to "Serbian" we are unable to determine whether he means Croatian, Montenegrin, Bosnian or Serbian *sensu stricto,* and in his reference to "Russian" printing shops he does not specify if they were Belorussian, Little Russian (Ukrainian) or Muscovite Russian. Mircea also uses the term "Galicia" which, like Transylvania, belongs to the past and is not used today. Galicia was the name applied to that portion of Poland lying on the northern slopes of the Carpathians which constituted an Austrian crownland between the years 1772 and 1918. After World War I it again became a part of Poland, and following World War II, a portion of this territory with its Polish-Ukrainian population became a part of the Soviet Socialist Ukrainian Republic with the city of Lwiw (Lwów) as its cultural center.

The summary of this portion of Mircea's article with a small correction and explanation is necessary to visualize the exact location of the discovery. It is approximately three hundred miles south of Lwów and four hundred miles south of Craców on the main trail from north to south in Central Europe.

With obvious great pleasure Mircea triumphantly exclaimed *Eureka* when he discovered "an unknown copy of the Cyrillic incunabula from Cracow, (1491), a Triod-Penticostar" [Penticostarion-Cvetnaja] among the old prints of the collection. Naming it the most important book in the collection, Mircea claims that it is the "first known Fiol print that reached, besides Ukraine and Western Russia (Belorussia), our area." If by "our area" Mircea means old Transylvania or the present province of Braşov, he is correct. On the other hand if he intends this to mean Rumania, he is mistaken.

There is no doubt that some, if not all, of Fiol's prints were in the possession of Makarios in Targovişte when he was preparing his own printings about 1507. We know, as a result of I. S. Sventsickiĭ's studies,[2] that a copy of Fiol's *Chasoslovec,* containing provenance notes from 1558 in Rumanian Cyrillic cursive, was discovered in Rumania near the Hungarian border in the nineteenth century. This copy of *Chasoslovec* is presently in the Ukrainian Museum in Lwów.

[2] I. S. Sventsitskiĭ, *Kataloh knih tserkovno-slavianskoĭ pechaty* (Catalogue of Church Slavonic Printing), (Zhovkva, 1908), p. 46.

Mircea is correct in stating that the Braşov copy of *Triod Pentecostarion* is the only one now preserved in Rumania. This allows him to wax enthusiastically about its uniqueness in his country and its bibliographic uniqueness.

The book presently is located in the St. Nicholas Museum of Rumanian Culture in Braşov (Muzeul Culturi Romanesti din Braşov. Braşov). To study it, approval must be obtained from the Ministry of Interior through the Department of Religious Affairs. Statements by Nemirovskiĭ and others that the book is in the National Museum in Braşov are incorrect and misleading.

Shortly after the announcement of the discovery, Mircea published an article in French, in which he presented the cultural background for the inception of Cyrillic printing endeavors: Cracow—Cetinje—Targovişte. He also underscores the close relations of Ruthenia ("Galicia" [Halicz], Volhynia and Kievan Rus') with southern Europe through commercial, cultural and religious connections especially with neighboring Moldavia and North Transylvania. Sobolevskiĭ's theory of the Moldavian provenance of Fiol's prints obtained confirmation in Mircea's findings of close religious and cultural relations: "For the south-east European zone, it is proof of the circulation of the book throughout the whole East Orthodox area, as well as of the exchanges in the frame of Rumanian medieval culture, of the spiritual values with the Ukrainian provinces. . . . The Rumanian countries, in particular Moldavia and northern Transylvania entertained with the Ukrainian centers relations, not only commercial but also cultural, religious and rich donations have been offered to churches and monasteries where the manuscripts had a notable place because of one common literary language—Slavonic, which the Rumanians used in their chancellery and their church."[3]

Without question the most valuable contribution of this article are the three reprints from the Braşov copy. The first reprint of page one (leaf 1 r.) of the book, originally blank, contains a very important provenance note located in the upper portion of the page. The second reprint (leaf 1 v.) has an illustration of the Crucifixion identical with the one found in *Osmoglasnik*. Beneath this illustration is the printer's mark, revealed for the first time. This revelation, unsuspected by scholars, is the most important finding. The third reprint gives the reproduction of the first printed page of *Triod Cvetnaja* on leaf 3 r., similar to those found in other known copies.

[3] Ion Radu Mircea, "Considérations sur les premières oeuvres imprimées à caractères cyrilliques," *Bulletin Association Internationale d'études du Sud-est européen* (Bucharest) X, 1 (1972), 111. "Pour la zone sud-est-européenne, c'est une preuve de la circulation du livre sur toute l'aire de l'Orient orthodoxe, ainsi que des échanges dans le cadre de la culture médiévale roumaine, de valeurs spirituelles avec les provinces ukrainiennes (Galicie, Volhynie, Kiev). Les pays roumaines—et plus particulièrement la Moldavie et le nord de la Transylvanie—entretenaient avec les centres ukrainiens des relations non seulement commerciales, mais aussi culturelles-religieuses, de riches donations étant offertes aux églises et aux monastères, où les manuscrits tenaient une place notable du fait d'une langue littéraire commune—le slavon—que les Roumains utilisaient dans leur chancellerie et leur Église."

Clarification is necessary. The first blank page—leaf 1 r. has a provenance note, second page leaf 1 v., has the Crucifixion and printer's mark. They are facing the first printed page which is marked as leaf 3 r. Where is leaf 2 in the Braşov copy? Mircea stated that the first two leaves were glued together and this is the practical reason for the absence of leaf 2. Mircea marked the page with the Crucifixion as being on leaf 2 v. This clarifies the numbering of leaves by Mircea, however, it does not explain another enigma; are the pages glued together really blank? It appears they were not checked by Mircea, or at least we have not been informed about it. Szandorowska on our request studied the above pages and found that there is some Cyrillic inscription between them, however illegible. The proper authorities were notified, and they promised to investigate this during the microfilming of the book in Bucharest.

There is still another deviation from the original form in the Braşov copy which was rebound about 1600. At that time one blank leaf was added to the front and one to the back of it. The volume had been rebound in leather on which were impressed by cold iron (i.e., embossed) beautiful medallions with the busts of contemporary celebrities such as Luther, Melanchthon, Erasmus, and others. In all probability the book was rebound in a Protestant Saxon (i.e. German) bindery shop in Braşov. It is not the original binding, for that we must look elsewhere. The Braşov copy had one leaf torn out: leaf 114. It was replaced by one written by hand. Mircea's study established that the watermark on this leaf was from the paper mill in Braşov and could be dated 1598–1600. Through this we learn the time of replacement and rebinding of the book.

In the first article making the announcement of the discovery, Mircea indicated that the book contained many interesting provenance notes pertaining to the date, places, owners and even the price of the book. These notes reconstruct the history of the book from its appearance in Rişnov up to the present. We do not know, however, in what way or when the book reached Transylvania. Many students from Hungary attended Cracow University. For example, a church reformer of Transylvania, Protestant humanist Johannes Honterus (1498–1549), (his monument still stands in Braşov), studied in Cracow and there published several editions of his Latin Grammar and *Rudimenta Cosmographica.* As a religious reformer he could have had a special interest in Orthodox books. Possibilities of acquiring books directly from commercial sources existed or, equally possible, the book was acquired via Lwów through its religious connections with the Orthodox segment of the Transylvanian population. The latter is most plausible.

The inscription of the first page (leaf 1 r.) in Slavonic-Cyrillic gives the following information:

> This book called Pendicostar was bought by the priest Smadul, son of Aldea from Rişnov, in the province of Braşov for seven florins and given to the church in the same locality that it may serve him for praying, and to his sons and his grandchildren and his

great-grandchildren. And witnesses are: The protopop [priest] Toma from the holy church in Braşov and Vasil Şofran and Dumitru son of Mircu and Stefan Grajd from Ẓarnesti, in the year 7049 (1541).[4]

No doubt the date is authentic, as Mircea, to his credit, checked the data pertaining to the witnesses: The protopop Toma, a former page at the court of the Ban of Craiova before 1541, as well as two of the witnesses from Braşov are often found in this city's documents up to the year 1550.

The print also contains other provenance notes. On leaf 29 is an inscription in Slavonic from the sixteenth century, faded by time, with the signature of the donor: "I, the priest [pop] Smadul from Ẓarnesti." Mircea also reports another: "On the second cover there still remains another inscription from the seventeenth century, which states that the volume was the property of the St. Nicholas Church in Scheia."[4a]

On the basis of the last two provenance notes it can be surmised that *Triod* was transferred from Rişnov to Scheia at the turn of the sixteenth century. Mircea found additional proof of this in the previously mentioned handwritten replacement of a torn out leaf and rebinding of the book.

The most important feature in Mircea's first article is the reproduction and description of the printer's mark which he discussed extensively, concentrating his attention on its meaning. A thorough study of the whole copy, however, was published in a third article, "Primele Tipărituri Chirilice Şi Incunabulul Cracovian de la Braşov" (First Cyrillic Printing—Braşov's Cracow Incunabulum).[5] These three articles complement each other; as a result the full picture and value of the discovery could be obtained.

The description by Mircea of the newly discovered book coincides with all previous research pertaining to *Triod Cvetnaja,* with additional details heretofore never mentioned by other scholars. Presented below is the previously unknown printer's mark found on leaf 2 v. of the Braşov copy.

[4] Mircea, "From Cracow to Braşov," p. 52, column 1.

[4a] *Ibid.,* p. 51, column 2.

[5] Ion-Radu Mircea, "Primale tiparituri chirilice si incunabulul Cracovian de la Braşov," *Targovişte, Cetate A Culturii Romanesti. Partea I. Studii Si Cercetari de Bibliofilie* (Bucharest, 1974), pp. 111–127.

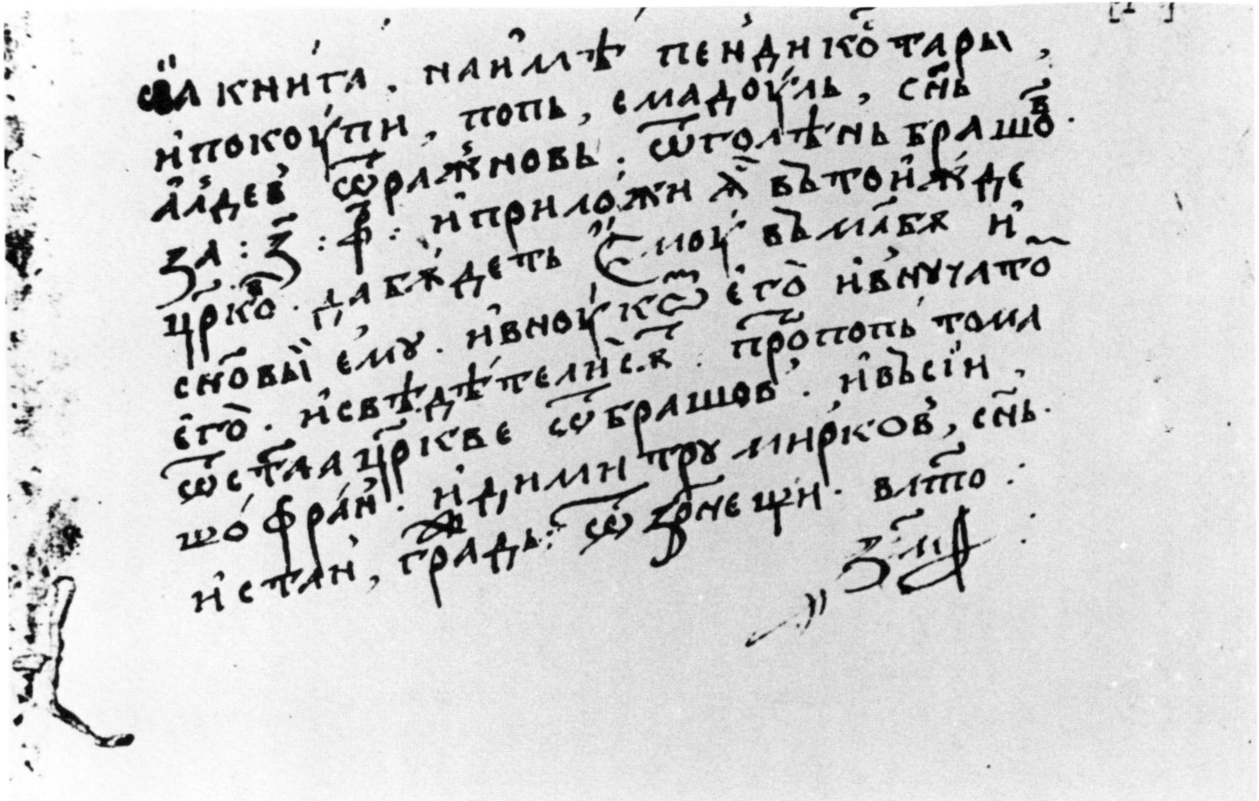

Fiol. *Triod Cvetnaja.* Braşov copy. Leaf 1 r. Donor's note.

The engraving is an entity in itself, communicating an important message, the name of the printer. In style, composition and execution it resembles Fiol's printing mark on his *Chasoslovec* and *Osmoglasnik*. That it is a separate entity is indicated by the rectangular frame in a heavy continuous line which encases the drawing and which is similar to that in the Crucifixion. Mircea does not give its dimensions. According to our calculations, it would be ca. 37/125. The printer's mark represents a band, a strip, which Mircea calls an *eşarfa,* meaning band, sash or scarf. In this case it is a decorative band extensively curled on both ends as well as in the center. The inscription is in Cyrillic capital letters.

ШБЄЙПОЛТЬ ФИОЛЬ

Shveipolt Fiol is our transliteration. While differing slightly from Mircea's interpretation of some letters in his first article, there is no doubt that the inscription indicates the printer was Shveipolt Fiol. There are indistinct characters after the letter "T" in the first word and after the letter "L" in the second. They represent reduced vowels, the so-called "jer." Normally there should be a "hard jer" Ъ after the letter "T" and a "soft jer" Ь after the letter "L." What we found here is that for both of them there is the same character, "soft jer" Ь. We mentioned that Sobolevskiĭ first stressed this erroneous use of the "soft jer" sign for both forms in colophons in *Chasoslovec* and *Osmoglasnik*. It is characteristic for Belorussian and Ruthenian regions during that period, while in Russia it does not appear.[6]

This is all that can be observed from the reproduction. According to Mircea who studied the original copy, the printer's mark was "printed in black, the drawing was added after printing the discrete accents with red at the scarf."[7]

The revelation in this obscure printer's mark delivers the undeniable proof that *Triod Cvetnaja* has its printer's identification. This eliminates any doubt that this book was printed by Fiol, and not by anyone else in 1493 or later as Nemirovskiĭ suggested. We may assume that *Triod Postnaja* has also some identification. The printer's mark and colophon in *Chasoslovec* and *Osmoglasnik* reveal that Fiol's printing press was from the beginning a legitimate business and open enterprise, each product from it was signed with his full name. All suppositions of some clandestine and underground activity therefore have no foundation.

No less important is the illustration located above the printer's mark. It is the identical picture of the Crucifixion which is known to be in *Osmoglasnik*. After the disappearance of the copy of *Osmoglasnik* in Wrocław, it is possible again to

[6] A. I. Sobolevskiĭ, "Zametka o iazyke pechatnykh izdaniĭ Shvaĭpol'ta Fiola i Skoriny" (Note on the Language of Fiol's and Skaryna's Prints), *Chteniia v istoricheskom obshchestve Nestora-letopistsa,* Kiev, 1888, II, 192–193.

[7] Mircea, "Primale tiparituri chirilice si incunabulul . . ." p. 122.

study the illustration in the original because of the Braşov copy of *Triod Cvetnaja.* The description of this picture will be based on a reproduction communicated to the author by Eliza Szandorowska, a National Library of Warsaw librarian, who examined it in Braşov.

This discovery changed numerous opinions and misconceptions; therefore it is necessary to begin the description and characterization of Fiol's typography with a thorough study of this illustration. The interest in this illustration has a long history. At the beginning of the seventeenth century it was mentioned by Kopystenskiĭ and first described at the beginning of the nineteenth century by Jerzy Samuel Bandtkie in his *De primis Cracoviae in arte typographica incunabulis dissertatio,* published in Cracow in 1812. Bandtkie discovered a copy of *Osmoglasnik* containing the illustration in Wrocław where it was a part of the Rediger Collection, which became a part of the City Library. In 1874 this book was taken to St. Petersburg, where facsimile copies were made. The detailed description of the Crucifixion illustration made by Władysław Nehring, a professor of Wrocław University, was utilized by Golowatzkij, Karataev and others. The present study will be based on the Braşov copy.

The illustration (leaf 2 v.) represents the Crucifixion of Christ. The composition of the picture concentrates on the figure of Christ hanging on the cross. On one side of his feet are two figures representing Saint John and Saint Joseph of Arimathaea, according to Better, Sichyns'kyi, Nemirovskiĭ and others. Chojecka is of a different opinion claiming that the second figure is Saint Longin, which frequently appears in the pictures of the Crucifixion. Strangely this time Saint Longin has none of his military accessories. On the other side are the Blessed Mother and three women mourners. A polygonal wall in the background is approximately two-thirds of the total height of the picture. Above the friezed wall the background is uncluttered and clear, suggesting the sky.

The composition of the picture, although quite cluttered in the lower portion, in the upper portion accents the cross with the Christ figure. The asymmetry of the left to the right side of the lower part of the picture can be explained by traditional influences. Most of the pictures of that era place the figures of the Blessed Mother always at the right side of the crucified Christ. More women are usually grouped around the Blessed Mother than men who appear individually on the opposite side of the cross. Against the sky is outlined the cross with the figure of Christ, arms outstretched and nailed thereupon. The arched figure of Christ, resembling late Gothic silhouettes, presents a well built masculine body with delicately marked musculature, taut in the outstretched arms and torso muscles. Christ's head is lowered to the right shoulder. The agony is well emphasized in the expression on the face. The Blessed Mother's face upturned to Christ is of a delicately designed profile. The regular features express sorrow; her whole countenance reveals a posture of pain and the gesture of the hand emphasizes her helplessness.

Triod Cvetnaja. Leaf 2v. Crucifixion with printer's mark.

The body of Christ hangs inert on the cross; the hips are covered with draped cloth coming down almost to the knees. The legs rest on a board-like support, where each foot is separately nailed. This is characteristic of the Orthodox presentation of the Crucifixion where the feet are always nailed separately: in the Roman Catholic presentation the feet are shown placed one atop the other and nailed without the support. In accordance with tradition a plate which bears no inscription is at the top of the cross.

However, following Byzantine custom in religious painting located on each side to the left and right of Christ's head, as well as the torso, are four words in abbreviated form, the symbols that these letters were painted in, meaning Jesus Christ NIKA (Victor). They have not been engraved in the woodblock from which the print was made according to Szandorowska's finding during her studies of this illustration *in situ.*

The figures of Saint John, Saint Joseph and the Blessed Mother all have halos drawing attention to their faces, elevated and attentively gazing up at that of Christ. One of the women accompanying the Blessed Mother is also gazing upward while the other two stand with heads bowed as in mourning. They all wear robes traditional in religious art, with sandals on their feet. Some believe that Christ has six fingers on each hand, but we can only find five.

The discovery by Mircea demands revision of the previous opinion that the Crucifixion in the Wrocław copy of *Osmoglasnik* was printed in many colors. According to Mircea the Crucifixion and printer's mark are in two colors: "Printed in black, the drawing has added after printing, discrete accents with red at the figures (personalities) and the scarf, as well as the known initials on the upper part."[8] Thus, we learn without any doubt from *Triod Cvetnaja* that the illustration is an imprint, and not as has been believed, a tipped-in picture; secondly the illustration is in two colors only, black and red. Which shade of red is difficult to ascertain from Mircea's statement. He uses the word "rosu" when referring to the illustration, and "chinovar" applied to the color of the headpiece and initials on the next page.

To clarify the discrepancy regarding the two-color or multicolor painting of the illustration: most likely the Wrocław copy had additional rubrication.[9] It was customary in Western countries to illuminate valuable codices elaborately. Such embellishment was also applied initially to printed books. This theory gains support from Estreicher's statement that: "The letter 'V' in *Osmoglasnik* is in three colors, red on blue and a dark brown field (background) with yellow stripes

[8] *Ibid.,* p. 122.

[9] Rubrication (from the Latin *rubrica,* red earth, especially red ochre): The coloring of initials, capital letters, captions, etc., in red, blue or other pigments in manuscripts and early books. Various techniques were used—painting, stamping, second printing, etc.

on the side."[10] This is an exceptional case, since no scholar ever mentioned any multicolored rubrication of Fiol's initials except in black and cinnabar.

Another argument to support our theory is that the illustration in *Triod Cvetnaja* has the letters in the upper portion of the picture, which are lacking in the Crucifixion found in *Osmoglasnik*. The rubricator, unaccustomed to this typical Byzantine form, covered those letters with paint. Rubricating the initial "V" he did not completely cover the original cinnabar paint on the edges, therefore Estreicher could suspect a fourth color—yellow.

The picture is encased in a rectangular frame by a heavy line. The size of the lithograph facsimile according to Karataev is 191 x 124 mm. Unfortunately Mircea does not give the dimensions of the illustration in *Triod Cvetnaja*. Most likely they are the same. The size of the illustration in *Triod Cvetnaja* measured from an accurate photograph is 193 x 124 mm.; together with the printers' mark 230 x 125 mm.

It is difficult to say whether they were impressed from the same woodblock. Both pictures look identical and cover the whole page; nonetheless beneath it, but only in *Triod Cvetnaja* there is the printer's mark. The explanation is simple: both books are folio-size. *Triod Cvetnaja* with 30 lines on a page had a 236 mm. column, while in *Osmoglasnik* with 25 lines on a page, the column has only 195 mm. This difference of about 40 mm. was sufficient for the placement of the printer's mark in *Triod Cvetnaja*. We may assume that the same arrangement probably was applied in *Triod Postnaja*. Regarding *Chasoslovec* with its size in quarto and a 147 mm. column, a picture of such dimensions could not be applied. Because of the necessity to fit the illustration to the dimensions of the 30 line column in *Triod Cvetnaja*, the printer eliminated the upper frame, also the frame on the right side of the printer's device to make it even with the dimensions of the Crucifixion. The only person who noticed this feature was Szandorowska.

The artistic merit of the Crucifixion varies among scholars from very moderate to exaggerated; Mircea appraises it as of "great beauty." Others link it with different schools, sometimes of opposite style and located thousands of miles from the place of the origin of Cyrillic typography.

V. Sichyns'kyi, among others, has disputed the origin of the *Osmoglasnik* crucifixion art and has suggested it was actually a piece of Ukrainian-Nurembergian woodcut art, as in his opinion, it resembles the German Nurembergian woodcuts of the 1480–1491 period. Still, he cannot deny basic differences:

> The composition of the Cracow [*Osmoglasnik*] woodcut was nevertheless independently executed. In accordance with the Greek-Orthodox rite, each foot of the Saviour is separately nailed to the cross. Resemblance to the Nuremberg woodcuts lies exclusively

[10] Karol Estreicher, "Günter Zeiner i Świętopełk Fioł," *Biblioteka Warszawska*, (Warsaw, 1867), III, 205.

in the character and type of the individual figures. In some details the engraving technique differs from that of the Nuremberg artists . . . *vignettes* [flags] and initials and also the type in Fiol's editions recreate, however, the old Byzantine pattern of the Ukrainian handwritten book.[11]

Actually whether a Ukrainian school of woodcut art based on German influence, such as Sichyns'kyi presupposed, actually existed in the fifteenth century is open to serious question. We do, however, agree that the woodcuts used by Fiol contain some Slavonic and conventional Byzantine elements, but these were commonly known and extensively applied in all East and South Slavic painting and woodcuts. The Slavonic-Byzantine style was well known in Poland as a result of political ties with the Ukrainians and Belorussians.

Already the first famous Polish historian of the fifteenth century, Jan Długosz, in his *Historia Polonica* known also as *Annales seu cronice inclyti Regni Poloniae* states that Jagello: "Gnesnensem, Sandomiriensem et Visliciensem Ecclesias, sculptura Graeca (illam enim magis quam Latinam probabat) adornauit."[11a] Jagello promoted many other artistic endeavors in the Slavonic-Byzantine style. Up to date there is a well-preserved monumental polychromy in the Catholic Church of the Holy Trinity in the castle of Lublin. It was completed on the 15th of August, 1418 by a Ruthenian artist Andrei. Frescos in this style, Slavonic-Byzantine, can be found in numerous other churches dating from Jagello's reign.[11b and 11c]. By the order of King Casimir the Holy Cross Chapel of the Wawel Cathedral was decorated in the same style in about 1470. There are Cyrillic inscriptions among the frescos and a noticeable similarity between the Chapel Crucifixion scene and the woodcut of *Osmoglasnik* and *Triod Cvetnaja.*

Predictably Nemirovskiĭ again sees Moscow influence in the composition of the *Osmoglasnik* Crucifixion scene. Thus "the engraved frontispiece could serve some iconographic image of the Crucifixion created in Western Ukraine, but it altogether follows Muscovite traditions,"[12] he writes. (Actually the term "frontispiece" is inaccurately applied to the Crucifixion in Fiol's book, since it does not precede

[11] V. Siczynskyj, "Die Anfänge der ukrainischen Gravierkunst im XV und XVI Jahrhundert." "Die Krakauer Komposition ist jedoch ziemlich frei ausgeführt. Nach griechisch-orthodoxem Ritus ist jeder Fuss des Heilands einzeln ans Kreuz geschlagen. Die Ähnlichkeit mit den Nürnberger Holzschnitten liegt ausschliesslich im Charakter und im Typus der einzelnen Figuren. Dafür weicht die Gravierungstechnik in einigen Details von der Nürnberger Technik ab, steht aber auf verhaltnismässig hoher Stufe. Die Vignetten und die Anfangsbuchstaben wie auch die Schrift der Fiolschen Ausgaben geben eher alte byzantinische Muster ukrainischer Buch-Handschriften wieder." *Gutenberg-Jahrbuch,* 1940, p. 239.

[11a] Joannes Dlugossius, *Historia Polonica* (Lipsiae, 1711), II, p. 659.

[11b] Juljusz Starzyński and Michał Walicki, *Malarstwo monumentalne w Polsce sredniowiecznej* (Monumental Painting in Medieval Poland) (Warsaw, 1922), pp. 40–43.

[11c] Starzyński and Walicki, *Dzieje sztuki polskiej* (History of Polish Art) (Warsaw, 1936), pp. 89–91.

[12] Nemirovskiĭ, *Nachalo,* p. 113.

the title page. The woodcut is just an iconic illustration.) While we do not find it difficult to agree with the first part of the quotation, the suggestion that the *Osmoglasnik* Crucifixion woodcut follows "Muscovite traditions" is ludicrous. At that time Moscow was following artistic traditions of the more culturally advanced Ukrainians, Belorussians and North Russians, not vice versa.

Nemirovskiĭ's attempt to find Moscow influences on all the Slavic nations even reaches to Poland herself: "At the end of the fifteenth century multi-person compositions of the Crucifixion became popular among Polish artists as a result of Moscow influence."[13] In the first place absolutely no cultural connections between the two countries existed at the time, and any Eastern art influence on Polish artists came only from the Belorussians and Ruthenians with whom they shared a common body politic. And Nemirovskiĭ overlooks the pertinent fact that Moscow was in no position to influence anyone in those days as its cultural level was the lowest of all the Slavic nations. Her history did not commence until 1147, over three centuries after the historical development of Kiev, Novgorod, Pskov, Polotsk, and other centers where East Slavic history and culture began and flourished. And for over two centuries the Tartars imposed unprecedented oppression on Moscow, which was not really alleviated until some ten years before Fiol printed his books. Obviously Muscovy was in no position to influence anyone in matters of art and certainly not a German artist living in Cracow, as Nemirovskiĭ would have us believe. Belorussians, Ruthenians, Serbians, Bulgarians and Rumanians were producing beautiful pieces of decorative art for their manuscripts (and soon after for their first books). Therefore, Fiol did not have to go to Germany for a pattern of artistic illumination for his Cyrillic books, or to Moscow for influence and inspiration.

Recently those who study the illustration are inclined to accept the theory that the Crucifixion is rather a local achievement in which the Ukrainian-Moldavian style prevailed. It does not exclude some technical influence from Nuremberg because of Wit Stwosz's domination in sculpture and woodcut art at that time in Cracow. The wood engraver could have been of Polish, Ukrainian, Belorussian or German descent remaining under the influence of the great master. However, it is interesting that the graphic style and form of the illustration is unique and has not been imitated.

The most recent and thorough study regarding the source of the Crucifixion illustration is presented in a comprehensive article by Ewa Chojecka. There all theories are discussed, citations from various foreign publications with diverse concepts adduced, and the conclusion is: "the source of inspiration could be from the local artistic environment. . . . It could have been iconic art from the central

[13] *Ibid.*, p. 110.

and eastern Carpathian area, a territory nearest to the Fiol press in Cracow."[14]

J. Kłosińska in her study emphasizes rather the relation to the south Slavic art centers: "The artistic origin of the Carpathian iconic paintings is not seen today so much as derived from the Ukrainian source, but rather as belonging to the Moldavian-Wallachian artistic milieu, transmitting influences from Serbia and Mount Athos."[15] But such minute dissection of the problem is beside the point because the studies of Carpathian iconic art are not yet complete. Chojecka is more convincing when she says, "the iconographic style of the Crucifixion revealed in the Cracow woodcut had not been restricted only to Ruthenian local art, but was part of the entire late Byzantine painting."[16]

All previous appraisals of the Crucifixion were practically in vain since any evaluation of a work of art, no matter how primitive or simple it might seem, from a reproduction is a contradiction in terms, especially when photocopies were made from a copy with painted-in colors. A new precise photocopy from the Braşov book has enabled us to give an accurate description; however, evaluation of the illustration should be made *in situ* by experts.

On the opposite page of the illustration a title page is expected but does not appear. Like the majority of incunabula, Fiol's books do not have title pages, although the use of title pages came into being in Italy and elsewhere about 1490. Necessary information pertaining to the books was given in two parts and in two different places. The "Incipit" (literally meaning "here begins" and used by medieval scribes at the beginning of a manuscript), which usually was on the first richly illuminated page, gave the author and title of the book. As for example the "Incipit" to *Osmoglasnik*: "With God we begin Osmoglasnik, the work of our Reverend Father John Damaskin."

All four of Fiol's incunabula contain "Incipits." The reproduction of the first printed page of *Osmoglasnik* will serve as an example of the decorative elements of Fiol's typography. At the top of the page is the headpiece, some call it flag, an angular knotty vignette in the South Slavic style. It represents three intersecting circles interwoven with a thong. A most accurate description is given by Mircea in his third article:

> The unique frontispiece,[17] printed with cinnabar . . . is composed of one single line of three double circles tied among them with semicircles which form in their center a cross of braided lines. At the two extremities of the upper and lower frontispiece, four bundles of

[14] Ewa Chojecka, "Wokół wyposażenia graficznego druków słowiańskich Szwajpolta Fiola" (Shwaipolt Fiol's Slavonic Printing and His Graphic Equipment), *Biuletyn historii sztuki* (Bulletin of the History of Art) (Warsaw, 1978(p. 234.

[15] J. Kłosińska, *Ikony. Katalog zbiorów. Muzeum Narodowe w Krakowie* (Icons. Catalog of Holdings. National Museum in Cracow) (Cracow, 1973), pp. 44–49.

[16] Chojecka, "Shwaipolt Fiol's Slavonic Printing . . . ," p. 233.

[17] Mircea uses the term "frontispiece" instead of "vignette."

braided stalks cross the circular motif and create a double diagonal in an *X* shape which is transmitted from one circle to the other. Finally, the two exterior circles from the left and from the right, do not close toward the central part, rather they continue in the central part forming here also the same system of diagonal in *X*.[18]

The frontispiece according to Mircea follows Moldavian ornamental motifs from old manuscripts:

> Such a model is inspired from the frontispiece of the manuscripts which it simplifies according to the needs of wood engraving. Judging by the frequency, we could say the uniformity, of this ornamental motif in Moldavia, so near Cracow, its identification in the Cracow frontispiece would not be excluded at all. In any case, it is not repeated in other printing shops from the first half of the sixteenth century.[19]

In his first article Mircea reporting the decorative elements of the first page states:

> The pages are illuminated in the beginning with a frontispiece of a Moldavian type, corresponding to the one on the books [manuscripts] copied in Neamt [Neamtu] by Gavril Uric between the years 1424 and 1450. The frontispiece is printed in red ink [cinnabar] as are the three initials.[20]

Interestingly, he emphasizes the "frontispiece" is in Moldavian style and corresponds to the one on the manuscript copied by Gavril Uric in the first half of the fifteenth century in Neamt, the famous cloister and fortress which played an important role in the history of Moldavia.

Perhaps we may yet uncover a Moldavian prototype of *Triod Cvetnaja,* or at least the source of the decorative elements used by Fiol. It is also possible that only a similarity exists. We know that all came from the south; and everything in Cyrillic is of Macedonian-Bulgarian origin. It could very well be that additional information pertaining to the beginning of Cyrillic printing will be uncovered in Rumania. During the fifteenth and sixteenth centuries Moldavia, with its highly developed culture, was closely connected with Poland and Ruthenia and had many contacts with Hungary and Bulgaria.

Beneath the angular flag which appears in all Fiol's books, the first stylized line of the "Incipit" is also printed in red. Caption letters, three lines in height, form this decorative clichéd line conforming to the traditional, illuminative "*vyaz'*" of Cyrillic script. Such clichéd lines are characteristic for titles of different parts of the book and also for captions of chapters.

The other decorative features are the initials also printed in red. Initials played

[18] Mircea, "Primele tiparituri chirilice si incunabulul . . . ," p. 122.
[19] *Ibid.,* p. 122.
[20] Mircea, "De la Cracovia la Braşov . . . ," p. 51.

an important role in medieval illumination. Rubricators were ingenious in creating a great variety of beautiful first letters which they decorated with many elements, human, animal, linear, floral, mythological and religious. The style of the first letters varied from country to country and from era to era, as did the format and size. As a rule of thumb, large, even enormous, initials were used at the beginning of the text, and these were most often elaborately decorated. Subchapters were started with smaller initials, and sentences began with still smaller ones.

In the West typography took about a hundred years to free itself of the medieval influence by reducing the size of the initials and the decorative content in general. Fiol started out with all the prerequisites of medieval manuscript features but quickly discarded elaborate initials and decorations which was cheaper, allowed him more space for the text and provided greater legibility. The improvement in his prints was rapid and obvious.

A study of initials in Fiol's books reveals three categories: (1) Woodcut knotty initials from braided stalks four to seven lines in height, some with teratological elements; (2) Plain calligraphic or floral initials four to six lines in height, some cast in metal; and (3) Capital or caption letters used as initials mostly as other initials printed in cinnabar.

In the illustration of the eighteen large initials used in Fiol's prints (p. 95) it is apparent they are of the same decorative style as the headpiece, the knotted flag above the "Incipit" of all four books. The shape of the caption letters does not differ from the design of the letters of the alphabet.

This type of ornamentation was known in all of the Eastern Orthodox countries. Fiol's wood engraver could have copied samples from Ukraine or from Moldavia. The source for the ornamentation and the script was Byzantium; however, it all arrived via Macedonia and Bulgaria. The motif of knotty decorations can be traced to the bas-relief in many churches, such as in the Church of Saint Sophia in Ohrid from the first half of the fourteenth century.[21]

Rubra (red ink) was, of course, an important element in the decoration of the first printing efforts. Fiol applied red ink both for the practical purpose of marking and distinguishing parts of the text for better legibility, this being an innovation in printing, and for the decorative effects.[22]

A generous use of red ink was characteristic of Cyrillic manuscripts, which were elaborate and as a rule filled with the red color used in various shades for initials and capitals, headlines in captions and chapter heads, tables of contents and as decorative elements, including headpieces. Red ink was also used in the West but mostly for decorative purposes only. However, use was made of other colors including gold and silver in the rubrication process.

[21] W. Molé, *Sztuka Słowian południowych* (The Art of the Southern Slavs) (Wrocław-Warsaw, 1962), pp. 86–90.

[22] It is customary to call it red, but in reality the color used in Cyrillic prints was cinnabar red.

Fiol followed Cyrillic manuscript traditions in the use of red. As a result his books are original in that Fiol printed in black and red with the two inks intermingling to achieve maximum legibility. As can be determined by the proof sheets now in the Jagellonian University Library in Cracow, Fiol's technique consisted of double printing (two imprints) from the same form. First the black ink was applied to the form and imprints made; then the corrector circumscribed those letters, words, sentences, phrases, etc., that were to be rubricated. In the meantime those letters, etc., were pulled out of the plate, underlays were installed and letters were inserted again. All of the same height, they were a few millimeters higher than letters to be printed in black. Next, the letters were covered with rubra (red ink); paper was spread on and pressed. Following this process the red letters were pulled out, the plate was covered with black ink and the second phase was carried through. Naturally, if the work was not precise, the colors overlapped at the edges.

In *Chasoslovec* and *Osmoglasnik* on the last pages there are identical colophons beneath the printer's device which were impressed from a woodcut. The printer's device is in the late Gothic style as is the one in *Triod Cvetnaja*. They were used to identify the printer, therefore were presented in contemporary form. Fiol's trademarks reveal his full name or initials. Those colophons give the location with the Cracow coat of arms resembling the city seal. His trade signet  indicated that he is a bookseller.

The device 61 x 122 mm. presents the coat of arms of the City of Cracow, three towers above a gate with open doors located beneath the center tower. A band of ribbon extensively curled flows from each side of the coat of arms. In the left portion of the ribbon appear four Cyrillic letters—"Z KRA"—and the same number of letters are in the right section—"KOVA," meaning "from Cracow." In the upper corners in Latin are the initials "S" and "V" for Shvajpolt Veil. In the lower corners are two identical printer's signets. The picture is encased by a rectangular frame of a heavy line. The woodcut does not indicate accomplished artistic ability, but by no means is it primitive. The artist of this woodcut is unknown, as is the case in all the woodcuts which appear in Fiol's books. The colophon in *Chasoslovec* is set in seven lines. It is identical in *Osmoglasnik* but set in six lines.

That is all with which Fiol chose to decorate his books. The sparsity of illuminative elements of his prints is unusual for those days. There are no elaborate miniatures, borders, captions or other ornaments common in contemporary incunabula.

Medieval codices were always elaborately illuminated and the pioneers of printing followed their highly decorative style. Gutenberg's *Bible* and those of his successors were very beautiful, although no more so than the manuscript texts from which they were taken. Illumination was an integral factor of handwritten books. The first printed books contained all the marks and features of the hand-

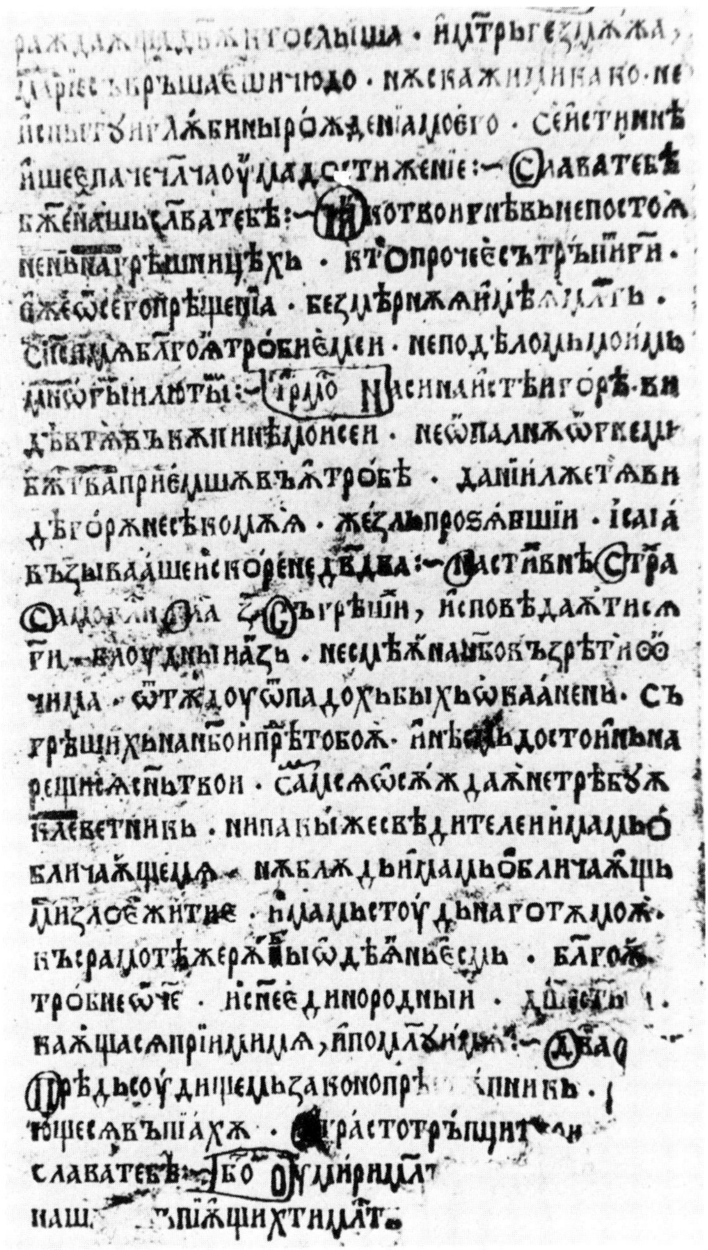

Triod Postnaja. Fiol. Cracow, c. 1491. Proofreading sheet of leaf 137 verso, with circled letters which should remain red — in print.

written books. It took over fifty years of the incunabular period before typography found the new forms and features to produce what we consider a modern book.

Actually Fiol tended to curtail rather than expand on the illumination contained in contemporary manuscripts. As his printing activities increased, he decreased the illumination features. His first print, for instance, was much more illuminated than those that followed.

Evaluating Fiol's accomplishments is not simple. Judgment could be determined from various points of view, but some pertinent information is not available to us. Some scholars complain that many errors in the texts are found and that their proofreading left much to be desired. Nemirovskiĭ has stated that because of the errors left by the proofreaders they would not have been tolerated in Russia and would have been condemned by church councils and synods. Nemirovskiĭ fails to reveal exactly how he was able to determine the books were printed and sent to Russia on order from that country on the one hand, and yet states that they would have been condemned on the other. Fortunately the books were printed for the Eastern Orthodox Church in the Polish-Lithuanian Commonwealth and no such action was even considered there. And as Kopystenskiĭ has stated, Fiol's books were not only accepted in Belorussia and Ukraine, they were highly respected there.

Technically Fiol's books can be considered deficient on several counts, nonetheless they have their value and merits. They do not differ from other incunabula; they follow the established modes of the day. What was different about them was the Cyrillic type with its specific characteristics and illumination that followed the patterns developed by the scribes of Slavonic-Byzantine manuscripts. There is no innovation in the decorative components of Fiol's typography. The Cracow printer developed nothing new; but, more important, he did preserve the Orthodox liturgical manuscript illuminative tradition. These traditions were followed by Cyrillic printers for the next three centuries. The print and illumination of Fiol's books are thoroughly in the Eastern Orthodox spirit; however, his printer's devices and marks are in contemporary late Gothic decorative Western style.

In comparison to the books produced by Skaryna and those of both Makarios, Fiol's prints were mediocre. Skaryna's books contain Nurembergian typographical and illuminative influences; those of the two Makarios were influenced by the Venetian printers. Fiol's Cyrillic typography was executed in a genuine Orthodox Slavonic-Byzantine style. He, along with Borsdorf, created Cyrillic printing by adhering to the text and spirit of Cyrillic manuscripts and illuminations which the two of them must have found a fascinating novelty. However, Cyrillic was not new to either Dr. Skaryna or the two Makarios and, under the spell of Western culture and the excellent typographical achievements of Venice and Prague printing, they introduced foreign cultural elements into their own Cyrillic prints. But in the capital of Catholic Poland two German craftsmen executed four books that were more in the spirit of Orthodox Slavic style than any of the other pioneers of

Cyrillic typography. To these Germans, Borsdorf and Fiol, Cyrillic type was something new and unique. Fascinated by its beauty, they accepted and preserved the purity of design.

Printers were obliged to provide the bookbinder with specific instructions pertaining to the method of putting the material together. In the binding process sections of leaves folded in proper sequence are called "quires." For obvious reasons it became commonplace during the early years of printing to mark each quire. These markings were usually placed beneath the text in the lower right-hand corner, occasionally in the bottom middle part. Signatures are usually on the recto, but infrequently they appear on the verso of the leaf. Both numbers and letters of the alphabet were used to mark quires. These quire marks came to be known as signatures.

As quires were not identical, nor the same size, nor seldom the same dimension, the signatures varied in incunabula. A quire could be composed of two, three, four, five or six folio size sheets folded once, twice or more times. As a result of this lack of uniformity terms came into being to designate the various quires: a "binion" is two inserted sheets creating a section consisting of four leaves and eight pages; a "ternion" is three inserted sheets equaling six leaves and twelve pages; a "quaternion" is four inserted sheets of eight leaves and sixteen pages (the most commonly used even today); a "quinternion" is five inserted sheets of ten leaves and twenty pages; a "sexternion" is six inserted sheets of twelve leaves and twenty-four pages. There is no uniformity; therefore a book could contain some binions, some ternions, some quaternions, and so forth. The varieties and complexities in marking sections appear awkward, but Bošnjak who studied signatures in Slavic incunabula states:

> Besides "quaternions," in Slavic incunabula one finds "binions" (two inserted leaves), "ternions" (three inserted leaves), "quinternions" (five inserted leaves), "sexternions" (six inserted leaves), etc. The list of Slavic incunabula contains data on the marking in those works in which there are signatures with the designation as to the number of leaves for quires, such as for instance 4 (binion), 6 (ternion), 8 (quaternion), 10 (quinternion), 12 (sexternion), etc.[23]

The printer's instructions to the bookbinder as to the order or sequence of the quires was most important, and especially so due to the lack of pagination. Registers of signature marks were developed primarily for the use of bookbinders. They were also helpful to printers for the purpose of keeping records.

The register of quaternions from *Triod Cvetnaja* (Braşov copy, leaf 364) is self-explanatory: "*To est' lichba do toi knihy iako imaiut' tetradi byti ot počhatku az'*

[23] Bošnjak, *A Study of Slavic Incunabula,* pp. 138, 140.

тоє личбадо тоиѣ книгы какъ дають тетрадь быти
ѿ початкꙋ азъ до конца. о днатетрапол же
дно ѣнты о днлнпол мадрꙋгого азъ до конца.

а	зі	лв	мн	ѯд	па
в	иі	лг	мѳ	ѯє	пв
г	ѳі	лд	н	ѯѕ	пг
д	к	лє	на	ѯз	пд
є	ка	лѕ	нв	ѯи	пє
ѕ	кв	лз	нг	ѯѳ	пѕ
з	кг	ли	нд	о	пз
и	кд	лѳ	нє	оа	пѳ
ѳ	кє	м	нѕ	ог	ч
і	кѕ	ма	нз	од	р
аі	кз	мв	ни	оє	ча
ві	ки	мг	нѳ	оѕ	чв
гі	кз	мд	ѯ	оз	чг
ді	кѳ	мє	ѯа	ои	чд
єі	л	мѕ	ѯв	оѳ	чє
ѕі	ла	мз	ѯг	п	чѕ

Chasoslovec. Fiol. Cracow, 1491. Leaf 383 v. Register of quires.

do konca . . ." (This is a set of numbers to this book, how the sections should follow from the beginning to the end . . .).

There are some peculiarities. The printer started with number 1 and ended with number 189; however, there are listed only 183 numbers on the list of quires. Six numbers are omitted: in quire XI, numbers 60, 61, 62, 63, in quire XXI, numbers 124 and 125. Besides this, in quire IX instead of number 50 there is number 41 listed twice and in quire XXIII numbers 200 and 201 instead of 140 and 141. In spite of these irregularities the books were correctly assembled.

All four of Fiol's books contained signatures consisting of Cyrillic numbers located in the lower right-hand corner. They are not found on all of the preserved copies due to the trimming of the paper during the binding and rebinding process.

Application of signatures differs because sections in Fiol's books are varied. The first print, *Triod Cvetnaja,* consists of 31 sexternions with signature marks on the first six leaves of the section; *Triod Postnaja* contains 32 quinternions with signatures on the first five leaves of each section; *Chasoslovec* has 48 quaternions with signatures on the first and third leaf of each section; and *Osmoglasnik* consists of 21 quaternions with signatures on the first four leaves of each section.

Fiol's progress in technique is obvious; he started with sexternions in *Triod Cvetnaja,* advanced to quinternions in *Triod Postnaja* and reached quaternions, the most used and most convenient quires, in *Chasoslovec* and *Osmoglasnik.* While *Chasoslovec*'s system of marking was slightly complicated, the marking of signatures on the first four leaves of *Osmoglasnik* was most simple and efficient. The insertion of a register of quires in all prints indicates the high professional level.

It is customary to describe how the old manuscripts and books were bound. As early as the beginning of the second half of the fifteenth century, the art of bookbinding was presented by a University of Cracow professor, Paweł Żydek of Prague. Manuscript No. 257 of the Jagellonian Library, written in the years 1453 through 1463, contains his description of all the phases of the bookbinding process, listing tools and materials used. Paweł Żydek stated the bookbinder first made grooves in wooden boards; next he tied the folded sections of vellum or paper tightly together with leather cords; the ends of the cords were inserted into the grooves of the wooden boards. The leather covering the boards was decorated, protected with knobs and equipped with a clasp. Materials and tools used by bookbinders were: wooden boards, press, straps, looms, hammer and other tools.[24]

The binding of the preserved copies of Fiol's books which were done in Cracow coincides closely with the above description. They consisted of wooden boards covered with blind tooled leather, decorated in linear and floral motifs. The covers were equipped with two copper clasps.

The art of bookbinding in Poland was superior in quality. It had started in monasteries as early as the twelfth century. The Cracow annals of 1404 note the first lay bookbinder. Soon the art of bookbinding became popular. Educated people and scholars engaged in it. Illuminated bookbinding flourished in the fifteenth and sixteenth centuries. In Source Material at the end of his book Ptaśnik named over 80 bookbinders active in Cracow between the second half of the fifteenth and the first half of the sixteenth century. From these documents much can be learned about the guild laws, bookbinding tools, relations with goldsmiths,

[24] Anna Lewicka-Kamińska, "Dzieje oprawy książkowej w Polsce. Stan badań, problematyka i postulaty" (History of Bookbinding in Poland. State of Research, Problems and Postulates), *Dawna książka i kultura* (Old Books and Culture), (Wrocław-Warsaw, 1975), p. 159.

Sample of Polish binding.

etc.[25] One scholar who generally ignores the books of Slavic nations states: "It is of interest to observe that gold-tooled bindings were executed at Cracow, both before and after 1500."[26]

In Poland in the fifteenth and sixteenth centuries, Cracow and Lwów were two important goldsmith centers. The first with its Italian influences was well known by Western Europe, and the second with Arabic influences was well known in Eastern Europe and Asia Minor. Their influence is revealed in the decorative motifs and goldleaf application in the binding of books in Poland, and their specific character was greatly admired by connoisseurs.

E. Ph. Goldschmidt in *Gothic and Renaissance Book-Binding* points out that Cracow was an important center of book production and binding. This was closely connected with the needs of the Jagellonian University, a prominent educational center in Central Europe during the fifteenth and sixteenth centuries. Goldschmidt's thorough study of two books in the original Cracow binding (found in his own private collection) was the basis for his statement that gilding in Poland began earlier than in Germany. He believes this technique came from Italy by way of Hungary.[27] This is partially true because gilding came to Poland directly from the East via Lwów, the second important center of the art and craftsmanship of binding. From the fifteenth century, binding in Lwów was under Byzantine and Arabic influence. Armenian craftsmen were instrumental in introducing these Eastern elements.

Paul Adam was correct in determining the intermingling of Western Italian and Eastern Greek (Byzantine) rudiments in the Polish binding art. This was the basis for the development of a new original style and technique in Polish binding in the sixteenth century.[28]

The five hundredth anniversary of Polish printing resulted in articles and books on this subject. In the field of bookbinding the study by Anna Lewicka-Kamińska is of special value, since it reviews all research done to date and formulates a program for future studies.[29] Another interesting study by Maria Krynicka covers the aspects of decorative figural stamping.[30]

[25] Jan Ptaśnik, "Cracovia impressorum . . . ."

[26] Douglas C. McMurtrie, *The Book, The Story of Printing and Bookmaking* (New York, 1943), p. 544.

[27] E. Ph. Goldschmidt, *Gothic and Renaissance Book-Bindings* (London, 1928), vols. 1–2.

[28] Paul Adam, "Über polnische Einbandkunst im XVI Jahrhundert," *Allgemeiner Anzeiger für Buchbindereien*, (Leipzig, 1925) nr. 32, pp. 684–685.

[29] Anna Lewicka-Kamińska, "Dzieje oprawy książkowej w Polsce," pp. 144–168.

[30] Maria Krynicka, "Elementy figuralne dekoracji polskich opraw książkowych i ich związki z grafiką w pierwszym trzydziestoleciu XVI wieku. Komunikat" (Decorative Figural Elements in Polish Bookbinding and Their Graphic Associations in the First Thirty Years of the XVI Century. Communiqué) *Dawna książka i kultura* (Old Books and Culture) (Warsaw-Wrocław), pp. 169–183.

9
Fiol's Heirs

The dissemination of Cyrillic printing was rapid. Within a few years after Fiol's trial, Cyrillic was being printed far south in Montenegro, in Italy and Rumania. It finally came into its own with Dr. Skaryna's presses in Prague and Wilno. Each and all of these printing shops made an important contribution in producing Cyrillic incunabula. No study of the subject could be complete without the description of the prints produced by each.

THE INCUNABULA OF MAKARIOS OF MONTENEGRO

In 1493 a printing shop was founded in Obod-Cetinje, in Montenegro, under the auspices of Prince Gjurgje Crnojevic (George the Black). Eight printers and an auxiliary staff operated four presses. The Montenegrin prints were characterized by numerous initials, capital letters, flags, illustrations, and excellent type. From 1494 to 1496 the Montenegro shop produced the following books:

1. OSMOGLASNIK prvoglasnik (Octoechos I)
Osmoglasnik prvoglasnik or I, the first part, Odes I–IV. (Obod-Cetinje), hieromonach Makarije, January 4, 1494: 4°. 269 leaves, 30–31 lines. Print black and red. Typographical and ornamental values are very rich; however, basically following Fiol's example. About 40 copies have been preserved.
2. OSMOGLASNIK petoglasnik (Octoechos V)
Osmoglasnik petoglasnik or V, the second part, Odes V–VIII. (Obod-Cetinje, hieromonach Makarje, 1494). 4°, 30 lines. The only one of Makarios's prints known with 6 illustrations. Printed in black only, size 80 x 210 mm. Other details unknown as only a part of one book, fortunately containing all six pictures, has been preserved.
3. PSALTER s posledovanjem
Cetinje, hieromonach Makarije, IX, 22, 1495. 4°, 348 leaves, 27 lines. Print black and red. Colophon. Print, as in the two above, is well executed and recorded. Many copies are preserved, one in the United States at the Harvard University Library, Cambridge, Massachusetts.

Osmoglasnik — prvoglasnik. (Octoechos I.) Makarje. Cetinje, 1495. Second leaf recto. Preface to the *Osmoglasnik.* Above — a small flag stylized in the Byzantine with Crnojevic's coat-of-arms. Initial p — stylized in Italian.

4. TREBNIK

Trebnik—Prayer Book

(Cetinje, hieromonach Makarije, c. 1496). 8°, 23–24 lines. Colophon missing. Only 184 leaves preserved, therefore not all details are available.

5. CHETVEROEVANGELIJE

Chetveroevangelije—Four Gospels

(Cetinje, hieromonach Makarije, c. 1496.) No details because not a single copy has been preserved; only a transcription of 1548 found in Slavonia, Yugoslavia.

НАЧЕЛО СВѢТЫИХЬ ОСМОГЛА
СНИКОУ . творенїе прѣподобнаго ѡца наше
го Іѡанна дамаскуна . вь соуботу вечерь на
малѣи вечерни . на гн вьзвахь стхры глась . а
Вечернѧѧ наше млтвы . прїими стыи гси
и подаждь намь ѡставленїе грѣхомь .
ꙗко ты едниь еси , ꙗвлеи вьмирѣ вьскрсенїе :.
Ѡбьидѣте люди сиѡнь иѡбь имѣте его . и
дадите славоу вьнемь , вьскрсшомоу из
мрьтвынхь . ꙗко ть е бь нашь . избавлеи
насьѡ беззаконїи нашихь :.
Прїидете людїе поемь и поклонимсе хоу .
славеще его иже измрьтвынхь вьскрсенїе .
ꙗко ть е бгь нашь . иже ѡ льсти вражїе мирь
избавлеи :. повтори , а . слава . и нинѣ бо :.
Всѐ мирноую славоу . ѡ члкь прозебшоую ,
и влдкоу рождьшоую . нбсноую дверь
вьспоемь марїю двцоу . беспльтныимь пѣснь
ивѣрныимь оудобренїе . та бо ꙗвисе нбо
а

Osmoglasnik — prvoglasnik. (Octoechos I) Makarje. Cetinje, 1494. First leaf recto. Beginning. Above a small woodcut vignette knotty flag in the South Slavonic style, black impressed.

Before 1525 two other printing shops specializing in Cyrillic were established in Venice; one by Božidar Vuković, born at Podgorica (now Titograd) in Montenegro; the second by Bozidar Ljubović and his sons Djuradj and Theodor. On July 7, 1519, Vuković published the Psalter, Part I, and in October 1520, Part II. Ljubović started in Venice and then, in 1523, transferred his shop to Gorazde in Bosnia, his birthplace. Neither printing shop contributed anything outstanding but continued the Makarios style.

BOOKS PRINTED BY MAKARIOS IN TĂRGOVIŞTE

About 1507 a printing shop was established in Tărgovişte, Wallachia, under the auspices of L. Bassarab, voivod (prince) of Ugrowallachia (now Rumania).[1] The Tărgovişte print is characterized by a large size type, well cast, big initials, large capital letters, headpieces about half the size of the page, and rich flowery ornamentation in the Byzantine style. From 1508 until 1512, the monk and priest Makarios (Makarije)[2] produced the following books:

1. SLUZHEBNIK—MISSAL—Liturghierul (Rumanian) Missal: The book containing all that is said and sung at Mass during the entire year.
Tărgovişte, Makarije, November 10, 1508. 4°, 128 leaves, 15 lines. Signatures marked on the first and verso side of the last leaf of each section. No pagination, supplementary marks, punctuation marks. Print black and red. Six head ornaments in South Slavonic-Byzantine style impressed from 3 woodcuts. Numerous woodcut knotty initials 4 to 6 lines high.
2. OSMOGLASNIK—Oktoikh
Tărgovişte, Makarije, August 26, 1510. 2° (folio). 200 leaves, 20 lines. Signature marks the same as in *Sluzhebnik*. No pagination, supplementary marks, punctuation marks. Three head ornaments from woodcut blocks. Big knotty initials.
3. CHETVEROEVANGELIJE—Evangheliar (Rumanian).
Four gospels—the first printed in Church Slavonic preserved to present times. Tărgovişte, Makarije, June 25, 1512. 2° (folio), 289 leaves, 20 lines. Signatures marked the same way as in two previous books. No pagination, supplementary marks, punctuation marks. Magnificent edition executed elaborately. In front of each Gospel there are great head ornaments (three new, one from *Osmoglasnik*). Nine smaller ones in front of prefaces and indices. Many knotty initials.[3]

DOCTOR FRANCIŠAK SKARYNA'S PRINTS

Francišak Skaryna (1485?–1540) was born in Polotsk, Belorussia. He received a Liberal Arts degree in Cracow and his Doctorate of Medicine in Padua. A highly intelligent humanist, he began his printing endeavor in Prague in 1517. He extended his printing activities to Wilno in 1520. The first known printer of East Slavic birth, he produced the first translation of the Bible in the Belorussian vernacular. The products of his printing shops were equal to those in Western

[1] Djordje Radojicić, "Die erste Wallachische Buchdruckerei (1506–1512)," *Gutenberg Jahrbuch* (1960), p. 35.

[2] Title and name of the printer from "Afterword" at end of book. Also note that the printing was under the auspices of L. Bassarab.

[3] L. Demeny, "L'imprimerie cyrillique de Macarios de Valachie," *Revue Roumaine d'Histoire*, VII, (1969), 549–574.

Europe. His books printed in Wilno, small in size, are called "Slavic Elsevirs" after the name of the famous Elsevir prints in Leyden and Amsterdam.[4]

1. BIVLIA RUSKA
Bible. Full title in translation: "The Ruthenian Bible translated by Doctor Francis Skaryna of the famous city of Polotsk, to the glory of God and the enlightenment of the common people."
Prague. Francišak Skaryna, 1517–1519, 4°, 23 Biblical books under separate titles, altogether 1,200 leaves (2,400 pages), 49 woodcuts. Language: Belorussian with the exception of the Psalms, which as liturgical songs, were printed in Church Slavonic but with Belorussian glosses on margins.
2. MALAIA PODOROZHNAIA KNIZHKA (Little Traveller's Companion Book), Wilno. Francišak Skaryna, September 1522, 12°, 436 leaves, 5 woodcuts. Language: Old Church Slavonic with contemporary Belorussian influences. This *Little Traveller's Companion Book* is a combination of religious songs and prayers in the style of the so-called *Liber viaticus.*
According to Nadson: "The book is divided into five large sections; *Psaltyŕ,* or Book of Psalms, together with ten canticles from the Old and New Testament; *Časoslovec* or the Book of Hours, containing ordinary, or unchangeable parts of daily church offices; *Akafisty,* consisting of a number of religious hymns and prayers; *Šestodneveć,* containing selected proper, or variable, parts of daily offices for every day of the week; and finally *Posledovanie cerkovnaho sobranija,* or a short church calendar. In addition a detailed table of contents is at the end of the book."[5]

Until 1971 it was accepted that Skaryna opened his printing shop in Wilno around 1525 and that the first book printed there was *Apostol.* In 1972 Moshe Altbauer, professor of Hebrew University in Jerusalem, while studying at the Royal Library in Copenhagen, found a copy of *Malaia Podorozhnaia Knižika* with a calendar and complete Paschalia (dates of Easter and other moveable feasts). We learned from it that Skaryna began printing books at Wilno at least by 1522 and that the first book printed was the *Little Traveller's Book.* After a thorough investigation of the newly discovered Paschalia, this information was announced by Alexander Nadson, director of the Belorussian Francišak Skaryna Library and Museum in London.[6] Skaryna probably transferred his printing shop from Prague to Wilno in 1520 and that part of his property in Wrocław was seized

[4] V. V. Stasov, *Razbor rukopisnogo sochineniia g. Rovinskogo: "Russkie gravery i ikh proizvedeniia"* (An Analysis of Mr. Rovinski's Manuscript: "Russian Engravers and their Works"), (St. Petersburg, 1864), p. 32.

[5] Alexander Nadson, "Skaryna's Prayer Book," *The Journal of Byelorussian Studies,* (London, 1972), 340.

[6] A. Nadson, "Kniha Skaryny ŭ Kapenhahiene" (Skaryna'a Book in Copenhagen), *Bozhym Shliakham,* London, 1971, Nr. 5 (128), 9–11.

Bivlia Ruska. Dr. F. Skaryna. Prag, 1517–1519. Title page.

Portrait of Dr. F. Skaryna. Woodcut from Bivlia Ruska.

by town authorities. This delayed the printing in Wilno for about one year. Documents found in Wrocław do not reveal any details.

3. APOSTOL—full title: DEIANIIA I POSLANIIA APOSTOLSKAIA. Full title in translation: "The Book of the Acts and Epistles of the Apostles, called Apostol, edited with God's help, by Doctor Francišak Skaryna of Polotsk." Wilno. Francišak Skaryna, March 1525, 8°, 351 leaves. Language: Old Church Slavonic with contemporary Belorussian influences.[7]

[7]Vitaŭt Tumash, "Bibliiahrafiia skaryniiany" (Bibliography of Skoriniana), *Zapisy*, Whiteruthenian Institute of Arts and Sciences, (München, 1970), kniha 5, 193–198.

Although Skaryna's prints were executed in the first quarter of the sixteenth century, they are taken into consideration in this work because the efforts of Fiol, Makarios of Cetinje, Makarios of Tărgovişte, and Skaryna were the real beginning of Cyrillic printing for all Orthodox Eastern and Southern Slavic nations. Actually some scholars suggest the year 1525 as the ending of the incunabula period. While it may not be necessary to consider extending the date from 1500 for Western Europe, it is advisable to accept the later date for Cyrillic printing which started late, officially in 1491. Therefore, Skaryna's prints could be called incunabula. He was the first printer of fully developed Cyrillic printed books.[8]

The printing history of the Slavic nations is as follows. Among all Slavs the first printers were the Czechs (Bohemians). They established the first printing shop at Plzen (Pilsen) just after 1468, produced the first books (both secular and religious) in the vernacular Slavic language, *Kronika Trojańska* (History of Troy), presumably appeared in 1468. Among the thirty-nine known incunabula titles produced in Bohemian printing houses, the most prominent is the first Bible in Slavic published in 1488 in Prague by Jan Kamp. The most magnificent print among all Bohemian incunabula is the Bible published by Martin Tishnov (Tišnov) in Kutna Hora on November 14, 1489. The book has 612 two-columned leaves in folio with 117 woodcuts, most of which cover an entire page. The print is black and red. The printer's mark with crown and King Wladislaus's monogram, W., indicate the work was done under the auspices of the king of Bohemia and Moravia. Wladislaus was the grandson of Władysław Jagiełło (1348–1434), the founder of the Jagellonian dynasty and the Commonwealth of Poland-Lithuania. The Czechs used Gothic and Latin alphabets.

Croatia occupies a prominent second position in the history of Slavic printing. It was the only nation among Western Catholic countries which, from the tenth century, was permitted to have the liturgy in the Slavonic language. The script was Glagolitic. The Croats, for centuries in close contact with Venice and Rome, early printing centers, developed Glagolitic printing very early. The first Croatian incunabulum was the *Misal po zakonu rimskogo dvora* (Missale Romanum), printed on February 22, 1483, in Venice in the printing shop of Andreas Torresanis (Andreas de Asula). Altogether nine incunabula were printed in Glagolitic, some in Venice, some in Croatia.

And, of course, in 1491 Fiol, Turzo and Borsdorf became the pioneers of Church Cyrillic typography which was continued by Makarios in Cetinje and Makarios in Targovişte. Their products were Church-Slavonic prints for the use of all the Eastern Orthodox nations, as apt for the Eastern Slavic countries as for Serbia, Macedonia, Bulgaria and Rumania. Poland was the birthplace of Cyrillic

[8] Symon Braha, "Doktar Skaryna ŭ Maskve" (Doctor Skaryna in Moscow), *Zapisy*, Whiteruthenian Institute of Arts and Sciences, (New York-München, 1963), Vol. 2, 11–34.

printing, which was refined and improved in Montenegro and Wallachia. All three printing presses existed briefly and disappeared without a trace except for the dozen books they produced which set the pattern for Cyrillic Church Slavonic printing and served as an inspiration for the further development of Cyrillic typography.

Skaryna perfected Cyrillic typography in the sense of producing modern books. Influenced by Czech printing in the vernacular, he was acquainted with international as well as Cyrillic printing. Therefore, he was well prepared to pioneer Slavic printing in the vernacular. Not only did he continue Cyrillic printing; more important, he was the first to print in the vernacular Belorussian language. As Symon Braha correctly pointed out: "After the Czech Bible, his Belorussian Bible was the second printed in a native Slavic language. Doctor Francišak Skaryna established the first printing shop in Belorussia as well as in all of Eastern Europe."[9] His ultimate achievement was the creation of completely modern books as printed today. His books are more than incunabula *sensu stricto*. Big folio sized liturgical service editions were avoided. He printed books of various sizes[10] for secular use, with title pages, pagination, space between words, regular ligatures. And most important, the design of the type did not follow the manuscript pattern; it was the creation of original modern Cyrillic typography. In the preface to the *Engravings of Francišak Skaryna* (Hravjury) published in Minsk in 1972, L. Barazna extols the excellence of Skaryna's illumination.

There are two theories relative to the effect Fiol's prints had on the Cyrillic printers who followed him; according to one they served as a source of inspiration and a model; the other suggests that subsequent Cyrillic printing developed separately.

Chronologically Cyrillic printing developed in three centers following Fiol: the Montenegro shop in Cetinje (1494–1496), Tărgovişte printing in Moldavia (1508–1512) and Skaryna's Belorussian printing enterprise in Prague (1517–1519) and Wilno (1520–1525).

As to the first center in Cetinje, most scholars agree that Fiol influenced Makarios's printings, to what extent has not really been established. Golowatzkij speaks of this as an obvious fact; according to him, all Balkan, Ukrainian and Russian printing in the sixteenth century was influenced by Fiol's printing endeavor. But again, this statement is not based on thorough research.

It has been suggested that the Cetinje Cyrillic prints were in some way a continuation of Fiol's endeavor. This theory is strongly supported by Bošnjak: "There can be no doubt that there are multitudinous similarities between these two printing establishments in respect to types, initials, initial clichéd lines and other

[9] *Ibid.*, p. 4.

[10] *Bivlia*—4⁰, *Apostol*—8⁰, *Malaia podorozhnaia knizhka*—12⁰.

features. Could it be that all these similarities were accidental? . . . One would, indeed, hardly be able to believe that the first Cyrillic establishment exercised no influence on the second, when one considers the almost identical editions of both these presses. By and large, science has ignored this problem to date."[11]

Not denying that in general Bošnjak is right, we cannot agree with the conclusion that Fiol's books and those produced by Makarios of Cetinje are "almost identical." No doubt Makarios was well acquainted with and influenced by Fiol's achievements; nevertheless, a comparison of Fiol's *Osmoglasnik* with Makarios's *Osmoglasnik* shows great graphic and artistic advancement in Makarios's work. It is understandable that each printing shop was advancing and must have prepared its own new type for printing a greater number of books. Each new set of type was better as a result of previous experience, and was improved with innovations.

Another factor is evident. The accomplishments in Venice, one of the most famous centers of European incunabula printing, influenced Makarios and helped to solve technical problems which Fiol had been obliged to work out by himself. Often this was not as beneficial for Makarios as it might appear. Following Western technique, Makarios cast the type with diacritical marks joined, which immensely increased the amount of type. Borsdorf had made the marks separately, an original invention and advancement.

There could be no doubt or question as to the typographical superiority of Makarios's Montenegrin prints. In this we agree fully with Bošnjak:

> Makarije must have been either a calligrapher or an engraver; thus he may well have participated in the making of the types, drawings, flags and pictures. In his works Makarije contributed the beginnings of individual chapters in the form of a stylized first line impressed by the cliché technique as in the first Cyrillic printing office. The flags, as well as some initials, are similar to those found in Fiol's works. There can be no doubt but that Makarije was a great master; his works surpassed even Fiol's by the beauty of characters and the elaboration of certain details.[12]

Another aspect must be taken into consideration: the individual character of all incunabula or rather those of each printing shop, since each workshop had its own style. It is well known that incunabula, especially in the early period, have more in common with old manuscripts than with modern printing for two reasons: First, handwritten manuscripts were prototypes for the first books, and it took some time before printers stopped following their pattern and created their own typographical characters. Second, first prints, like manuscripts, are unique and unrepeatable because there were no standards in type-making and settings. There-

[11] Bošnjak, *A Study of Slavic Incunabula,* pp. 90–91.
[12] *Ibid.,* pp. 94–95.

fore Makarios's prints were different from Fiol's and also brought innovations. Montenegrin prints without any doubt were used as patterns by all printing shops in the Balkans during the sixteenth century.

The third printing workshop of pioneering status was the one in Tărgovişte, Ugrowallachia. It produced three books between 1508 and 1512 which influenced printing in all of the territory now known as Rumania, the eastern part of the Balkans, and Ukraine. Unfortunately, to date, scholars have not paid too much attention to it; however, Golowatzkij over a hundred years ago stressed that:

> The very great resemblance in the exterior appearance of the letters [type] in books printed in the XVI century in Kronstadt or Ugrowallachia is striking. It may be attributed to the circumstance that the same manuscripts of Bulgarian-Russian origin served as models for both printing shops, or perhaps some interconnection actually existed between both printers, who perhaps were followers of Fiol, may be definitely decided by future research.[13]

Golowatzkij reached his conclusions by comparing the text of Fiol's *Osmoglasnik* and the Cetinje *Osmoglasnik,* as well as Fiol's *Osmoglasnik* and the Tărgovişte *Evangelium.*[14] Laymen would not notice a difference; but specialists do, inasmuch as they agree the Balkan Cyrillic prints especially follow Fiol's type and contain many other characteristic elements of the Cracow printing shop. But more thorough comparative studies are necessary.

Presently some scholars identify without reservation Makarios of Cetinje with Makarios of Tărgovişte. This automatically solves all questions for them; they conclude that Cetinje influenced Tărgovişte and the books printed in Wallachia were in some way a continuation of the Montenegrin printing shop. G. J. Koliada, who represents this view most emphatically, says that after the invasion of the Turks

> the founder of Montenegrin printing, Makarij [Makarios], transferred his activities to Ugrowallachia, then closely connected with the Slavic world in cultural endeavors. Here he laid the foundation of Rumanian typography. There are preserved three books which he printed there: *Sluzhebnik,* 1508, *Oktoikh* 1510, *Chetveroevangelye* 1512. . . . From the typographical point of view the *Chetveroevangelye* of 1512 is in no way less valuable than books printed by Makarios in Cetinje. The design of the letters is on the whole the same as in Montenegrin prints; dimensions, however, are larger which makes it more solemn. Heights of 10 lines in the Montenegrin edition are 69 mm., in *Chetveroevangelye* of 1512, 91 mm. Considerably changed are the initials; they represent braids on a black

[13] Golowatzkij, "Sweipolt Fiol und seine Kirillische Buchdruckerei . . . ," p. 440.

[14] Fiol's *Osmoglasnik* from 1491 and *Cetinje Oktoich* from 1493–1494, also Fiol's *Osmoglasnik* and *Chetveroevangelium* at Tărgovişte 1512. *Ibid.,* pp. 446–448.

> or red field without frames. This way it achieved harmony of braid initials, braid headpieces and the print.[15]

Koliada is correct in many respects; nevertheless he overlooks the study of Fiol's prints and this makes his conclusion incomplete. Thus we have two opposing theories: Bošnjak's connecting the Tărgovişte printing press with Fiol, and that of Koliada who traces it to the Montenegrin printing establishment. There is no doubt that Fiol's printing press influenced Montenegrin printing. Koliada's statement therefore supports, however indirectly, the theory of technical progression from Fiol's shop to Makarios's in Cetinje and the Tărgovişte establishment.

As to Belorussian printing, Tumash, an authority on the subject, expresses his opinion in an unpublished letter as follows:

> Skaryna's type was original in design; he did not imitate the type of other printers. Skaryna based the design of his type mainly on the Belorussian half-uncial used in manuscripts. However, with his knowledge of Latin prints acquired during his studies in the West, he formed his Cyrillic type under the influence of "antiqua" with rounded Latin script shape, and thus developed the first true typographic Cyrillic types.

His type was later copied by the printing shops in Nieśwież (1562) and Vasil Ciapinski in Ciapino near Polotsk around 1576.

As a humanist educated in Cracow and Padua in the first decade of the sixteenth century Skaryna was surely aware of the existence of Cyrillic prints in Cracow, Montenegro, and Venice. The fame of Fiol's prints had spread throughout Belorussia and Ukraine, as stated by Archimandrite Kopystenskiĭ. Tumash himself has admitted that Fiol's prints were published primarily for Belorussia. How can it be supposed that his books did not influence Skaryna? The followers of the theory that all the first Cyrillic printing shops developed independently cannot explain this enigma.

In the West the general opinion is that Roman printing influenced Cyrillic printing from the very beginning:

> As far as Slavic printing abroad is concerned, the strong influence of Roman type demonstrated itself much earlier. . . . The title page of F. Skaryna's *Bivlia ruska* [Prague 1517–1519] has several characters which are direct borrowings from the contemporaneous Roman type and others which are Cyrillic characters modified under the influence of Roman type. The same is valid, to a certain extent, for books printed in Cracow [1491].[16]

[15] G. J. Koliada, "Iz istorii knigopechatnykh sviazeĭ Rossii, Ukrainy i Rumuynii v XVI i XVII vekakh" (From the History of Printing Ties of Russia, Ukraine and Rumania in the XVI and XVII Centuries), p. 83.

[16] I. L. Kaldor, "The Genesis of the Russian Grazhdanskii Shrift or Civil Type," *Journal of Typographic Research,* vol. 3 (1969), 341.

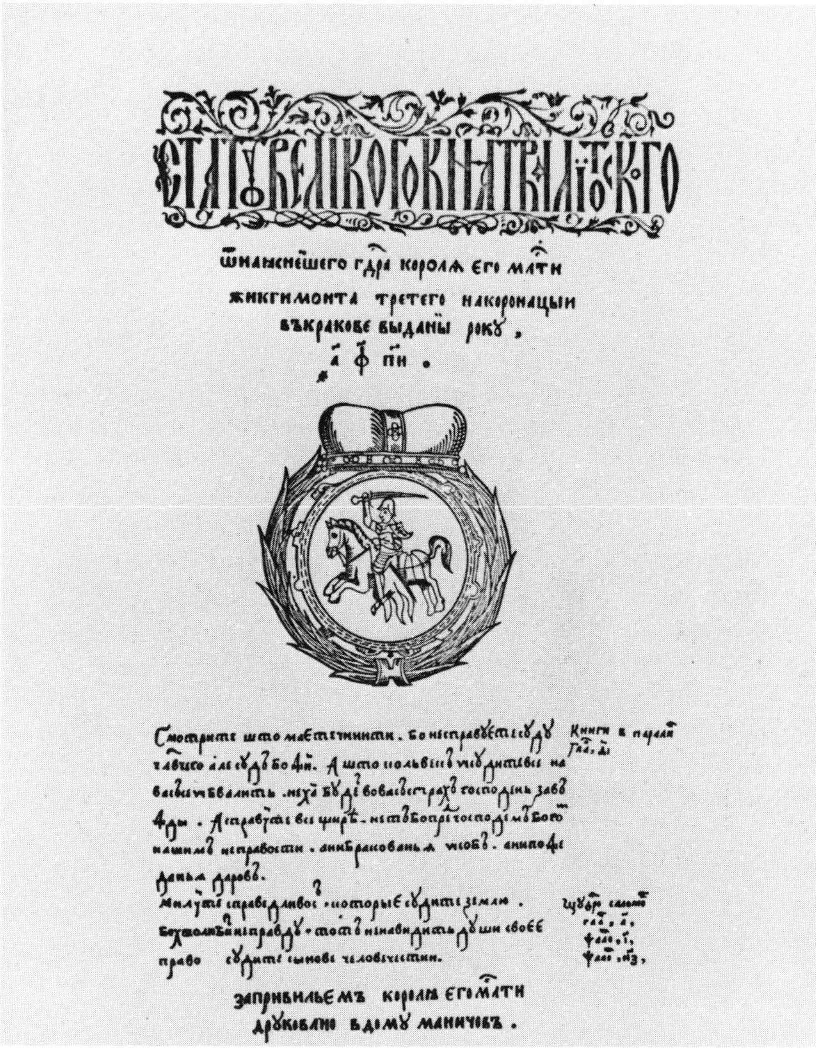

СТАТУТЪ ВЕЛИКОГО КНЯЗСТВА ЛИТОВСКОГО

ѿ наяснейшего г(о)с(у)д(а)ря короля его м(и)л(о)сти
Жикгимонта третего на коронацыи
в Кракове выданы року,
‚АФПН.

Смотрите што маете чинити. Бо не справуете суду
чл(о)в(е)ч(е)ского але суду Бож(е)го.

Книги в парали(помено)н. глава ДI

Милуйте справедливост, которые судите землю.

Премудр(ость) Соломон(ова) глава А.

Запривильемъ короля его м(и)л(о)сти
друковано в дому Мамоничовъ.

Belorussian Cyrillic-italic type by Hryn Ivanovich of Zabłudów in Wilno, 1583.

There is some foundation for such a statement regarding Skaryna's types; however, Kaldor is inaccurate when he relates this idea to Fiol's prints.

With all the small differences and subtleties, for the first two centuries Cyrillic books remained generally script-like, an amalgam of uncial and half-uncial, with only one exception: the Mamonich Cyrillic-italic type, created by Hryn Ivanovich of Zabłudów in Wilno, 1583, at the famous Belorussian Cyrillic printing shop called "Mamonich's House."

The cursive sloping type known as italics (the invention of Francesco Griffo Aldus Manutius in Venice around 1500 based on the "cancelleresca corsiva" of the Roman papal chancellery) was developed in Belorussian printing under the influence of Belorussian shorthand which was used in the chancellery of the grand duchy of Wilno. The Belorussian italics are most decorative and shapely, a less sloping Cyrillic italic and very different from anything else known in all Eastern Slavic printing. (See sample on page 144.)

Scholars generally felt that all Balkan Cyrillic printers followed the pattern of the Cetinje printing press. Jagić made such a statement after studying the Makarios *Osmoglasnik* [Octoechos]: "Bozhidar Vukovic's edition of the *Octoechos* of 1537 looks like a reprint of the oldest Cetinje print."[17] The same statement applies to later printers; they did not deny that Fiol's prints were to an extent a pattern for Makarios. But if we look at the six illustrations of Makarios's *Octoechos,* Part II, we can easily find an Italian influence which combines Italian decorative elements in vignettes with the Byzantine picture located in the center. Decorative initials in Makarios's *Octoechos I* are more Latin in style than Cyrillic, but this does not eliminate Fiol's influence on the design of the type and composition of the book. Gutenberg is the father of all printing, but Fiol is the father of Cyrillic typography.

In our examination of the prints of the three pioneering shops we are able to establish the following similarities and differences: the type is very similar in spite of all the improvements introduced by Makarios in Cetinje. Makarios did not allow himself to be influenced by Western printing except for the use of the newly developed Greek printing in Venice where he acquired improved forms of some letters. Sidorov stresses this very clearly.

> If Venice was a good school for the early Balkan Slavic printing, the latest in reciprocal influence shows on the late Venice printing. The prints of Božidar Vuković in Venice in the first half of the XVIth century follow the devices established by Makarije.[18]

This made his type better, but not necessarily much different from Fiol's. In respect of the Tărgovişte type we cannot agree with Koliada that it was more influenced by Cetinje than by Cracow. On the contrary, the Tărgovişte type looks

[17] I. V. Jagić, "Ein Nachtrag zum ersten Cetinjer Kirchendruck vom J. 1494," *Archiv für Slavische Philologie,* 25, 1903, 629.

[18] A. A. Sidorov, "Khudozhestvenno-tekhnicheskie osobennosti . . . ," p. 59.

like that of Fiol. While the type dimensions are larger and the page dimensions smaller, the type is very similar.

Characteristic of Tărgovişte print is the letter *M* with its descending middle part. It was taken from Borsdorf's Cracow type; Cetinje did not have such an *M*. The diacritical marks in the Tărgovişte prints are cast separately as they were in Borsdorf's type. We do not wish to imply that Tărgovişte prints do not have their own peculiarities, but they do have much more in common with Fiol's prints than with the Cetinje books or those of other West Balkan or Venetian provenance. All of the prints are black and red; the Cracow and Tărgovişte prints indicate artistic ingenuity while Makarios's Cetinje prints are more uniform in the use of red ink, as are Skaryna's. The technique of applying colors in the Cracow and Tărgovişte prints was the same; Makarios used the system then prevailing in the West.

What is most striking is the lack of Western influence in the Cracow and Tărgovişte prints, either in type or in decorative elements. The latter are purely Slavic-Byzantine braids in headpieces, initials, flags, etc., while in the Cetinje books they are a mixture of Western and Slavic. Skaryna's decorative elements are Western. The composition of the books, however, is similar in all three printings. In the triangle with its vertex in Cracow and a base situated between Cetinje, Montenegro and Tărgovişte, Rumania, Cyrillic printing was being developed for all Eastern and Southern Orthodox Slavic churches, including Rumania.

The value of any discovery can best be measured by its influence on posterity. The year 1525 closes the first incunabula period of Cyrillic printing during which a fully developed typography by Skaryna began. The second period encompasses fifty years (1525–1575) during which Cyrillic printing spread over Eastern Slavic Orthodox territories, especially those which had no opportunity to participate in the earlier development of Cyrillic typography, i.e. Russia and some parts of Ukraine.

Necessity is the mother of invention. The demand for ecclesiastical books in the newly acquired territories (after conquering Astrakhan and overthrowing the Tartar supremacy) inclined Ivan the Terrible to approve the establishment of a printing press. Consequently, over a hundred years after Gutenberg and over 70 years after Fiol's printing endeavors, the first official printing press was organized in Moscow. The founders were a deacon, Ivan Fedorov, and a wood engraver, Piotr Mstislavets (1563–1566).[19] They produced two books: *Apostol* and *Chasovnik*.[20] Soon after printing the second edition of *Chasovnik,* their shop was destroyed and burned by a mob. Moscow from the fourteenth century developed *scriptoria* which supplied the Orthodox Church with liturgical books. They were

[19] A. S. Zernova, "Pervopechatnik Petr Timofeevich Mstislavets" (First Printer Petr Timofeevich Mstislavets), *Kniga: Issledovaniia i materialy* (The Book: Research and Materials) (Moscow, 1964), IX, 77–111.

[20] *Apostol*—one of the most widely used books in the Orthodox Church, which contains the Acts of the Apostles and Epistles.

under the strict control of the Muscovite Church hierarchy and in the course of time this developed into a monopoly which practically survived up to the time of Peter the Great. It is understandable that printing was considered a threat to the scribers' guild and consequently Fedorov and Mstislavets were forced to leave Moscow. Both men, being persecuted by Church authorities, escaped to Poland where they were given asylum.

Since the second period of Eastern Slavic printing is dominated by Fedorov's achievements it would be advisable to study his ties with the masters of the first Cyrillic printing period. The majority of scholars agree that Fedorov and Mstislavets were well acquainted with the books of Fiol and of both Makarios and Skaryna. Nemirovskiĭ expressed the opinion that Fedorov spent some time in Cracow and perhaps studied at Cracow University. Russian scholars and the majority of Ukrainians stress his close connection with the Cracow and Târgovişte schools of printing rather than with Cetinje and Skaryna's press.

Let us cite the few basic influences of Cracow and Târgovişte prints on Fedorov as presented by A. A. Sidorov:

> Feol's books, the first in the entire Slavic printing, have been authoritative and, obviously also reached the old Muscovy. Ivan Fedorov's technique of two color printing is similar to that used by Feol. . . . The technique of Feol's editions is closer to Ivan Fedorov's than the technique of Makarios's Montenegro editions. . . . Closer to the Moscow prints are the Rumanian editions of Makarios, 1508–1512 [in Târgovişte]. Here we find fantastic large woodcut initials later adopted by Moscow. But Moscow did not follow Makarios in one respect—in utilizing slightly too huge self-contained woodcut headpieces sometimes covering half a page.[21]

Although other scholars and more details could be cited, we agree with P. M. Popov in his summary of the results of Russian and Ukrainian scholars' studies and research regarding Fedorov:

> As masters of Fedorov's printing craftsmanship we should recognize Szwajpolt Fiol and Makarios, a prominent printer first in Montenegro, then in Rumania. The relationship in technical details of the first Moscow prints with the Balkan prints is much more striking than with the chronologically closer products of B. Vuković's prints in Venice and F. Skaryna's in Wilno.[22]

In the fifteenth century the destruction of Novgorod by Tsar Ivan III (1475–1478) closes the splendid era of icon painting which flourished in that city. Andrey Rublyev (1370–1430), one of the greatest artists, worked in Moscow. His excellent

[21] A. A. Sidorov, "Khudozhestvenno-tekhnicheskie osobennosti," pp. 58–59.

[22] P. M. Popov, "Pochatok knyhodrukuvaniia u slov'ian, XV–XVI st." (Beginning of Slavic Printing in 15th–16th Centuries) in *Knyha i drukarstvo na Ukraïni,* AN URSR, (Kiev, 1964), ch. 1, p. 15.

work inspired followers. With the Novgorod artisans brought to Moscow, this city became the center of icon painting by the sixteenth century. But it is noteworthy and characteristic that neither Fedorov nor Mstislavets reveals any striking influence of this highly developed art in their work.

Mieczysław Gębarowicz, a Polish scholar now living in the U.S.S.R., promotes the notion that Ivan Fedorov was the pioneer-founder of all Slavic printing:

> The history of Russian printing, especially its beginning in the territories of the ancient Polish Commonwealth belong undoubtedly to the most interesting chapters of the history of the Renaissance. This printing, as is well known, was begun in Cracow, where in 1491 and undoubtedly in the following year, there appeared for the first time books printed in Russian. In spite of all the efforts of Francišak Skaryna, still thirty years later in Wilno, printing failed to strike any permanent and durable roots. It finally did happen, but not until the end of the third quarter of the sixteenth century thanks to the work of a Muscovite, Ivan Fedorov, a personage still quite mysterious to this day.[23]

As is evident, by using "Russian" as an umbrella term, Gębarowicz obscures the distinction between Old Church Slavonic and the various vernaculars and downgrades the accomplishments of everyone except Fedorov, a patently unjust and unhistorical position.

In the very same article Gębarowicz discusses the activities of another well known printer, the Polish Szymon Budny who in 1562 printed *Katechisis* [Catechism] in Belorussian in the town of Nieśwież; however, in the above cited statement he completely ignores that achievement and those of other predecessors.

Gębarowicz not only disregards the fact that South Cyrillic printing, which was highly developed in the first three quarters of the sixteenth century, influenced all Eastern Slavic territories; he also ignores the content of the very documents used in his own studies. Gębarowicz cites the epitaph on Fedorov's grave, which states that Fedorov "restored neglected printing." It was neglected, but only in Russia, not in Belorussia or elsewhere. In the epilogue of *Apostol,* printed in Lwów in 1573–1574, Fedorov states "when settled in Lwów he followed in the footsteps of some men chosen by God." Those documents can in no way be interpreted to mean Fedorov was the founder. However, he was one of the pioneers, a very important one indeed, but nevertheless only a follower, since we know of several predecessors, Fiol, both Makarios, Skaryna and others.

Fedorov was well acquainted with their works and especially with those of Skaryna. Proof of this is found in his prints. Fedorov's *Bukvar* (Primer), printed in Lwów in 1574, contains material for reading practice at the end of the book.

[23] Mieczysław Gębarowicz, "Iwan Fedorow i jego działalność w latach 1569–1583 na tle epoki. I. Poprzednicy" (Ivan Fedorov and His Activities in the Years 1569–1583 against the Background of the Era. I. Predecessors) *Roczniki Biblioteczne* (Library Annals), XIII, 1–2 (Wrocław-Warsaw, 1969), p. 5.

Texts with references to the Proverbs of Solomon were taken from Skaryna's Bible with only slight linguistic adaptations.[24]

After him there were in the Grand Duchy of Lithuania which encompassed all Belorussian territories other printing shops and printers mentioned by Gębarowicz. How he reached the conclusion that Fedorov was the founder of all Eastern Slavic printing is a mystery.

Based on facts and documents, we conceive a true picture of Fedorov to be as follows:

> He was the founder of Muscovite Russian printing, the printer of *Apostol*; and of two editions of *Chasovnik* in Moscow from 1563–1566; he was not, however, the sole printer but worked together with Piotr Mstislavets, the designer of the first Muscovite type. *Apostol* was well printed and illuminated. Soon after printing the second edition of his *Chasovnik*, both men, being persecuted, escaped to the Grand Duchy of Lithuania where they were given asylum as well as printing opportunities by the Belorussian magnate G. A. Chodkiewicz. In 1568–1569 they printed *Uchytelnoe Evangelie*. From September 26, 1569 to March 23, 1570 Fedorov without Mstislavets printed *Psaltir with Chasoslovec*. Russian scholars complain that both prints were mediocre in type and in illumination, and not as splendid as the Moscow *Apostol*. They attribute this to Chodkiewicz's demand that the books be delivered quickly. The truth, however, was that Piotr Mstislavets left Fedorov and the two men never met again.[25]

In losing Mstislavets, Fedorov lost one of the most prominent type designers and woodcutters in the early history of Cyrillic printing. Fedorov was forced to hire a new man, Hryn Ivanovich of Zabłudów, who was not as talented as Mstislavets. The departure of Mstislavets was the real cause of the decline in workmanship.

The latest results of research done by Belorussian scholars reveal that Fedorov was only a technical executor not a publisher of books printed in Zabłudów. Vitaut Tumash in the summary of his latest study states:

> Hetman Chodkiewicz was the initiator, owner and *spiritus movens* of the Zabłudów printing house and the chief publisher of the books published there. Attribution by some authors of such a role to Ivan Fedorov is without foundation. In Zabłudów Ivan Fedorov and Piotr Mstislavets were merely technical executors of the Hetman's plans and his will; there they were printers, not publishers, or editors.[26]

This statement also explains why Mstislavets left Zabłudów. He was too proud

[24] A. Nadson, "Padruchnik Fedarava i Skaryna" (Fedorov's Primer and Skaryna), *Bozhym Shliakham*, (London, 1972), XX, No. 5–6 (133–134), 8–11.

[25] Zernova, "Pervopechatnik Petr Timofeevich Mstislavets," *Kniga*, IX, 77–111.

[26] Tumash, "Hetman Ryhor Khadkevich i iahonae vydavetstva" (Hetman Ryhor Khadkevich and His Publishing House), *Zapisy*, Byelorussian Institute of Arts and Sciences, (New York, 1976), Vol. 14, 3–42.

to remain only a subordinate technician, so he went to Wilno. There he was able to work independently and put into operation his own ideas in the field of printing.

Fedorov started his third phase of printing in 1572, this time in Lwów with all of his tools and equipment, some of which were of Moscow origin including Mstislavets's type. There he printed the Lwów *Apostol,* which was a copy of the one he had printed in Moscow, except for a different Epilogue. Neither *Apostol* is in the vernacular but rather in the Old Church Slavonic with local "adopted" words. The Lwów *Apostol,* published on February 15, 1574, is bigger than the one printed in Moscow with more illustrations, woodcuts, vignettes, head ornaments, tail ornaments, initials, etc. Russian scholars stress, however, that the proofreading is not as proficient as in the Moscow *Apostol.* The type of the Moscow *Apostol*—really the Mstislavets type—was used by Fedorov's engravers in the Lwów *Apostol.* No new type was engraved when replacing battered letters; the old type was carefully followed.

Another book was printed in Lwów in 1574, a primer for teaching the Old Church Slavonic language. This book, the first of its kind printed among Eastern Slavic nations, is truly Fedorov's greatest cultural contribution. It bears no title.

From a document of September 2, 1575, we learn that Fedorov was working for one of the most powerful magnates of Ukraine, Prince Ostrogski. The printing shop itself was installed in 1577 in the town of Ostrog. In the meantime, an editorial commission was created which sent scholars to all the Orthodox countries to search for the best texts of the Bible. Consequently, editorial work was performed by a special committee under the supervision of the professor and rector of the Ostrog Academy, Herasym Dany'lovich Smotryc'kyi, a Ukrainian. Fedorov was one of the members of this committee. He received the ready text and the printing was finished in 1581; however, some copies are predated 1580. The Ostrog Bible is Fedorov's greatest typographical achievement, but in spite of its magnitude, in the sense of size and illuminations, it brought nothing new to printing. It is not a revelation, but simply a continuation of what had been achieved previously by Fiol, Makarios, Skaryna, and a few others before him. In Ostrog, *Novyi zavet z Psaltirem* (The New Testament and Psalter) 1580 and *Chronologia* 1581 by Andrei Rymsha were printed simultaneously with the Bible. The texts for all three prints were prepared very carefully. This was the contribution of the Ostrog Academy's Belorussian and Ukrainian scholars. Taking all this into consideration, we agree with P. M. Popov's opinion that "The Ostrog prints of Ivan Fedorov are striking not only by their high typographical perfection, but also by their scholarly character, naturally in accordance with the conception of those times."[27] Fedorov could not realize his dream in Russia, but only in the Polish-Lithuanian Commonwealth. The *Ostrog Bible* is a Ukrainian achievement.

[27] Popov, "Pochatok knyhodrukuvannia u slov'ian," in *Knyha i drukarstvo na Ukraïni,* p. 32.

Fedorov's *Ostrog Bible* 1580–81.

While not denying Fedorov's accomplishments as the pioneer of printing in Muscovite Russia and Ukraine, for Gębarowicz to pronounce him the founder of Russian printing (in the sense that encompasses all Eastern Slavic nations) is at the least a misconception. Fedorov was a founder of typography in Moscow, and his merits in Russian and Ruthenian-Ukrainian printing were indeed enormous, especially for the Ukrainian nation where he deserves the honor to be called "Honestus Ivanus Fedorovich, litteram Ruthenorum impressor." Ukraine made him famous.

In Western incunabulistics the rule is that the location of the printing press designates the national affiliation. While the personality and nationality of the printer are not unimportant, whatever they may be, his products belong to the country in which they were printed. Thus, the Venice printing shop and all the prints of Jenson, a Frenchman, the most prominent printer after Gutenberg in Europe, are recognized as Venetian or Italian, not as French. Prints of Stanislaus Polonus, a Pole, and Meynard Ungut, a German, in Seville are acknowledged as Spanish. Fiol's prints are Polish-Lithuanian-Belorussian and Ukrainian because they belonged to the Commonwealth, and all four participated equally in the history and achievements of the Polish-Lithuanian body politic.

The language of the incunabula print does not give any right to the nation using that particular language to claim it as its own. Incunabula whether printed in Greek, Hebrew, Aramaic, Old Church Slavonic, etc. belong only to the places and countries where they were originally printed, and to the printers. Therefore, incunabula ordered by somebody, such as *Statuta Episcopalia* ordered in foreign countries by Polish bishops, does not make them Polish. If they were done in Augsburg, Cologne or anywhere else, those towns have the right to claim them as theirs.

Fedorov as a printer does not belong only to Russia, in spite of his nationality. He worked in the following cities of the Polish Commonwealth: Zabłudów, 1568–1570; Lwów, 1572–1574; Ostróg, 1578–1582 and again in Lwów in 1583 where he died and was buried. For certain he worked in Moscow in 1563–1565 and less certainly in the late 1550s. According to Western rules and customs he is a Ukrainian as well as a Russian printer. Working in Russia, Belorussia and Ukraine, he became a partner and cultural pioneer of the great printers promoting the progress of the Renaissance epoch. Through his achievements and devotion, he brought honor and distinction to his native land. He was instrumental in initiating a close relationship between Russia and the West. Humanistic circles of the Polish Commonwealth promoted the idea of a union between different cultures and nations, as well as religions. Fedorov joined the trend. Indeed, he is the most prominent printer in the second phase of Cyrillic printing, which was centered in Ukraine.

In the creation and development of Cyrillic printing Muscovite Russia owes everything to her Western neighbors, Belorussia, Ukraine and Rumania. The basic difference between Muscovy and all other Slavic nations was that Muscovite printing shops, from the very beginning until the second half of the eighteenth century, were not only under direct state control, but were owned by the state. Private citizens in Muscovite Russia did not have the right to print, nor could anything be printed outside the state printing establishment. For us, it is difficult to comprehend this authoritarian censorship which encompassed everything, since printing in the West was a free enterprise from its very inception. There was no state supervision nor any national government presses. Rulers such as the Moldavian Voivodes and Montenegrin princes could and did subsidize printing. The Polish King Stefan Batory did, indeed, have a field printing shop to inform the nation of his achievements during his military campaigns, but that endeavor was his private affair, not a national institution.

No special achievements in Russian printing occurred until the simplification and improvement of the Cyrillic script introduced by Peter the Great in 1708. With the simplified Cyrillic half-uncial began the creation of the various vernacular Slavic scripts based on the Russian so-called "grazhdanka" for lay use. The Orthodox Church retained the Old Church Slavonic Cyrillic script for religious purposes in all nations. The preponderance of Russia in the field of writing dates only from the eighteenth century.

To avoid any misinterpretation in presenting the development of printing in the Polish-Lithuanian Commonwealth it is necessary to mention that printing in Lithuania was not limited to Cyrillic printing since Lithuanian typography was bilingual. The official language of the Chancellery of the Grand Duchy was Belorussian and Cyrillic script was used in all official acts and documents. Printing in the Lithuanian vernacular came about much later, as did Polish printing—since Latin was used initially. Humanism and the Reformation were instrumental in the rapid expansion of native languages, literature and printing in all of Western and Central Europe. Cyrillic typography was first used for church purposes in the Old Church Slavonic language before it was adopted for native languages. Skaryna printed a Bible in the native Belorussian language in 1517. The first book in the Polish language, called then *lingua vulgaris Polonica,* was printed between 1505–1508 in the Haller printing shop under the management of Casper Hochfeder. The name of the book *Historyja umęczenia Pana naszego Jezusa Chrystusa, na pienie polskie wydana* (History of Our Lord Jesus Christ's Passion, Edited in Polish Descant) was described by Michał Hieronim Juszyński in his two volume work: *Dykcjonarz poetów polskich* (Lexicon of Polish Poets) (Cracow, 1820, II, 423). Since this small book in octavo has not survived to the present date, the majority of prominent scholars asserted that the first book in the Polish language appeared in 1513 in Cracow, the *Raj duszny* (*Hortulus animae*—The Soul's Paradise),[28] a

[28] Biernat of Lublin, *Raj duszny — Hortulus animae* (Cracow, 1513).

Page from the *Grazhdanska azbuka* [a book dealing with the reformed alphabet] with the mark of Peter I, 1710. L. V. Cherepnin: *Russkaja paleografia* (Russian Paleography). Moscow, 1965, p. 446.

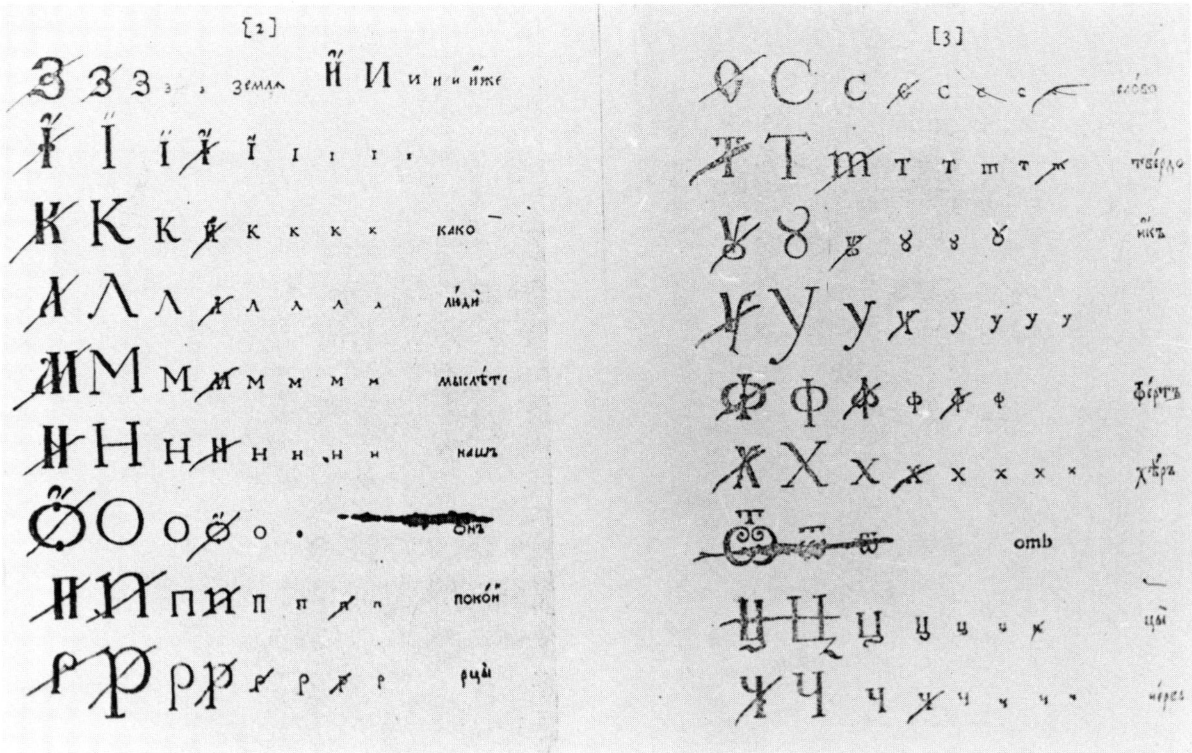
[2]
земля
иже
како
люди
мыслете
нашъ
онъ
покой
рцы
[3]
слово
твердо
икъ
фертъ
херъ
отъ
цы
черв

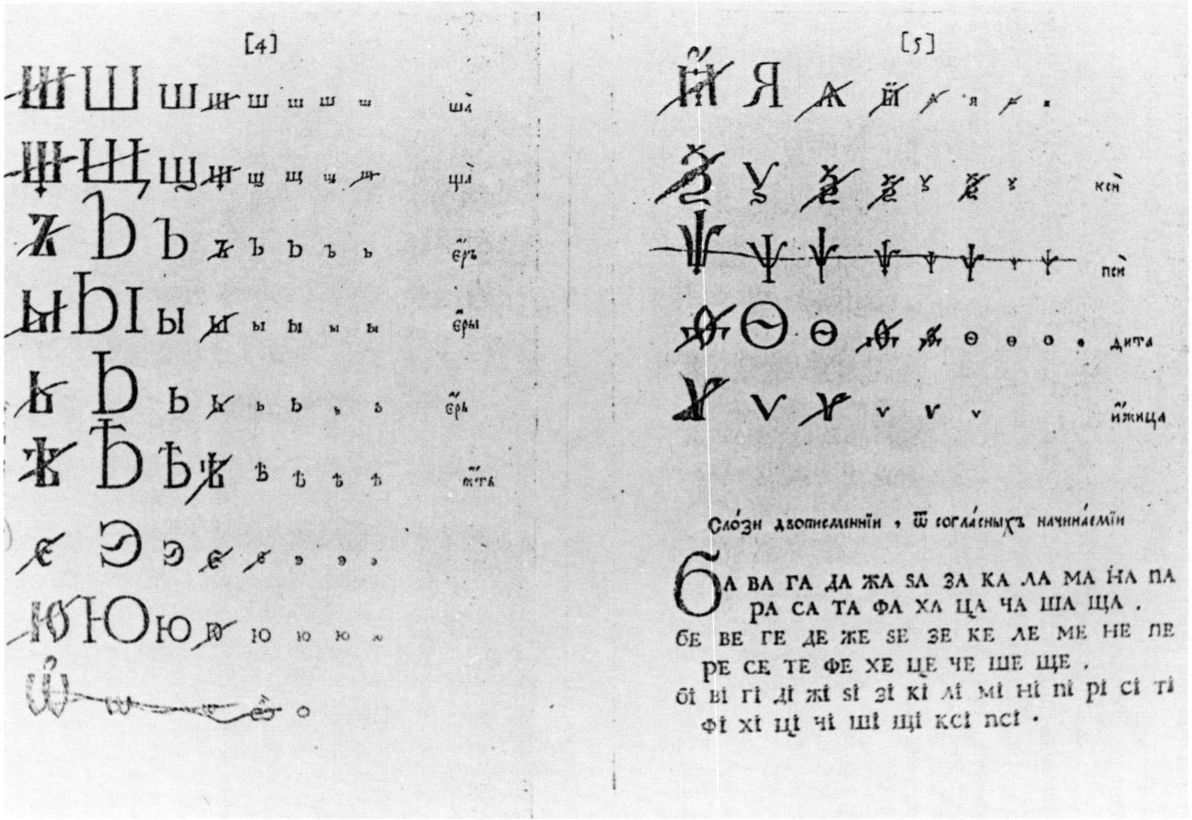
[4]
ша
ща
єръ
єры
єрь
ять
[5]
кси
пси
фита
ижица
Сло́зи двопименнии, ѿ согла́сныхъ начина́емии
БА ВА ГА ДА ЖА ЅА ЗА КА ЛА МА НА ПА
РА СА ТА ФА ХА ЦА ЧА ША ЩА.
БЕ ВЕ ГЕ ДЕ ЖЕ ЅЕ ЗЕ КЕ ЛЕ МЕ НЕ ПЕ
РЕ СЕ ТЕ ФЕ ХЕ ЦЕ ЧЕ ШЕ ЩЕ.
БІ ВІ ГІ ДІ ЖІ ЅІ ЗІ КІ ЛІ МІ НІ ПІ РІ СІ ТІ
ФІ ХІ ЦІ ЧІ ШІ ЩІ КСІ ПСІ.

prayer-book by Biernat of Lublin, whose printer was Florian Ungler. The Lithuanian nation with the acceptance of Christianity used the Latin alphabet. The Lithuanian language appears in print for the first time in 1547 with the publication of *Catechismusa prasty śadei* by the prominent humanist and follower of the Reformation Martynas Mazhvydas, one of the founders of the Lithuanian literary language. The book was printed in Königsberg (Polish Królewiec, after World War II Kaliningrad), capital of East Prussia, then a vassal state of the Polish-Lithuanian kingdom. The first book printed in Lithuanian appeared in Wilno in 1595—the *Katechism* by Mikalojus Daukša.[29] The dominant language in print in Lithuania up to the eighteenth century was Belorussian. Ironically this was systematically being replaced not by the native Lithuanian, but by the Polish language, except for the official acts and documents which remained in Belorussian.

[29] Juozas Jurginis, "Vilnius. Pierwsze przekłady książek polskich na język litewski i ich znaczenie kulturalne" (Wilno. First Translations of Polish Books into the Lithuanian Language and Their Cultural Importance), *Dawna książka i kultura* (Old Books and Culture), (Wrocław-Warsaw, 1975), pp. 316–329.

10

Incentives behind the Creation of Cyrillic Typography in Cracow

Several theories as to the motivation behind the Fiol-Turzo printing enterprise exist—and each contains a grain of truth. First among them is the economic one, that the printing of Cyrillic books was purely a business enterprise. Given what we know of both Fiol and Turzo, we may assume they began publishing Cyrillic books assured that they would turn a profit. However once that activity posed a threat to Fiol, he was quick to turn his back on it and seek other avenues of enrichment. He quickly gave up his "heresy" and his printing shop on order of the Church because it was no longer a safe and paying proposition.

Fiol was immediately released by the Inquisitor once he admitted wrongdoing and promised to cease such activities. That he was let off so easily, with really no more than a slap on the wrist, indicates influential people brought power to bear on his behalf. Which leads us to the theory that the printing of the Orthodox books was either a political and/or a religious affair and those who inspired it and financed the enterprise were able to, and did give, Fiol protection when his activities ran afoul of the authorities. Actually Turzo, Fiol's sponsor, was himself powerful enough to protect the printer, but Turzo was a businessman, not a politician. While his interests were broad, and he had connections in official government circles, he was never personally interested in politics. Moreover, he was a good Catholic and his son was a Catholic prelate.

Subsuming various political and social aspects of Fiol's printing activities, Kuziela wrote:

> Estreicher and A. Brückner suppose that it was the result of an order given by some German firms; Morawski, of Cracow University, sees in it the hand of a Polish king; Bandtkie and Ptaśnik assume that the printing was influenced by the Cracow Slavonic Benedictines and initiated by Lithuanian magnates such as Gasztołd and Sołtan, to support the union between Catholic and Orthodox churches through the publication of liturgical books in Cyrillic. The Ukrainian historian of literature, Ivan Franko, on the contrary, connects the Cracow Cyrillic printing with the Ukrainian magnate, Prince Ostrogski (a staunch anti-unionist).[1]

[1] Kuziela, "Der Deutsche Schweitpold Fiol . . . ," p. 77.

Kuziela, however, was not satisfied with any of these explanations and attempted to find some signs of Ukrainian nationalism in Fiol's prints. Drawing on the sentiment of his own times, the end of the nineteenth and beginning of the twentieth centuries, he came to the fantastic conclusion that Fiol's books were inspired by a Ukrainian national movement of the fifteenth century which was centered at Lwów. He even made mention of a long list of books which he said were to have been printed by Fiol in the interest of Ukrainian nationalism. The prominent Ukrainian historian, M. Hrushevs'kyĭ, however, discounts the idea of Lwów as the Ruthenian or Ukrainian (the terms are synonymous) capital:

> Ruthenia's "capital" in the fourteenth and fifteenth centuries was rather insignificant . . . [Lwów] rose quickly as the capital and settlement *Poloniae militantis,* residency of the Latin Archbishop, "general starosta"—magistrate of Ruthenian territories, "Ruthenian voivode," etc. The Ruthenians in Lwów were living in an Orthodox ghetto, a small Ruthenian quarter which was located in the neighborhood of the Jewish ghetto and apart from the privileged Catholic townspeople-citizens who would not let them occupy the market place. (It was a small street running east of the market place which has, to date, retained its name "Ruthenian Street" and, in addition, one small cross street now called *Blacharska*).[2]

The influential elements in Ukraine—the wealthy landowners and the church hierarchy—all had close ties with Poland and Lithuania. The Polish Commonwealth was the only protection from the Tartars who, from the beginning of the thirteenth century plundered and devastated Ruthenia to the extent that the southeastern part of the territory became a no-man's-land. This section came to be called in the fifteenth century Ukraine (Ukraine, u-"at." kraj "land" or "border"). The Tartars were an almost constant menace; they overran and burned Kiev, the capital, in 1482 and again four years later devastated the whole territory. During this period no one in Ruthenia was considering independence—actually just the opposite. The Ruthenians were seeking closer ties with the Polish-Lithuanian state as protection from the Tartars and from the Muscovy Grand Dukes, and also with an eye toward the liberty, cultural development and commerce it offered.

These ties were especially important to Lithuania. Her great adversary, Muscovy, claimed to rule over Rus' and the Eastern Slavs because of religious and tribal ties. Olgierd, the founder of the Grand Duchy of Lithuania (which encompassed most of the territories that were formerly the Grand Duchy of Kiev) wrote the Constantinople Patriarch and complained that Lithuania had two main enemies—the Teutonic Order and Moscow. The Teutonic order used Christianity as a pretext for conquest and subjugation of pagan Lithuania in the name of the Pope, while the Muscovite Grand Dukes applied the same method to the Belorussians and the Ukrainians in the name of Orthodox Church unity.

[2] M. Hrushevs'kyĭ, *Istoriia ukraïns'koï literatury* . . . pp. 151–152.

Moscow had only later become a political factor of importance. The first news of her existence did not come until 1147 and soon thereafter she became a vassal of the Tartars and only then became dangerous to other Russian principalities. During the period from 1240 until her liberation from the Tartars in 1478 Muscovy got all her powers from the strength of the Golden Horde and became dominant among the Russian principalities by applying unscrupulous methods. In discussing the rise of Moscow the well-known historian Bernard Pares states:

> As we have seen, the Tartar invasion was a wholesale calamity, destroying possibilities of development in Galicia, isolating Novgorod from the rest of the water road, leading indirectly to the subjugation of much of the water road itself to Lithuania and, through Lithuania, to Poland. The new Russia of the backwoods of the Middle Volga and Oka was thus politically cut off from Europe. Not far off, on its eastern side, were the frontiers of Tartar occupation, and it was itself squeezed dry by the exactions of their tax-gatherers and reduced to a sheer struggle for existence. This destroyed all common political interest. This newly settled area split into a number of principalities, which constant subdivision made smaller and smaller, until many of them were little more than private estates. Here civilization had been completely thrown back, learning was almost lost, art in decline; and it is from this state of subjection, demoralization, and individual egotism that we must trace the beginnings of the power of Moscow.[3]

No wonder the Belorussians and Ukrainians joined the Polish Lithuanian United Kingdom, being afraid of Moscow's church policy and political supremacy.

The Metropolitans of Kiev, during the thirteenth century, were the only symbol of unity of Orthodox Rus' which was destroyed politically by continuous Tartar invasions. Metropolitan Cyril left Kiev in 1299 and settled in Vladimir. His successor Peter, due to clashes among the pretenders to power, accepted Ivan I Kalita's invitation to Moscow and settled there temporarily in the hope that one day he would be able to return to his Kievan Metropolis. He soon became famous for his daring journey to the Tartar capital. Upon his death, he was raised to sainthood for his good deeds during his lifetime and for the miracles which occurred at his tomb. He was not a Muscovite; he was a Ruthenian and his sojourn in Moscow lasted only slightly over a year; nevertheless, Moscow claimed him as her saint. His successors remained in Moscow, and this sustained the Moscow rulers' argument that there is but one Orthodox Church capital—Moscow, and one political center for all Rus'.

The idea of a religious union with the Orthodox Church started to occupy some Polish statesmen, both Catholic and Orthodox, in the belief this would be the best solution to the danger posed by Moscow. Soon the Popes started to push their own concepts of a union in order to regain power over all Christianity by accepting

[3] Bernard Pares, *A History of Russia* (New York, 1965), p. 78.

Moscow's political preponderance over the Eastern Slavs. The situation became very complicated, and it remains so today.

The fifteenth century was a time of great struggle between those who wanted a union and those who opposed it. Queen Jadwiga tried to accomplish it through cultural enterprises. For example, from Prague she invited Slavic Benedictines who used the Glagolitic script and the Old Church Slavonic language to teach the people about Catholicism and to establish religious and cultural contacts between the Poles, Lithuanians and Eastern Slavs. Furthermore, she promoted the translation of the Bible from Latin into Polish, and there was a rumor she herself owned Cyrillic manuscripts and could read Cyrillic. Archmandrite Kopystenskiĭ was deeply convinced that this was true: "Polish Queen Jadwiga was occupied with the study of the Slavic Bible, and the works of the Church Fathers translated into Slavonic."[4] Kopystenskiĭ was wrong; Queen Jadwiga did not know Old Church Slavonic. However, the Jagellonians knew Cyrillic well and many Cyrillic manuscripts were in the court library.

The idea of increasing Slavic manuscript books was at least a century older than Turzo's enterprise which multiplied them by print. We can be sure the Jagellonians did not object to the printing of Fiol's books in Cyrillic, a project which had the support of such Belorussian magnates as Sapieha and Sołtan as well as many Poles. Ukrainian Prince Ostrogski also showed special interest.

The most plausible explanation for the Cracow Cyrillic printing is the hypothesis that the printing of Orthodox books was a political and religious idea of some prominent circles at the Cracow royal court. There the most influential and powerful personalities of Poland, Lithuania, Belorussia and Ukraine were represented and fought for control. Kuziela, while maintaining a generally reserved attitude towards Poland, holds to this theory because he was unable to change the historical fact that at the turn of the fifteenth and sixteenth centuries Cracow was a cultural center not only for central Europe—but also for Belorussia and Ukraine:

> In the first place, one must realize that at the end of the fifteenth century Cracow was a much more important European cultural center for Western Ukraine than is generally accepted. Cracow was then located fairly close to the Ukrainian ethnic territories and possessed a very influential Ukrainian spiritual and ecclesiastical colony. In addition to many representatives of the aristocracy and nobility (especially from Lithuania) active at the royal court were huge masses of students from Ukraine and Belorussia studying at Cracow University or en route to the West.[5]

Kuziela is correct except for a minor inaccuracy: the University matriculation book does not reveal the names of many Ruthenians.

[4] Golowatzkij, "Sweipolt Fiol . . . ," p. 427.
[5] Kuziela, "Der Deutsche Schweitpold Fiol . . . ," pp. 77–78.

Several special factors other than those stated earlier made Cracow very important. No other country in the West, not even Bohemia which was then quite powerful, had any significant contacts with Eastern European Slavic nations. Byzantium, which had dominated Eastern and South Slavic nations, ceased to exist as a cultural and religious force when Constantinople was seized by the Turks in 1453. Cracow and Wilno filled the vacuum and became the political and cultural centers of the Western Rus' nations.

Belorussia was closely associated with Lithuania. The *Cambridge Medieval History* describes these events as follows:

> The main thread of Russian history runs in North-Eastern Russia, where Moscow was rising to importance under Gedymin's contemporary Ivan Kalita. But the real successor of Kievan Russia, as historians have now realized, was not Moscow, alien partly in race and wholly in political ideas to Kiev, but the new Russo-Lithuanian State. . . . The Russian principalities had come to look upon Lithuania as their saviour from Tartar rule, since the Lithuanian princes, behind their impenetrable barrier of marsh and forest, could defy the Khan of the Golden Horde with impunity. Thus Polotsk, long under Lithuanian influence, became subject to Lithuania in 1307; Vitebsk soon followed. Podlasie with Brest was seized by Gedymin in 1315; Minsk was occupied soon after. By his victory on the Irpen in 1320, Gedymin conquered the princes of the Kiev region, though Kiev itself, since the departure of the Metropolitan to Vladimir in 1300, had lost the last shred of its political and commercial predominance, its place having been taken partly by Lemberg [Lvov, Lwów] and partly by Gedymin's new city of Vilna. Gedymin had thus brought under his rule all White Russia and a large part of Little Russia, and had established a loose union of Russian principalities not unlike the Kievan union of an earlier age.[6]

While the Grand Duchy of Lithuania was ruling the whole of Lithuania, Belorussia and most of Ukraine, Belorussian culture and language became dominant to the extent it was difficult to determine which was the real ruler—Belorussia or Lithuania. This Belorussian influence extended so far in fact that in the fifteenth and sixteenth centuries Lithuanians were mistakenly acknowledged as ethnic Slavs. The contemporary historian, Hartman Schedel, writing of Lithuania in his *Chronica Mundi* of 1493, stressed "das gezueng diss Volks ist Windisch" (the language of this nation is Wendish). All Slavs in territories deemed German were called Wends by the Germans.

Culturally Belorussia dominated all Rus' in the fifteenth and sixteenth centuries. Its high culture was prominent in the upper classes of Lithuania and the Belorussian language became the language of learned people. Up until the eighteenth century state acts and documents of the Grand Duchy were written in this language using Cyrillic script. It was also a court language which prevailed up to

[6] *The Cambridge Medieval History* (New York, 1936), VI: 1561.

Ivan Fedorov. *Bukvar.* Lwów, 1574.

the beginning of the sixteenth century when the sons of Casimir, educated in Cracow, inherited the throne and the Polish language began to dominate everyday use. Nevertheless, the official language in Poland's acts and documents remained Latin.

Along with the Belorussian language and cultural influences the Orthodox Church extended its influence. It penetrated deeply into Lithuania and many magnates and part of the nobility accepted the Orthodox rite. Ukraine was also Orthodox while some of its principalities were directly under Polish rule. These princes and lords became a part of the establishment and many were in the King's court in Cracow. Consequently Orthodoxy became a religious as well as a political problem during the fifteenth century in Catholic Poland and in the Grand Duchy of Lithuania which was a quarter Catholic and three-quarters Orthodox.

To gain a clearer view of this complicated situation in Poland during the fifteenth and sixteenth centuries, let us cite a prominent author, the 1980 Nobel laureate in literature and University of California professor, Czesław Miłosz:

> Ever since the Middle Ages, when the borders of the Grand Duchy of Lithuania embraced populations speaking several Eastern Slavic dialects, these dialects, along with the Cyrillic alphabet, had been used in official documents. But also the ruling nobility of Lithuanian stock gradually abandoned the use of their native tongue, switching to Slavic in its Polish or Eastern Slavic variety. . . . The official language of the Duchy was called Ruthenian, and in the sixteenth century it already showed signs of a division into a northern variant, i.e., Byelorussian, and a southern variant, Ukrainian. But the linguistic situation was extremely fluid, and Ruthenian absorbed many Polish words. Some texts sound practically like Polish texts written in Cyrillic with Eastern Slavic case endings added. . . . In any case, nobody who studies the life and institutions of the Grand Duchy and the history of the Reformation there can bypass such rich material, consisting of edicts, regulations, juridical formulas, and, occasionally religious polemics. The first Bible in the vernacular (the work of Franciszek Skoryna) to be published within the borders of the "Respublica" [the Jagellonian Commonwealth] was, as we have already mentioned, not in Polish but in Old Byelorussian. A monumental juridical work, the *Lithuanian Statutes,* was published in Old Byelorussian in Wilno in 1529. . . . Let us add that the two languages stood on an equal footing, and the lords of the Duchy used Old Byelorussian when speaking in public in Warsaw.[7]

Addressing all the people of the Grand Duchy in the third edition of the Statute of the Grand Duchy of Lithuania (Code of Civil and Criminal Law), the Vice-Chancellor of the Grand Duchy, Lew Sapieha, in 1588 stated with pride that this work was presented in the native language: "If it is shameful for some nations not to know their laws, how much more is it so for us, who have our laws written not in

[7] Czesław Miłosz, *The History of Polish Literature* (London, 1969), p. 106.

some foreign language, but in our own."[8] It is noteworthy that the language was not Lithuanian nor Polish, but Belorussian. It shows how the cultural borderlines intermingled and were voluntarily accepted in those days.

A short poem by J. K. Paškievič (Pashkevich), a Belorussian poet of the early seventeenth century, expresses the sentiment of the times:

> Poland blooms with Latin genius,
> Lithuania with Ruthenian.
> *Sans* this in Poland thou will not prosper,
> *Sans* that in Litva seems a jester.
> Latin to one a tongue bestoweth,
> One *sans* Ruthenian downfall knoweth.[9]

This verse voices the modern and humanistic political ideology of the Polish-Lithuanian Commonwealth in that period. When the principle of *cuius regio, eius religio* (the religion of the ruler is the religion of the state) was dominant throughout the entire world as the tragic result of religious struggle, Poland was a country where the free union of nations prevailed with cultural and religious freedom.

The prominence of Belorussia in the Lithuanian state during the fifteenth and sixteenth centuries was the result of the dominance of its culture and language in the court. This facilitated the accommodation of those regions of Ukraine which joined the Polish-Lithuanian Commonwealth. Belorussia supplied the church with scriptures and priests. Shortly it became apparent that the demands became so enormous that the *scriptoria* were unable to fulfill these requirements. (With the fall of Byzantium, the situation became rather critical.) Leading Belorussian and Ukrainian magnates as well as Orthodox church officials came to the conclusion that only the magic art of printing would be able to replace the manuscripts destroyed by the Tartars.

The center of the printing activity was Cracow and a thorough historical study of government and Church establishments of the Polish-Lithuanian Commonwealth might possibly reveal who was the initiator. This is emphasized by the Polish scholar Maria Błońska:

> Attempts at ascertaining the names of the inspirers and actual founders of Fiol's printing press, the first press in the world to print Church Slavic liturgical books in Cyrillic type, have been unsuccessful so far. Also unknown are the organizers of trade in these books, which were produced in Cracow, but intended solely for export to the Grand Duchy of Lithuania. Because it seems certain that the inspirers of Fiol's printing press were members of this section of the Lithuanian-Ruthenian society which gravitated

[8] Alexander Nadson, "The Memoirs of Theodore Jeŭłšeŭski, Assessor of Navahrudak (1546–1604), *The Journal of Byelorussian Studies,* (London, 1968), 271.

[9] *Ibid.,* p. 271.

towards the Western, Polish culture. The lines along which investigations by historians of printing should proceed in this respect could only be determined by a research on Polish-Lithuanian cultural and religious relations in the fifteenth century conducted jointly by historians and church historians.[10]

It is obvious that only in Cracow (where culture, art and ideas were given free expression as a result of the enlightened and liberal Jagellonian rule) could the idea of printing Orthodox books in Cyrillic have been born, either to support the Orthodox Church or to acquaint Catholics with a rival rite.

Polish circles were not particularly eager for the Ecclesiastical Scriptures in their national language because Latin was the official language of the Catholic Church and also the language of the upper classes. Almost everything was written and printed in Latin up until the sixteenth century. Only a few Polish songs, a bit of poetry and a few translations of religious works, including the Bible, were written in the vernacular.

On the other hand the Orthodox Church needed books for two reasons. The Tartars' persistent invasions had devastated Ukrainian lands, burning churches and ecclesiastical manuscripts. Upon the restoration of peace, books were in great demand. The idea of mass production of books by means of printing, therefore, could only have been born in Orthodox circles—and industrial Cracow could and did easily respond to the demand.

Secondly, the Orthodox authorities were engaged in an effort to upgrade the educational standards of their priests to conform to the level of the Roman Catholic priesthood. Intellectuals thought of the masses; Skaryna emphatically underscored this by stating on the title page of his Bible that it had been translated for the purpose of enlightening the common people. Here was a Belorussian scholar and printer expressing the trend of Polish Humanism and the Renaissance.

Already at the beginning of the fifteenth century the most enlightened ideas about human rights to life, and liberty, also to religious freedom, were expressed by the professors of Cracow University. The ideas expounded by the Cracow School of Law regarding the law of nations were far in advance of contemporary European learning.

The rector of Cracow University, Stanisław of Skalmierz, in his study on the nature of just wars, argued that only a war of defense could be considered just and condemned aggression of any kind. Another rector, Paweł Włodkowicz, delivered at the Council of Constance, 1414, an extraordinary treatise: *De potestate papae et imperatoris respectu infidelium* (On the Power of the Pope and Emperor with regard to the Infidels). Condemning religious wars and defending the principle of

[10] Maria Błońska, "Próba nowego spojrzenia na dzieje krakowskiej oficyny drukarskiej Szwajpolta Fiola (około 1483–1491) (An Attempt at a New Look into the History of Szwajpolt Fiol's Cracow Printing Press) (ca. 1483–1491), *Rocznik Biblioteki Narodowej* (National Library Yearbook), IV. (Warsaw, 1968), p. 62.

Wit Stwosz, Callimachus' tombstone, Cracow, 1496.

state sovereignty, he extended it to the pagans, pointing out that they must not be converted to Christianity by force. He articulated four maxims: (1) It is not permissible to convert by force. Pagans are brethren. (2) Just war is a war for peace only. (3) War for the purpose of conversion by force is a crime. (4) All laws based on crime are invalid.

Promoting freedom of religion the Polish delegation at both Councils, in Constance (1414) and in Florence (1439), supported and advocated union with the Eastern Church. Those ideas dominated Polish Humanism during the fifteenth and sixteenth centuries and in 1572 were instrumental in introducing the law of equal rights for all denominations in the Polish-Lithuanian Commonwealth.

When Catholic reactionary circles discovered that the Orthodox were supporting Cyrillic printing, they eliminated the enterprise in Cracow through the offices of the Holy Inquisition. It was done anonymously but the order came from the top level of the establishment. Fiol was arrested and Turzo was persuaded to close the business, and not even his own son, a Catholic canon, could come to his aid.

Chivalry was then shown by the winning side by destroying neither the books nor the printing shop and by forgiving Fiol. No damage was done to Turzo's property and even the bail for Fiol's release was paid by other Cracow citizens and not by Turzo. Everything went so smoothly that our supposition of the printing presses being moved to purely Orthodox territories does not seem far-fetched at all.

However, Orthodox circles had learned the technicalities of mass production of books. Workers leaving Cracow soon spread this knowledge throughout the Balkans and Eastern Europe. It was a by-product of a political ideal which became one of the most valuable aspects in the history of many Slavic nations.

Fiol's trial and the events that followed had been kept in low profile since no one in Cracow wanted to stir up a commotion while the ailing King Casimir was still alive. His attitude toward the Orthodox Church and the Cyrillic Old Church Slavonic Scriptures was favorable and well known. The Orthodox Church was, after all, the church of his mother, Queen Sophia.

Unquestionably the Jagellonians were under the spell of Belorussian culture. King Casimir ordered the following Cyrillic inscription in Old Belorussian to be put on the monument to himself and his wife, Elizabeth of Austria, in the famous Byzantine "Ruthenian" Chapel in 1478, which was a part of the Catholic Cathedral Church at the royal Wawel Castle in Cracow: "With the volition and wisdom of the Almighty God the Father the inscription in this chapel was made at the command of the powerful King, His Majesty Casimir, with God's grace the King of Poland, Grand Duchy of Lithuania and Ruthenia, ruler and sovereign of Prussian duchies, lord also of many other lands; and Her Majesty the Queen Elizabeth, of the imperial family, granddaughter of His Majesty Emperor Sigismund, the ruler

"The Crucifixion," Russo-Byzantinian polychrome in the Holy Cross Chapel, Cracow, 1470.

of Austria, Bohemia and Hungary, in the year of Our Lord's Nativity 1498."[11]

While Turzo, Fiol and Borsdorf were the instruments which established the first Cyrillic printing office and were therefore the pioneers of Cyrillic printing, the inspiration more than likely did not come from them. It may have come from highly placed persons in the King's entourage who formed the government and administration of Poland, Lithuania, Belorussia and Ukraine.

From the beginning of the fifteenth century, conceived for religious and political purposes, the idea of a great union of all peoples under the aegis of Poland and Lithuania was gradually implemented culminating in the unique act of union known as *Unia Lubelska* (Lublin Union) of 1569 which survived for centuries. Simultaneously, the growing tendency toward a union between the Catholic and Orthodox Churches was crowned with the *Unia Brzeska* (Union of Brest) of 1596 which has partially survived under the name of the Uniat Church. The concept of Cyrillic printing had been born in a similar atmosphere. It did not survive in Cracow but that city was the first sponsor and inspiration for Cyrillic printing in all Eastern and Southern Slavic nations. The Cracow Cyrillic incunabula are one of the most interesting results of the farseeing and broadminded policies and concepts of the Jagellonian times which were permeated by humanism. And it came about, not by words but by deeds, the establishment of a brotherhood and unity of nations and religions which is still a dream of mankind.

The names of those who were instrumental in bringing forth this Cyrillic printing press in Cracow are an enigma and perhaps will never be solved by researchers, however, this was the product of Polish culture. Its essential quality was tolerance and profound understanding of Christianity. From these elements arose tolerance toward other faiths, races and nations. In a period when the principle "cuius regio, eius religio" prevailed Polish rulers stated that they were not rulers of their subjects' consciences. No wonder then that in this atmosphere in the capital of Catholic Poland, Cracow, the first in the world Cyrillic printing shop was created, in accordance with the progressive spirit of the Jagellonian Commonwealth.[12]

[11] A. L. Sobolevskiĭ, "Starshie perevody russkikh katolikov" in *Materialy i izsledovaniia v oblasti slavianskoĭ filologii i arkheologii* (Materials and Research in the Field of Slavic Philology and Archeology) (St. Petersburg, 1910), *Akademiia Nauk. Otdel. russ. iazyka,* vol. 88, no. 3, 193–194.

[12] Krystyna M. Olszer, ed., *For Your Freedom and Ours. Polish Progressive Spirit from the 14th Century to the Present* (New York, 1981).

Appendix 1
Description and Characteristics of Fiol's Prints

I. TRIOD CVETNAJA

Triod Cvetnaja, a folio size volume, was most likely the first of the four books known to have been printed by Fiol. The three first pages are blank. On page four (leaf 2 verso) a woodblock frontispiece illustration, presenting the Crucifixion and beneath it the printer's mark, opens a new chapter in the history of printing.

The text begins on the following page (leaf 3 recto). At the top of this first printed page is a knotted headpiece impressed in red; beneath it also printed in red is the first stylized line of the Incipit. Its caption letters 3 lines in height form the decorative clichéd line conforming to the traditional Byzantine-Slavonic illumination "vyaz'."[1]

There are no decorative initials on the first page of *Triod Cvetnaja.* Throughout the entire book, however, numerous initials appear, altogether about ninety of various forms and sizes. The arrangement is chaotic with a predominance of large initials over smaller ones, accumulation in some parts with long intervals in others. The first one-third of the book has approximately two-thirds of all the initials.

From the thirteen woodblocks of knotted initials shown in the illustration on page 95, sixty-three imprints have been made. The woodblock for the letter "V" was used 20 times, for "B"—10, "T"—8, "G"—7, "P"—6, "S" and "R"—5 times each, "CH" and "I"—only once each. Those of seven lines in height were used in preference to the smaller ones. On the first 120 leaves there are 42 knotted initials, the remaining 246 leaves contain altogether only 20 imprints.

The plain floral initials were used sporadically except the initial "T," six lines in height impressed 7 times. Altogether from all of the four floral initials shown in the illustration on page 95, there were 10 imprints made.

The following three lines in height capital letters were used in *Triod Cvetnaja* as initials:

[1]See p. 103, *ante.*

They all were applied less than twenty times. It is difficult to be precise in these matters because in different copies there are some small deviations. For instance on leaf 289 verso of the copy in the Lublin Catholic University Library two initials "V" are impressed. They vary distinctly in appearance. The one in the lower part of the page can be considered as the regular character from the set of capital letters of the alphabet. In the upper portion of the same page there is another initial "V." Its appearance and setting seems to be poorly executed as if it were thrown into the text later. Also below the text an ornamental figure of the same letter "V" is strangely stylized. There may be more of such variations in different copies especially when considering page 116 verso of the Lublin copy (illustration p. 173) with an initial "B" laboriously illuminated, not to be found in the other copies. These extras could have been added by different owners, as were commentaries and provenance notes found in the margins indicating these books had been extensively used.

The illuminative elements in *Triod Cvetnaja* accentuated by the application of the cinnabar-red color to special words, sentences and paragraphs are striking, but the execution of the print is poor. The lines are not straight; the margins are uneven (especially the right one), and the entire setting is primitive.

Due perhaps to the typographical shortcomings as well as spillage of type composition of whole pages, re-setting was necessary. This had been the reason for the obvious differences on certain pages. Among the copies and fragments of *Triod Cvetnaja* in the Polish libraries two variants, A and B, have been established. In quires 21 and 23, three sheets 127, 142 and 143—with corresponding leaves 240 and 249, 267 and 270, 268 and 269 reveal differences in the setting of whole pages.

In her article Maria Błońska presented the illustrations of page 240 from variant A (copy presently in the Warsaw National Library) and variant B (copy in the Cracow National Museum).[2] By examining an illustration of the same page 240 from variant B (copy in the Lublin Catholic University Library) the differences between variant A and B can be easily ascertained. The variations are mostly in the allocation of different words, letters, diacritical marks, elimination of some duplication of words, consequently changing the length of lines. The meaning in the text was not always the reason for changes. The text remained the same.

Szandorowska found while studying *in situ* that "the Braşov copy of *Triod Cvetnaja* is another variant in comparison to the researched Polish copies. It is a composite of the two known variants of the text, described in the literature as

[2] Maria Błońska, "Próba nowego spojrzenia na dzieje krakowskiej oficyny drukarskiej Szwajpolta Fiola (około 1483–1491)" (An Attempt at a New Look Into the History of Szwajpolt Fiol's Cracow Printing Press (ca. 1483–1491) *Rocznik Biblioteki Narodowej* (Yearbook of the National Library) (Warsaw, 1968), IV, 56–57.

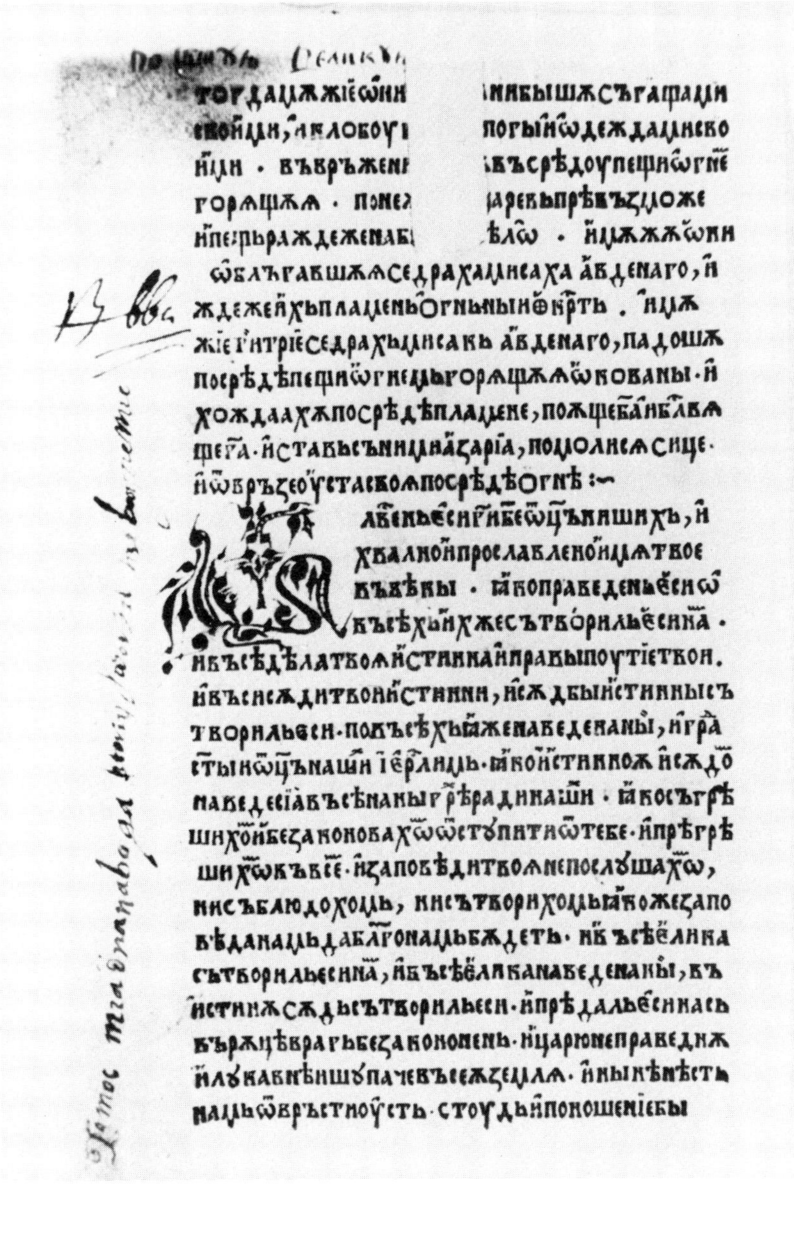
тогдацѫжїеѿни инибышѧсъгастадли
євойцѧи, аклобоу погыиѿдеждацнєво
иди · въвръжен късрѣдоупещиѿгнє
горѧщѫѧ · понеж царевьпрѣвъздоже
ипещьраждежена ѣлѡ · идѫжѫѿни
ѿблъгавшѫѧседрахадинсаха авденаго, и
ждежеихьпладеньогньныиѿкрть · идѫ
жїе гнтрїеседрахьднсакь авденаго, падошѫ
посрѣдѣпещиѿгнедьгорѧщѫѧѿкованы · и
хождаахѫпосрѣдѣпладене, пожщебаиблвѧ
щега · истававъницдназарїа, подолнсѧсице ·
иѿвръзеоустасвоѧпосрѣдѣогнѣ :~
лвеньесигибеѿцънашихъ, и
хвалнойпрославленоидѧтвое
въвѣкы · якоправеденьесиѡ
въсѣхьихжесътворильесинна ·
ивъсѣдѣлатвоѧистиннайправыпоутїетвои.
ивъсиеждитвоиистинни, иеждбыистинныс
творильеси · покъсѣхьяженаведенаны, игра
стыиѿцънашихъ ієрлимь · якоистинною иеждо
наведесїавъсѣнаныгрѣраднинашн · якосъгрѣ
шихоибезаконовахѡѿстѹпитиѿтебе · ипрѣгрѣ
шихоѡкъвсе · изаповѣдитвоѧнепослѹшахѡ,
нисъблюдохоць, нисътворихоцьякожезапо
вѣданацьдаблгонацьбѫдеть · ивъсѣелика
сътворильесинна, ивъсѣеликанаведенаны, въ
истинѫсѫдьсътворильеси · ипрѣдальесинась
въръкѹврагьбезаконопень · ицарюнеправеднѫ
илѹкавиенишѹпачевъсеѧземлѧ · инынѣнѣсть
нацьѿвръстиоустъ · стоудьипоношенїебы

Fiol. *Triod Cvetnaja.* Leaf 116 v. Lublin Copy.

variant A or B. In the Braşov copy we have to do with the combining of the variant in the setting: B + A + A."[2a]

Characteristically changes of whole pages, as well as single lines (which in *Triod Cvetnaja* are numerous) are in no way connected with any typographical improvement. They are solely vocabular, orthographic, etc., without any consideration for alignment of words, straightening of the right margins, esthetic, etc. The right margin of variant A appears to be more uniform than in the later re-set variant B.

Triod Cvetnaja does not have a title page or colophon, but has an important feature—the register of sections. Mircea and Szandorowska report that this register of sections is located on the last page. This coincides with the description of sections based on a study of the Warsaw National Library copy that will be presented. Fortunately in this copy the signatures placed in the lower right-hand corner are well-preserved and aid in following their arrangement.

Fiol used numbers starting with the number one to mark signatures. All leaves were counted whether they were printed or blank. The first printed leaf in *Triod Cvetnaja* is the third and it has number 3 in the lower righthand corner.

Before discussing the arrangement of signatures we must note that *Triod Cvetnaja* consists of 31 sections, sexternions, which means 6 folded sheets giving 12 leaves or 24 pages. The printer places signatures only on the first six leaves of the folded sheets leaving the next six unmarked, because Fiol simultaneously printed two pages.

The next page will show the method used by Fiol in placing signatures, giving a few sections as examples with special attention to the first and last sections.

Briefly, the formula for the arrangement of signatures is as follows: Sections multiplied by leaves less blank leaves equal the total number of printed leaves and, multiplied by two, give the total amount of printed pages in the book.

Sections		Leaves		Blank Leaves	Printed Leaves
I	x	10	–	2	8
II–XXX	x	12			348
XXXI	x	12	–	2	10
31 sections				4	366

[2a] Eliza Szandorowska, "List do Redakcji w sprawie nieznanego sygnetu drukarskiego Szwajpolta Fiola" (Letter to the Editor in Reference to the Unknown Printer's Device of Szwajpolt Fiol) *Biuletyn historii sztuki* (Bulletin of the History of Art), vol. XLII (Warsaw, 1979), p. 232.

Section	Leaf No.	Signature Cyril.	Signature Arab.[x]
I.	1		
	2		
	3	Г҃	3
	4	Д҃	4
	5	Є҃	5
	6		
	7		
	8		
	9		
	10		
II.	11	Ѕ҃	6
	12	З҃	7
	13	И҃	8
	14	Ѳ҃	9
	15	І҃	10
	16	А҃І	11
	17		
	18		
	19		
	20		
	21		
	22		

Section	Leaf No.	Signature Cyril.	Signature Arab.
III.	23	В҃І	12
	24	Г҃І	13
	25	Д҃І	14
	26	Є҃І	15
	27	Ѕ҃І	16
	28	З҃І	17
	29		
	30		
	31		
	32		
	33		
	34		
IV.	35	И҃І	
	36	Ѳ҃І	
	37	К҃	
	38	К҃А	
	39	К҃В	
	40	К҃Г	
	41		
	42		
	43		
	44		
	45		

Section	Leaf No.	Signature Cyril.	Signature Arab.
V.	47	К҃Д	24
	48	К҃Є	25
	49	К҃Ѕ	26
	50	К҃З	27
	51	К҃И	28
	52	К҃Ѳ	29
	53		
	54		
	55		
	56		
	57		
	58		
XXXI.		Р҃ПЅ	186
		Р҃ПЗ	187
		Р҃ПИ	188
		Р҃ПѲ	189

x Cyril.Arab. means Cyrillic number and its Arabic equivalent.

Cyrillic numbers and their Arabic equivalents

In placing signatures some errors were committed, noted for the first time by Karataev. Consecutive numbering was disrupted by omissions of some numbers or substitution of one for another. Numbers 60, 61, 62, 63, 124 and 125 were completely omitted: substitutions were made using number 41 instead of 50, 64 instead of 66, 200 instead of 140 and 201 instead of 141. Naturally, due to such deviations, the signatures in the last section do not correspond with the actual number of leaves. Such discrepancies shall be noted in other books. In spite of all the shortcomings, the binding in some inconceivable manner was accomplished correctly. The end result proved to be satisfactory.

Thanks to the efforts of Szandorowska we are able to present a photocopy of the register of sections in the Braşov *Triod Cvetnaja.* The heading and setting of figures is similar to the other known examples; however, in comparison with the register of sections in *Chasoslovec* it appears quite primitive.

Triod Cvetnaja (the *Pentekostarion* in Greek) is an Orthodox liturgical book containing all the variable portions of the services from Easter Sunday to the eighth day after Pentecost, the most solemn and festive fifty day period of the Church year in the Orthodox Rite. We would like to stress that the title of the book is misleading. The Orthodox Easter services do not contain canons with three odes as in the Lenten season. Fiol's book does not mention the name *Triod Cvetnaja.* The name was adopted later as an analogue to the *Triod Postnaja.* Contents of *Triod Cvetnaja* given by Karataev.[3]

Bibliographical description (Résumé)

Triod Cvetnaja (Tsvyetnaya) Pentacostal Triodion.

Szwajpolt Fiol. (Cracow, ca. 1491). 2°.

366 leaves, 725 printed and seven blank pages—1st, 2nd, 3rd at the beginning also last four. Printed pages have 30 lines, 7.8–7.9 mm in height. The printed area averages 236 x 125 mm., however, some of the lines are up to 140 mm. There is a total of thirty-one sections, sexternions. The exception is the first section with only ten leaves and the last with eight leaves. Signatures, Cyrillic numbers in the lower right corner of the first six leaves of the sexternion. Register of sections on leaf 364. No pagination. Supplementary marks, punctuation marks. Print in black and red. No colophon.

Illuminative features: one woodblock—Crucifixion and printer's mark on leaf 2 v., knotted frontispiece on leaf 3 r., headpieces stylized and initials throughout the whole book.

Two variants of *Triod Cvetnaja,* A and B, are known. Changes in sections twenty-one and twenty-three, leaves 240 and 249, 267 and 270, 268 and 269

[3]Karataev, *Opisanie slaviano-russkikh knig,* pp. 12–13.

constitute variant B with no technical improvements or change in text, only the replacement of some sheets. The Braşov copy represents a new variant, B + A + A. The details are unavailable.

Paper with three different watermarks has been used in this book.

Preserved copies:

The print was in oblivion for a long time. There was no published description of Fiol's *Triod Cvetnaja* for two hundred years after the publication of Zachariĭ Kopystenskiĭ's *Palinodia* in 1621. Then in 1819, a copy was discovered by K. F. Kalaĭdovich who was able to prove that Fiol had produced it. Soon afterwards many other copies were uncovered. Nemirovskiĭ's studies have established that twenty copies and three fragments of the *Triod Cvetnaja* are still in existence:

> To date we are aware of the location of twenty copies of Cracow's *Triod Cvetnaja*. Three copies are in the State V. I. Lenin Library of the U.S.S.R. in Moscow, and three in the State Historical Museum in Moscow; two copies are in the State M. E. Saltykov-Shchedrin Public Library; one copy is in each of the following institutions: the Lwów State Scientific Library; the Central Library of the Academy of Sciences of the Lithuanian S.S.R., Vilnius; the Lwów State Museum of Ukrainian Art; the Lwów Historical Museum of Ancient Russian Art in Moscow; The Library of MGU; Eparchial Library in Szentendre, Hungary; the National Library in Warsaw; the Library of the Catholic University in Lublin; the National Museum in Cracow; the Pontificio Istituto per gli Studi Orientali Library in Rome; and in the New York Public Library. Besides these, there are two known fragments of the *Triod Cvetnaja*; one in the Ossoliński Library in Wrocław and one in the Wrocław University Library. A small fragment (2 leaves) is in the State Scientific Library in Lwów. Full copies of the *Triod Cvetnaja* are very rare. The best one is in the State Historical Museum in Moscow.[4]

Since Nemirovskiĭ made this accounting a copy was uncovered in Braşov, Rumania.[5] We were fortunate in locating an unaccounted fragment in the United States containing 29 leaves which came from the territory south of Lwów, not too far from Braşov. Therefore twenty-one copies and four fragments of the *Triod Cvetnaja* are now known to exist.

Nemirovskiĭ's publications have a void regarding details of the copies located outside the U.S.S.R. Here are citations of details found in reliable sources regarding some of Fiol's prints preserved in the West.

Braşov copy

The most valuable relic of all the preserved Fiol prints is without doubt the copy

[4]Nemirovskiĭ, *Nachalo*, pp. 163–164.

[5]R. Mircea, "De la Cracovia la Braşov: incunabulul din 1491" (From Cracow to Braşov: An Incunabulum of 1491) *Magazin istoric*, 8 (Bucharest, 1972), pp. 50–51.

discovered in 1971 in Braşov, Rumania. It was thoroughly discussed and described earlier. However, whatever is known regarding this copy is exclusively through Ion Radu Mircea. Included here is the complete bibliographical résumé of *Triod Cvetnaja* presented by Mircea in his article, "Primele tiparituri chirilice şi incunabulul Cracovian de la Braşov."

Description

Paper size 30.5 x 205 [mm.] watermarks (sun, crown, circle cut by line with an x at the tip, on leaf 114), the watermark of the sheet of paper from Braşov (1589–1600).

364 leaves in 31 fascicles, first one of 10 leaves, 29 of 12 leaves, last one of 6 leaves, signature in the lower right side, each sheet numbered with Cyrillic digits (thus only the first 5, 6 or 4 leaves; from г҃ to р҃кв, first two leaves not numbered <а҃>,<в҃>) one white, the other with a woodcut on the back, glued together.

Signatures 60, 61, 62, 124, 125 are omitted; 50 (н҃) replaced with м҃г; 66 (ѯ҃ѕ) replaced with ѯ҃д; 141 (р҃м) replaced with с҃; leaf 114 missing was replaced with handwritten text on Braşov paper from the end of the sixteenth century.

Last page (p. 119 [?], verso) has the table of signatures. At the beginning and at the end, a leaf was added during the repairs of the binding.

30 lines, the size of the print block is 12.5 x 23, titles and some initials in red ink. Often the initial letter is a little away from the rest of the word or in the case of an overlapped letter.

Overlapped letters with diacritical marks for с, ж, п, н, г, or without diacritical marks for м, д, т, х, as well as the wavy line denoting abbreviations and digits. Their position is not exact, but often displaced backwards, seldom forward. Punctuation is reduced to commas and periods; to denote paragraphs, regardless if the line is started da capo or not, two periods followed by the same wavy line as in the case of digits are used. The printer uses two colors, black and red (especially for the titles and initials).

Ornamentation. The text is adorned by a woodcut, a Moldavian style frontispiece and by numerous initials of the same kind.

On the recto of leaf 2 there is a German style engraving of the Crucifiction, of great beauty. Well known from the other printings from Cracow, the name of the German printer, in the shape of an unfurled sash, is added at the bottom, in an orthography unknown to the specialists: Швѣнполтъ Ѳiолъ (in other printings it appears as: Швайнполтъ Фѣолъ). Printed in red, subtle accents were added to the black drawing after the printing to the personages and to the sash, as well as the known initials і҃с х҃с н҃ к҃ on the upper side.

The unique frontispiece, printed with a border, from leaf 3 on is composed of a single row of three double-circles connected by a semicircle that forms a cross-like interweaving in the middle. At the two extremities of the frontiespiece, four bundles of stalks interweave while going through the circular motif and create double diagonals in the shape of an X which goes from circle to circle. Finally, the two exterior circles from left and right do not close in the central part, but continue in the central part, also forming the same system of diagonals in the shape of an X. Such a pattern is inspired from the frontispieces of manuscripts, which are simplified according to the needs of wood engraving. Judging from the frequency —we could say uniformity—of occurrence of this ornamental pattern in Moldavia, so close to Cracow, a resemblance to the Cracow frontiespiece should not be excluded. In any case, it is not repeated by any print shop in the first half of the sixteenth century.

Initials are of three kinds: some large, composed of weaved "stalks," seldom with animal-like elements, resembling those from Moldavian manuscripts from the fifteenth century. Others, simpler, have a calligraphic aspect, probably of same source.

A set of smaller initials present a large variety of forms which should be classified and reproduced.

The binding is of leather and wood, with metal locks and straps. It is elegantly stamped with a hot iron, with medalions of the face of Erasmus of Rotterdam, Melanchthon, Luther, and a circular inscription bearing their names; other inscriptions not yet identified. Taking after the clue provided by the date of the Brașov paper used to replace leaf 114 (1589–1600), the binding was done at the same time, probably in a shop in Brașov. The unusual ornamental patterns for the Slavic and Romanian books of that time as well as the title on the front of the binding in Greek characters) Πεндαχοσταρυ instead of Пинтикостаръ), seem to confirm this supposition.

The Contents. The text consists of the sermons from the second part of the "mobile" holy days of the year (those holy days whose date changes yearly), starting with Palm Sunday up to the 7th Sunday after Easter, called the Sunday of all Saints. A comparison with Triod Penticostar of Coresi and with older manuscripts does not show any essential differences.

Mentioned with special titles are:

Leaf 3	Friday evening
Leaf 8 vo.	Synaxarium on Lazarus Saturday.
Leaf 12 vo.	Saturday night, of the Good Lazarus.
Leaf 48 vo.	The Holy and Good Friday evening.
Leaf 56	Holy Saturday
Leaf 64	Holy Sunday
Leaf 71 vo.	Holy Sunday
Leaf 87	The third Sunday of the Mironositelor
Leaf 101	The fourth Sunday about the despre Slăleănog
Leaf 110 vo.	The Wednesday of the nijumătătimi Cineizecimei
Leaf 118 vo.	The fifth Sunday about the Good Samaritan

Leaf 134 vo.	The sixth Sunday about the Man born blind
Leaf 147	Holy Thursday
Leaf 150 vo.	The seventh Sunday of the Holy Fathers of Nicaea.
Leaf 191 vo.	Table of Signatures.

The drawing up. The text is in the middle Bulgarian style, so familiar to the Romanian texts, though it has a lot of eastern phonetical differences.

Annotations. Numerous annotations existed on the covers, on the inside, those on the first cover, written in red, were erased; others are on the pages of the text, and on the first leaf verso or second leaf recto, today glued together, one can see through transparency some that could not be deciphered yet. We will list only a part of the legible ones:

—Leaf 1 Г(оспод)и, спас(и) мои, горѣ тѧ, напрѣсталѣ.

—Leaf 1 vo. + СЇА

—Leaf 1 bi.

+ Сїа книга наимѣ Пендикостары / и покоупи попь Смадоуль, с(ы)нь Алдев ѡт Ражновь (sic!) ѡт голѣнь Брашов / за: з̃: ф(ло) р(инь) и приложи ѧ вь тоиждe цр(ъ)ков да бѫдеть е моу вь м(о)лбѫ и с(ы) новы емоу и виоукѡм его и свѣдѣтдли сѫт: прото попь Тома ѡт св(ѧ) етаа цр(ъ)кве ѡт Брашов и Въсїи Шофран и Димитроу, Мирков с(ы)нь, и Стан' Граждь ѡт Зр(ъ)нешти в л(ѣ)то Змѳ.

In translation: "This book called the Penticostar was purchased by Father Smadul son of Aldea of Rîşnov, County of Braşov, for the sum of 7 fiorins and he gave it to the church of the same place to be for prayer to him and his sons and his grandsons and his great-grandsons. And in witness thereof are: the archpriest Toma of the holy church of Braşov and Văsii Sofran and Dumitru son of Marco and Stan Grajd from Zărnesti in the year 7049 (1541)."

—Leaf 3 vo. at the bottom of the engraving бжевклоѱжїа влож ; this name appears to be ciphered Шбеиполть Ѳиоль

—Leaf 18 in red, cut off at binding (thus before 1600 + аз попа Смадоул ѡт Зернешть : I father Smadul of Zerneşti

—Leaf 43 ѱаломъ а̃, час а̃: г(лало)ли моем. в въскѫѧ./ ка б(ож)е. б(о)же мо/ ими (cut off at binding)

—Leaf 44 vo., up г̃ час ѱал. лв. рк. и̃. Next, crossed out in ink and erased

—Leaf 45 vo. ѕ̃ час. ѱал. нг̃. рлѳ кс̃.

—Leaf 46 vo. ѳ̃ час, ѯи ѯѳ. пе.

—Leaf 65 vo., bottom (different handwriting, cut off at binding)

въс Кр(ъ)стенїе Х(ри)ст(о)во видѣше о.. / .. се с(ве)т(о)моу г(оспод)оу Іс(оу)сꙋ единомоу / . . омоу Кр(ъ)стоу вое моу по села /... ем. и с(ве)тое въскр(ъ)сенїе твое поем ../.. ти бо еси (ог)ь наш развѣ бо / .. ого незнаем. и име твое нарї / .. <п>рїидѣте въси кри и по / ... І(соу)се Х(ри)с(то)во с(ве)т(о)моу въскр(ь)сенїе се /... де о(ь)ста радї радост въсегда бл(аго)с(ло)веште г(оспод)а, поем въ /... г(о) распѧтие бо прѣтрьпѣ. и / ... се въ мр(ътвѣ)мъ раздроуши.

—Leaf 68 (a crossed out note) пис̃ припел(е) ...

—Leaf 68 vo. (different handwriting)

припел(е). / + Х(ри)с̃това пас̃ха жив̃ . . . / тъв̃ на жирт̃ва а гог .. / радуите -- / радуи дево, радуи ис̃паки .. / тво с(ы)н въс̃к(ѣ)се из<б>а вен ѡт̃ гроба ... / + Те чахж але ... / вѣстите ал нас̃ ѡт. а .. / и те ѹбо и възъ .. / ыт̃ и Х(ристо)с̃ въскрес̃(е).

(lower, on the right corner) Пис̃ припел̃(е) поп̃(а)....ѡт̃ З<ер>—не <щ> Гежнов̃

Written by Pripele priest . . . from Zărneşti

—First cover "let it be known that I Pătru Cărăuşul have written ѡт̃ <кѣ> та цр<ъ>ков̃ ѡт̃ Шкеи̃ in the month of May дн̃ь к 7194 (1686)."

—Second cover, "Let be known that I, Văsii Hoban, have written when I was cantor of the church м<ѣ>с̃<ѣ>ца April 14 дни 7160 (1652)" (erased).

"Let it be known that I, Vasilachi Vasilievici, have written ѡт̃ с<вѣ>та цр<ъ>ков ѡт̃ Шкеи̃ Braşov ѻт̃ голкп̃ м<ѣ>с̃<ѣ>ца April 27, year 7160 (1652)". Written over an erased line: ("Let it be known that I, Radulu Puşcaşulu, have erased this."

"Let it be known that I, Barbul archpriest Vasii, have written к лѣт̃ 7171 (1663). м<ѣ>с̃<ѣ>ца April 9. аз̃ Барбѹл дїа<к> м<ѣсѣ>ца April 9."

И нѣ<п>дакни<к> аз̃ дїак̃ Барбѹ ѡт̃ с<вѣ>та цр<ъ>ков̃ ѡт̃ Шкеи̃ [1]

Copy in the Pontificio Istituto Per Gli Studi Orientali in Rome

With gratitude for the extensive cooperation of the Pontifical Oriental Institute in Rome and the assistance of Reverend Bernard J. Mrożek, S.J., it is now possible to present the bibliographical description of Fiol's books located in the Library of the Pontifical Oriental Institute.

In the catalogue of early Slavic printed books prepared by Reverend J. Krajcar, S.J., under number three, is the following notation:

[ТРИОДЬ ЦВЕТНАЯ]. (Triod Cvetnaja)
Kraków, Švejpolt Fiol; (1491)

2⁰, Neither foliation, nor pagination. Book has 31 gatherings, each 12 leaves, except for first with 10 leaves and last with 6 leaves only.

First leaf in our copy bears signature 15, i.e. fourth leaf of the third gathering (Antiphons for liturgy on Palm Sunday). It is, however, preceded by an unsigned leaf of the second gathering (Zacharias's prophecy at minor vespers on Lazarus Saturday). Last signed leaf bears signature 167 and is followed by two unsigned leaves (vesper prayer on vigil of Pentecost).

In each of gatherings 5, 6, 13, 14, one unsigned leaf is missing, in gathering 9 two unsigned leaves are missing. Also missing are leaves signed 64, 65, 66 (11th gathering) and leaf signed 150 in 25th gathering.

Und, 5. Kar. 5. Str.-Tol. 3 Sven. 92.[6]

This copy from the description in the catalogue is a defect. It appears upon close examination as a unique specimen. The preserved leaves are in excellent condi-

[6] J. Krajcar, S.J. "Early-Printed Slavonic Books in the Library of the Pontifical Oriental Institute," *Orientalia Christiana Periodica,* XXXIV, fasc. I, 1968. (Pont. Institutum Orientalium Studiorum, Roma), p. 108.

tion, except for a few which bear candle wax stains. Only one page is considerably mutilated, nevertheless the perforations were carefully patched with white paper and the missing words and letters are handwritten inserts. Altogether the preserved part of the copy gives the impression that the book was either rarely used or given excellent care. Proof of this is also evident in the luster of the ink which is radiant, like new. The missing leaves at the beginning and end, and those torn from within the book give the impression that this copy was vandalized. This suspicion is substantiated by the new binding in which nothing remained from the original. It most likely had been completly discarded and destroyed.

The new binding has no similarity to the original one. The wooden boards are covered with yellow leather without brass clamps so characteristic in the originals. In the upper section of the spine a gold-tooled binder's title appears on a red background: in four lines, the title, place and year: Triod—Cvetnaja—Cracow—1491 are presented in Cyrillic. The backbone must have been reconditioned since the assembled leaves are out of line and consequently some signatures in the lower margin have been cut off. The sequence of pages is kept in order, starting with one leaf from the second quire found at the beginning of the copy, whereas the text in consecutive sequence is from the leaf bearing the fifteenth signature.

The only provenance notes that are to be found in the copy appear on the front flyleaf of the new binding indicating they are from a later date. In the upper section of the upper flyleaf under number 2476 there appears in Cyrillic the name, place and year of the book.

Тріодь цвѣтная напечѣ в Краковѣ, вѣ 1491 г.

(Triod Cvetnaja printed in Cracow in the year 1491).

Below this inscription on a piece of paper glued to the flyleaf is a note in Latin:

Triod. (Temp. Pasch, 1491)

Oundolski, num. 5.

In the lower right side the date and price are written:

27/3/39/—R [rubles] 400.

The only information in addition to the name of the book in Cyrillic and Latin, is that this copy was acquired on March 27, 1939. The price 400 Rubles indicates the place of purchase, the U.S.S.R.

The name Oundolski needs clarification. B. M. Undolskii is the author of *Katalog slaviano-russkikh knig tserkovnoi pechati biblioteki A. J. Kasterina,* (Catalogue of the Slavonic-Russian Church Books in the A. J. Kasterin Library), Moscow, 1848.

There are very few notes and glosses in this copy. The ones that exist such as those on recto and verso of the leaf with signature РЛИ are difficult to decipher in its entirety with the exception of some words. The note on leaf with signature PNΘ is easier to decipher. From its contents we find it concerns Muscovite saints although the sentence is incomplete and consequently difficult to understand. We learn from these inscriptions: a. the handwritten texts are not commentary to the

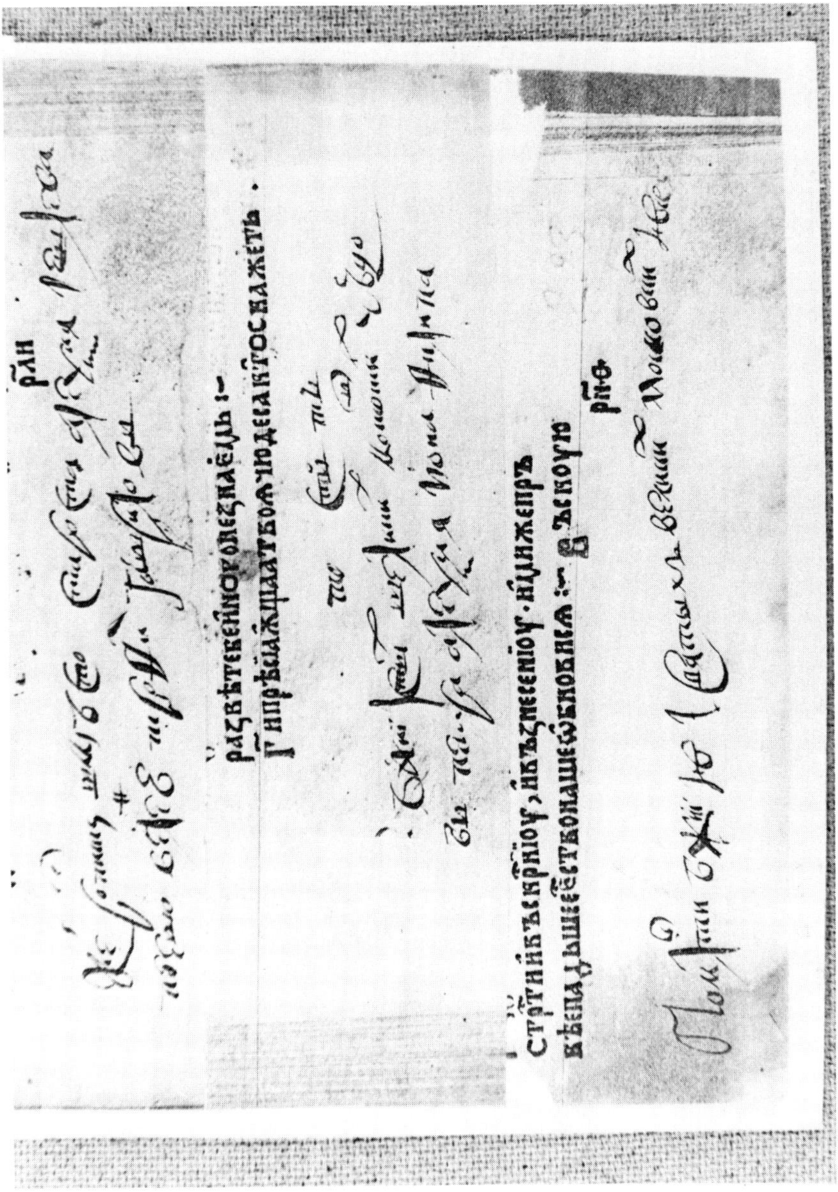

printed texts; b. a cursive script is of Muscovite variety from the end of the seventeenth or the beginning of the eighteenth century.

Polish Holdings

Data pertaining to Polish holdings of *Triod Cvetnaja* in the *Central Catalogue of Incunabula in the Polish Libraries*:

TRIOD'

5397 *Triod' cvetnaja.* [Cracow, Sveb. Fiol, ante 1491]. 2°. Karataev 5. Goff T-428. E[streicher] XXXI 322. GO [A. Kawecka-Gryczowa. *Catalogue of Incunabula in the Library of the Ossoliński Institute in Wrocław*] 322. KWr [B. Kocowski. *Catalogus incunabulorum typographicorum Bibliothecae Universitatis Vratislaviensis*]. 2823. K. Heintsch: "Studies regarding Szwajpolt Fiol." Part I, *Annals of the Ossoliński National Institute,* Vol. V. 1957. pp. 233–342. N. V. Varbanec, V. I. Lukyanenko: "Slavic Incunabula in the Saltykov-Shchedrin Library in Leningrad (GPB)," *Kniga,* vol. 2. 1960. pp. 196–201. M. Błońska: "An Attempt at a New View of the History of Szwajpolt Fiol's Printing Press." *Annals of the National Library,* IV: 1968. pp. 52–62.[7]

Wrocław University Library Fragment. (Index symbol: Wrocław-U)

Data from the Catalogue of Incunabula in the Wrocław University Library:

2823 TRIOD CVETNAJA
Cracow, Sweboldus Fiol, [ca 1491]. 2°
E[streicher] XXXI 322–3. Kopera col. 6–9. Wisl[ocki] 514.

Fragment: The only leaf preserved—102 [= р҃в].
Provenance note: [Valentinus Crautvald—XVI century.] Taken out from the bookcovers of incunabulum XV.Q.115,2—see nr. 2257. Sign.: XV. F. 547.[8]

This incunabulum was discovered, described and registered by Bronisław Kocowski, the author of *Katalog inkunabułów Biblioteki Uniwersyteckiej we Wrocławiu* (Catalogue of Incunabula in the University Library in Wrocław). Checking and verifying pamphlet volumes, he found in one of them (among the wastepaper used by the bookbinder) a leaf from *Triod Cvetnaja.* He established that it is

[7] Alodia Kawecka-Gryczowa, ed. Maria Bohonos and Eliza Szandorowska, compositors, *Incunabula quae in bibliothecis Poloniae asservantur.* (Bibliotheca Nationalis Polona. Vratislaviae-Varsaviae-Cracoviae. Ex Officina Instituti Ossoliniani, 1970), pp. 920–921.
TRIOD'
5397—Triod' cvetnaja. (Kraków, Sveb. Fiol, ante 1491). 2⁰. Karataev 5. Goff T-428. E XXXI 322. GO 322. KWr 2823. K. Heintsch: Ze studiów nad Szwajpoltem Fiolem. Cz. I. "Rocznik Zakł. Nar. im. Ossolińskich" T. V. 1957 pp. 233–342. N. V. Varbanets, V. I. Luk'ianenko: Slavianskie inkunabuly v sobranii Gosudarstvennoĭ Publichnoĭ Biblioteki im. M. E. Saltykova-Shchedrina v Leningrade (GPB). "*Kniga*" sb. 2 1960 pp. 196–201. M. Błońska: Próba nowego spojrzenia na dzieje krakowskiej oficyny Szwajpolta Fiola. *Rocznik Biblioteki Narodowej.* IV: 1968, 52–62.

[8] Bronisław Kocowski, *Katalog inkunabułów Biblioteki Uniwersyteckiej we Wrocławiu* (Catalogus incunabulorum typographicorum Bibliothecae Universitatis Vratislaviensis), Part 1–2, (Wrocław, 1959–1962), p. 846.
2823 Triod cwietnaja.
(Kraków, Sweboldus Fiol, ca. 1491). 2⁰.
E XXXI 322–3. Kopera szp. 6–9. Wisł 514.
Fragment: Zachowała się tylko karta 102 (= р҃в)
Prow.: (Valentinus Crautvald—XVI w.)
Wydobyte z okładzin inkunabulu XV, Q. 115,2—zob. nr 2257.
Sygn XV. F. 547.

leaf 102(р҃в) with the beginning of the liturgical text for the fourth Sunday after Easter. Provenance note from the beginning of the sixteenth century revealed that the owner of the book was canon Valentinus Crautvald. Another note in the *ex libris* states that it was the property of the Peter-Paulite Church Library.[9]

Information about the book in which a fragment of *Triod Cvetnaja* was found—the present incunabulum number 2257 in the Wrocław University Library:

2257 *Philelphus Franciscus*
Orationes cum quibusdam aliis opusculis
Venezia, Bartholomaeus de Zanis, 28 III [March] 1491. 4° HC 12923. BMC V 431. Pol 3139. Madsen 3217. Mead 3117. VBI 4247.
Second copy
Defective. Leaves CLIII–CLX of quire V[8] replaced with handwritten insertion from the XVI Century. Marginalia in Latin and notes from the XVI Century by two scribes.
Prov.:
1. V[alentinus] C[rautwald] XVI Century.
2. Property of Peter-Paulite Church Library [Ex libris] 73 . . . . . . Binding: Manuscriptic parchment wastepaper from the XV Century. The backbone—brown blind-tooled leather . . . Cracow binding. Beginning of XVI Century. Binding end papers: fragments of Cracow print ca 1491. Sweypolt Fiol: Triod Cvetnaja leaf 102. See nr. 2823.
Sign.: XV. Q. 115,2.[10]

Ossoliński Institute Library Fragment (Index symbol: Wrocław-O)

Notation from the *Catalogue of Incunabula in the Library of the Ossoliński Institute in Wrocław:*

322. Triod cvetnaja. [Cracow. Sw. Fiol. 1491] 2°
Karataev 5. Rev. Ign. Polkowski. "An Unknown Cracow Print from the XV Century: The work by *Franciscus de Platea Opus restitutionum usurarum et excommunicationum*" (Proceedings of the Philological Department of the Academy of Arts and Sciences, Vol. VIII and reprints)—with erroneous identification of the fragment as from *Triod Postnaja.* Reproductions of fragments in K. Heintsch, "Fragment of a Fiol Print in the Library of the Ossoliński Institute in Wrocław (*Ze skarbca kultury*—From the Cultural Treasury. Wrocław 1953, issue No. 2).
Frg. [fragment]: 2 leaves of section 30, namely first leaf, sign. 180 and twelfth leaf (identification of leaves based on information from the copy in the Lenin Library in Moscow).
Prov:
1. Stamp: Reverend Ignacy Polkowski

[9] *Ibid.,* Preface, p. xviii, also xxxi.
[10] *Ibid.,* p. 675.

2. [Prince Poniński Library, Horyniec].
Binding: Loose cardboard jacket, XX century—XV 428.[11]

This fragment composed of two loose leaves was discovered in Cracow by Reverend Ignacy Polkowski in the binding of another incunabulum of 1493, unknown Latin Psalter. Polkowski erroneously identified them as those from *Osmoglasnik*, later changed to *Triod Postnaja*. Karol Heintsch proved by his comparative study with a copy of *Triod Cvetnaja* in the Czapski Collection, also by that in the V. I. Lenin State Library of U.S.S.R. in Moscow, that the fragment is from *Triod Cvetnaja*. He gave a thorough description of both leaves, established signature and made reproductions of them.

Fragment consists of two leaves 347 and 358; first and last (12th) leaves of section 30 with signature р҃н.

In the Ossolineum Library this incunabulum carries the Inv. No. 19451. Both leaves are in a cardboard folder bound together with adhesive paper. The arrangement is awkward because when the leaves were put together the upper one became leaf 358 and the second leaf 347, which should be placed in reverse. When the leaves were assembled originally before they reached the Ossolineum, the owner, Rev. Polkowski was not aware of the error, and it has been retained in this manner to the present day.

Both leaves are in good condition although the edges of the paper are slightly damaged by insect borers. The section with the print appears well preserved both as to color and clarity. Only in certain sections there are traces of book-binders glue. No glosses or other inscriptions except a small Ossolineum ownership stamp on each verso side of the leaves.[12]

[11] Alodia Kawecka-Gryczowa, *Katalog inkunabułów Biblioteki zakładu im Ossolińskich we Wrocławiu* (Catalogue of Incunabula in the Library of the Ossoliński Institute in Wrocław), (Wrocław, 1956), p. 79.

322. Triod cwietnaja. [Kraków. Sw. Fiol. 1491].. 2⁰.

Karataev 5. X. Ign. Polkowski. Nieznany druk krakowski z XV wieku: dzieło Franciszka de Platea Opus restitutionum usurarum et excommunicationum (Rozpr. Wyd. filol. Ak. Um.t. VIII i odb.)—z mylnym rozpoznaniem fragmentu jako Triod postnaja. Reproduckcje fragmentu podaje K. Heintsch, Fragment druku Fiola w Bibliotece Zakładu im. Ossolińskich we Wrocławiu (Ze skarbca kultury. Wrocław 1953. zesz. 2). Frg.: 2 karty ze składki 30. a mian. karta pierwsza, sygn. 180 oraz karta dwunasta (oznaczenie kart na podstawie informacji i egzemplarza Biblioteki im. Lenina w Moskwie).

Prow.:
1. Piecz.: X. Polkowski.
2. [Bibl. XX. Poninskich, Horyniec].
Opr.: Lużne okładziny kartonowe, XX w.—XV. 428.

[12] Karol Heintsch, "Fragment druku Świętopełka Fiola w Bibliotece Zakładu im. Ossolinskich we Wrocławiu" (A Fragment of Fiol's Print in the Library of the Ossolinski Institute in Wrocław), *Ze skarbca kultury* (Wrocław, 1953), issue 2/5 pp. 87 and 94.

References:
Ignacy Polkowski, Rev. "Nieznany druk krakowski z XV w.: dzieło Franciszka de Platea *Opus restitutionum* . . ." (An Unknown Cracow Print from the XV Century: A Work by Franciscus de Platea's *Opus restitutionum* . . .) *Rozprawy Wydziału Filologicznego Akademii Umiejętności, Tom VIII* (Cracow, 1880).
Karol Heintsch. "Fragment druku Świętopełka Fiola w Bibliotece Zakladu im. Ossolińskich we Wrocławiu" (Fragment of a Fiol Print in the Library of Ossoliński Institute in Wrocław.) *Ze skarbca kultury.* (Wrocław, 1953), issue 2/5, pp. 78–94.

Czapski Copy. (Index symbol: Kraków-Czap.)

Data regarding the copy of *Triod Cvetnaja* in the National Museum in Cracow. Collection of Emeryk Hutten-Czapski.

Emeryk Count Hutten-Czapski (1828–1896), prominent authority in Polish and Russian numismatics, was the founder of a huge private collection composed of such items as coins, medals, arms, illustrations, drawings, pictures, also books, chiefly with old prints. Originally assembled at the Czapski estate at Stanków, Belorussia near Minsk, in 1894 it was brought to Cracow. Upon Czapski's death his collection was incorporated into the National Museum in Cracow in 1903. However, the bequest stipulated that this Special Collection should bear the name of the donor: "The Count Emeryk Hutten-Czapski Museum."

After World War II, with the general reorganization of the cultural establishments, all private collections became part of the National Museum in Cracow. This particular Special Collection is now Division III of the National Museum in Cracow and bears the name: "Collections of Emeryk Hutten-Czapski." The collection has three departments: Department No. 9 encompasses pictures, illustrations, drawings and watercolors; Department No. 10 numismatical cabinet and Department No. 11 old prints and manuscripts.[13]

Among the old prints and manuscripts is Fiol's *Triod Cvetnaja.* Czapski, who catalogued his precious books himself, very often made notations how and when the books were acquired. However, to date no such note has been found regarding this particular incunabulum among the Czapski papers. Since many of Fiol's books were seen in Belorussia by Kopistenskiĭ as early as the sixteenth century, and some that are preserved today in U.S.S.R. are from Belorussia, Czapski's copy could have been from this region. But it could have been acquired somewhere else because Czapski made many journeys throughout the Russian territories in the capacity of a high official and also as a private collector. The origin of the Czapski copy of *Triod Cvetnaja* thus remains unknown.

[13] Maria Kocójowa, "Zarys historii zbiorów Emeryka Hutten-Czapskiego" (Outline to the History of the Emeryk Hutten-Czapski Collection), *Rozprawy i sprawozdania Museum Narodowego w Krakowie* (Transactions and Reports of the National Musum in Cracow), XI (Cracow, 1976).

Triod Cvetnaja in the Czapski collection was catalogued by Czapski himself and this card is still the only available description of the book in the National Museum in Cracow catalogue.

No. XV 12. 149[1] 1 vol. folio
TRIOD CVETNAJA [in Russian alphabet]
Printed by Swiętopełk Fiol in Cracow 1491. [In Polish]
My copy has 2 pages л҃ѕ-р҃пє and 10 pages [not clear]
It begins: НО ѥМЪ ТРѠ Ѡ Є НѢСНИ... [leaf 70r.]
Ends with: ИѦБЄРЬ ИБИЛѪꙖБЦЄ.БѢРНЇНБЪЗБѢИЦИЄМЬ. [leaf 357r]

Whatever is missing is added in writing.
Triod Cvetnaja [in Polish] 587 7a/XV
N.J. 24792 [Inventory number].

Based on this catalogue card Feliks Kopera prepared his description of the book. In fact it is only a repetition of what was recorded by Czapski.[14] All findings currently presented are based on new material delivered graciously by T. Zapiór and B. Żulińska from Cracow, also taking into consideration information found on the Czapski catalogue card.

Description of the Czapski copy:

TRIOD CVETNAJA. Cracow, Szwajpolt Fiol. [ca. 1491] 2⁰. Variant-B. Defect. First leaf in this copy is the 70th (12th of quire 6). The last printed leaf is 357th (11th of quire 30). Inside only one leaf, 333, is missing. Most of the printer's signatures are preserved, some unfortunately have been cut off in the process of rebinding. In the upper margin of the printed leaves thorough foliation appears in pencil with Arabic numerals beginning with number 70 and ending with 357.

In place of 69 missing leaves at the beginning of the book, are 48 handwritten leaves of *Triod Cvetnaja.* This replacement was done on old paper with script endeavoring to imitate Fiol's Cyrillic characters. Pages 1 through 96 are thoroughly marked in Arabic numerals in pencil on the upper margin. The last missing 7 leaves are also replaced by handwritten text. They are neither paginated nor foliated. At the beginning of the handwritten text appears a heading in red: "Sunday of All Saints." The text under this heading is not a continuation of the text on leaf 357 verso. The manuscript ends with the words: "Virgin, Mother of God, plead for us and save us from eternal agony." According to B. Żulińska, who

[14] Feliks Kopera, *Spis druków epoki Jagiellonskiej w zbiórze Emeryka hrabiego Hutten-Czapskiego w Krakowie* (List of Prints from the Jagellonian Era in the Count Emeryk Hutten-Czapski Collection in Cracow), (Cracow, 1900), pp. 6–9.

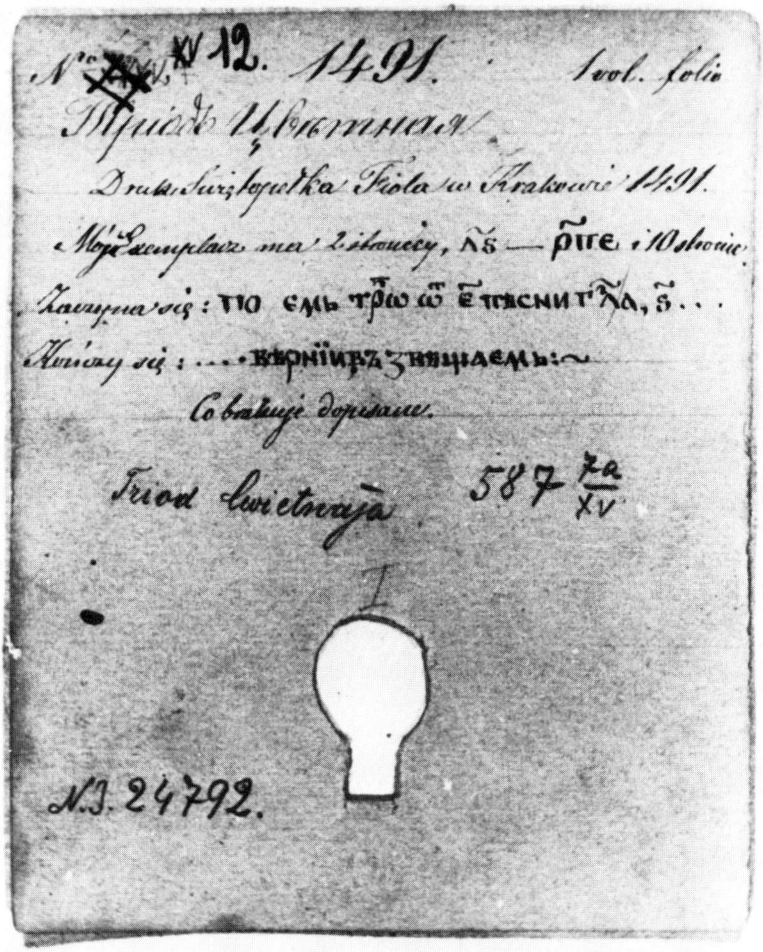

Catalogue card of Czapski's copy of *Triod Cvetnaja*.

provided the description of the Czapski copy, the handwritten part has some deficiencies and omissions. Differences also appear in the texts of the printed and handwritten parts, which upon closer scrutiny appear unrelated to each other. There are many glosses and marginal notes on both the printed and handwritten parts of this copy. All of them, with one exception, provide information and instruction regarding the text. It is noteworthy that some of the glosses are on separate scraps of paper glued to the margins.

Glosses and marginal notes to be found on the following leaves of the printed text: 70v, 72r, 77r, 78r, 79r, 84r-v, 86r, 87r-v, 89r, 90r, 91r, 92v, 97r, 100v, 102v, 119v, 122v, 123r, 124r, 125r-v, 127v, 128v, 135r, 138r, 143r-v, 146r, 149r, 151r-v, 152r, 154r, 157r, 158r, 159v, 160v, 161v, 162r-v, 171v, 174v, 175r, 176r, 177r-v, 189r, 192v, 196v, 197r-v, 203v, 210r, 211r, 216r, 218r, 219v, 221r-v, 223v, 224r, 225r, 231r, 232r, 236v, 238r-v, 242r, 243r, 248r, 256v, 261r-v, 263v, 264r, 267r, 268r, 269r, 270r, 271v, 272r, 277r, 278r, 280r, 281r-v, 283r, 284r, 286r, 287r, 288r, 289r, 290r, 291r, 292r, 293r, 295r, 296r, 297r, 298r, 302r, 312v, 316v, 322r, 325v, 326r.

Studying the handwritten replacements of missing leaves 1 to 69 at the beginning and the last seven of the book, are easily found differences in the texts and also in the script itself. At least three copiers, two for the front section and the third for the end part are discernible. The front part was executed with great care, making every effort to reproduce closely the original print. The end part, however, reveals an unpremeditated form of contemporary cursive with very moderate use of superscripts and diacritical marks.

The last handwritten page is interesting for its provenance notes. It is, however, difficult to understand them, because the paper was trimmed to the point where all the margins were cut away including some of the text. Only one name can be read: Khmolabinsky, the rest is undecipherable.[15]

Provenances:

1. In the lower margin of leaves 287 through 298 there appears under the printed column on the left side—each part on a separate leaf—the following seventeenth century ownership note:

Leaf 287r.—siya
Leaf 288r.—kni
Leaf 289r.—ga
Leaf 290r.—trieot
Leaf 291r.—arkhann
Leaf 292r.—ien(s)kogo
Leaf 293r.—poppa

[15]See p. 192, *post*.

Leaf 294r.—
Leaf 295r.—evsta (fia)?
Leaf 296r.—evsyeevva
Leaf 297r.—va
Leaf 298r.—tried? moiem?

The provenance note quoted above translated into English stands for: "This book Triod is the Arkhannienskiĭ priest's Evstafi Evseev." Note on page 298r. partly covered with a piece of paper is difficult to decipher and understand. The character of the script is different from the rest.

II. A printed *ex libris* of the Czapski collection is glued on the left endpaper of the front cover. The signature is No. XV. 12 and inventory No. 24792

The binding according to Maria Krynicka, an authority in this field, is contemporary to the time of printing. The wooden boards were covered with blind-tooled dark brown leather. What is left now are the bare boards with some remnants of the original leather covering. The binding is in very poor condition, and it appears that the covers were never renovated. The book, however, must have been rebound because the handwritten parts of lost leaves at the beginning and the end are not glued in, but sewn in together into the block of the remaining printed section.

Special note: Tadeusz Zapiór upon close examination of the Czapski copy discovered under the unglued left endpaper of the front cover, a leaf with Cyrillic printing, which was glued to the wooden board of the upper cover in an upside down position. Zapiór upon receiving permission from the proper authorities to unglue the entire endpaper ascertained that the whole page contained a religious text. It is still unidentified up to this date. Upon close scrutiny of the photocopy received from Zapiór, it can be positively determined that this fragment does not belong to any of Fiol's prints.

References:

Feliks Kopera, *Spis druków epoki jagiellońskiej w zbiorze Emeryka hrabiego Hutten-Czapskiego w Krakowie* (List of Prints of the Jagellonian Era in the Collection of Count Emeryk Hutten-Czapski in Cracow), (Cracow, 1900), Column 6–9. Kopera was the first scholar to publish information regarding the location and condition of this incunabulum. Unfortunately Kopera was more interested in Fiol the printer than in the print itself. Kopera did not elaborate in his summaries and did not add anything new.

E. L. Nemirovskiĭ, "Izdaniia Sh. Fiola, F. Skoryny i I. Fedorova v knigokhranilishchakh Varshavy i Krakova" (Publications of Sh. Fiol, F. Skaryna and I. Fedorov in the Book Vaults of Warsaw and Cracow), *Sovetskoe Slavanovedenie,* Issue 5, Moscow, 1975, pp. 69–71. On page 71 a short description of the Czapski copy with the above mentioned inscription.

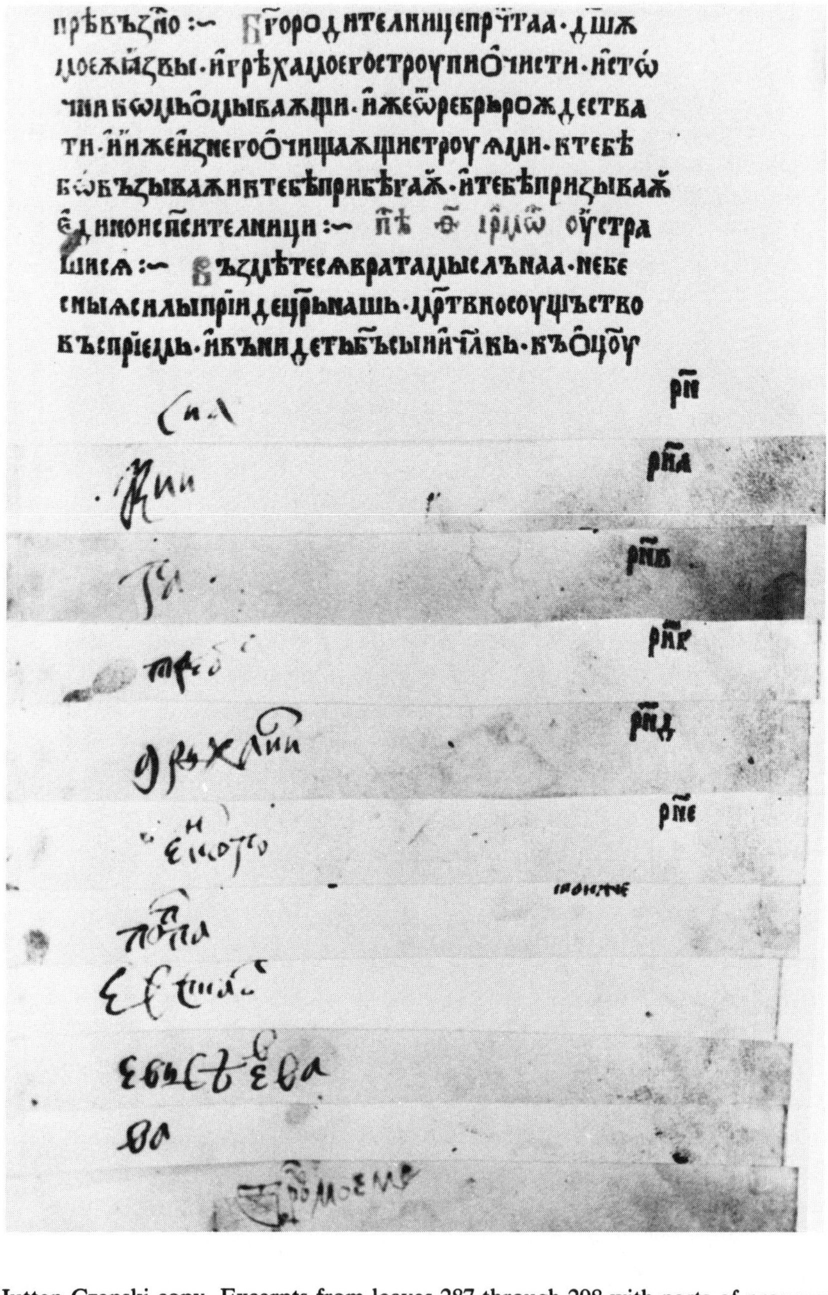

Hutten-Czapski copy. Excerpts from leaves 287 through 298 with parts of provenance note

Ex libris of Hutten-Czapski Collection

Lublin Catholic University Library Copy. (Index symbol: Lublin-KUL)

Data pertaining to the *Triod Cvetnaja* copy in the Catholic University Library in Lublin. Sign. Nr. XV. 206.

There is no publication up to the present regarding this copy except for a general description and note pertaining to the Lublin copy in the Central Catalogue under Inc. Nr. 5397, vol. II, pp. 920–921. Information given below is based on inquiries by the author and the study of the photocopy of the whole incunabulum graciously sent to him from Lublin as well as the photocopy of the Library catalogue card.

Translation of the above mentioned card: (recto and verso).

TRIOD
—cvetnaja XV. 206
[Cracow, Sveboldus Fiol, ante 1491], 2⁰
[leaves 315–318, 110–310]
Karataev 5, E. XXXI, 322–323. Centr. Cat. 5397
Variant B: different set of sheets:

РКЗ —127 = leaves 240 and 249
РМВ —142 = leaves 267 and 270
РМГ —143 = leaves 268 and 269

As an example:
Leaf 240r. (sheet РКЗ) line 26:

лепреестанноцоламфеесаеспстасадшацьнашоць :~,

Leaf 267r. (sheet РМВ) line 18:

кацьцоужьеныъвъдашжсѧ·ндїаволагръды;

Leaf 268r. (sheet РМГ) line 17:

ѡковнидѣньбы,пасцлинзаблгость·соугоубы.

Marginalia: Numerous in Cyrillic and in Polish.
Prov.: Ex Bibl. Capituli ritus graeco-cathol. Premisliensis.
Binding: newer pasteboard.
Special note from endpaper follows: "In the heading of the catalogue under the letter T, number zvi, (page 2073) is written: Place and year of publication: Venice around 1554 in the annotation 'Montenegrin order to print'. (Signature) Podolinskij."

While closely examining data found on the "main card" of the Catholic University Library in Lublin catalogue and comparing these data with information in the *Central Catalogue of Incunabula in Polish Libraries,* there appears to be a discrepancy in the latter regarding citations from leaf 240r.—see page 920 lines 1 and 2 from the bottom. Line 26 was cited as an example to substantiate the difference between variant A and B. Close scrutiny reveals that line 26 attributed to variant A actually is in variant B and vice versa. Verification of the other lines reveals that citations are correct. This error is in the *Central Catalogue of Incunabula in Polish Libraries.*

Description of the Lublin copy:

This copy is defective. The first preserved printed leaf is 110-N͠ζ, the last 318 with the missing four leaves 311, 312, 313, and 314. The arrangement of this volume is somewhat awkward. There are at the beginning the last four preserved leaves 315–318, followed by a block of leaves from 110 to 310. On most of the leaves the printer's signatures are preserved. In addition, in the upper righthand corner are certain markings in Arabic numerals of a later date. These are done in pencil. One of them in square brackets is in accord with the printer's signatures facilitating arrangement of leaves. The other one starting with number 1 marked above the number in square brackets begins with 315 as 1, 316 as 2, 317 as 3, 318 as 4, 110 as 5, etc. The book, unfortunately rebound according to the upper foliation numbers (which have no foundation in signatures), indicates that the bookbinder was not well-oriented in the subject matter and erroneously bound the last four leaves in the front of the book.

The condition of this copy appears to be varied. About 50% of the leaves are in good condition, clean, legible without any inscriptions or markings. About 25% are with notes, ranging from one or two up to the point where all of the margins are completely covered with inscriptions. The other portions of the leaves are more or less worn, soiled with candle wax, many of them with completely torn-off corners. Some of the leaves with missing corners were restored and texts replaced by handwriting on both sides, such as leaf 113. These worn, soiled and marked leaves are those in the portion of the book which had been most frequently used. Marginalia: All of these notes are in Cyrillic for the purpose of assisting the priest in the performing of his services, thus marks, such as vertical lines to divide the words, since there is no spacing between words. Four notations are in Polish. Three of them on pages 141r., 155r., and 192r., with some religious maxims and thoughts written in crude script, and one on page 410(?) a slightly frivolous note in legible and refined script. Special feature: on leaf 217v. in the left margin is one line of a musical score drawn in with a Cyrillic text.

Provenance note 1.

Ex libris. In the center of the endpaper of the front board is a glued-in rectangular *ex libris* sticker with a decorative border. The imprint in Latin in four lines states: *Ex Bibliotheca Capituli Ritus graeco-catholici Premisliensis.* In the first line of the imprint on the left of the "Ex" there is handwritten letter K L l K and to the right F 10. At the top of the page there are numbers from left to right: N.129/2 [most likely signature numbers] and following that the identification of print—1491 Krak[ow] in Cyrillic. Beneath the *ex libris* sticker appears the number XV. 206, the identification number assigned by the Lublin Catholic University Library.

Provenance note 2.

The first leaf of this book is a glued-in sheet of grayish handmade paper most likely from the nineteenth century. At the top in the center of the page appears in Cyrillic the title *Triod Cvetnaja,* below this the place of printing Kraków and the year 1491 both with question marks. Following the double spacing is a strange note partly in Cyrillic and partly in Latin: "V holovnim katalohu pod bukvoii . (-T) : zbi. (pag. 2073) stoyt napysano: Locus et annus editionis: Venetiis circiter 1554 in adnotatione "Chernokhortsy drukovat kazali" [in Latin], Podolinskiĭ" [in Cyrillic]. (In the heading of the catalogue under the letter T, number zvi (page 2073) is written: Place and year of publication: Venice around 1554 in the annotation "Montenegrin order to print." [Signature] Podolinski).

This annotation is simple to interpret. Before the copy was identified as Fiol's print an opinion prevailed that this copy of *Triod Cvetnaja* was printed in Venice in 1554 on an order from Montenegro. This classical confusion resulted from the mélange of different printing endeavors in the Balkans and Venice.

This is all that is known of the fate of the Lublin copy. Both provenance notes are of a later date. Anticipated early provenance notes usually found on the first and last blank leaves are lost with the missing first 109 printed leaves and the last 52. There is no evidence when the book was obtained by the bishopric in Przemyśl. The book in all probability reached the bishopric library in Przemyśl in the first half of the nineteenth century after it had been rebound. Theologians later corrected the errors in binding and applied foliation which were then shown in

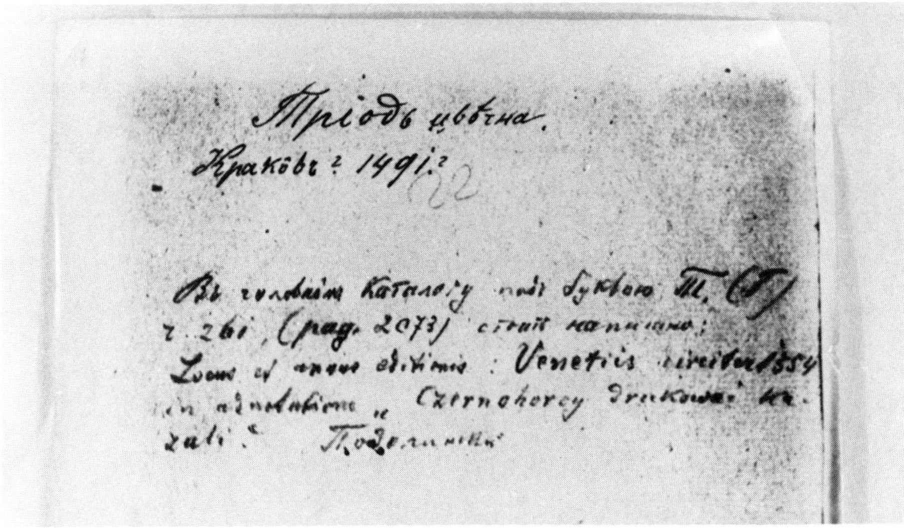

Fiol. *Triod Cvetnaja.* Lublin copy. Provenance note on glued-in first leaf.

brackets in accordance with Fiol's signatures. When and how it was transferred to its present location in Lublin will be discussed subsequently.

The library card indicates that the binding is made of newer pasteboard. Dr. Błońska states that the backbone is covered with dark leather (probably calfskin) with traces of gilding. The endpaper used in binding is of handmade quality, grayish-blue in color.

Warsaw National Library Copy. (Index symbol: Warszawa—N).

Data regarding the copy in the National Library in Warsaw.

Triod Cvetnaja, Inc. F, 1350

Cracow, Szwajpolt Fiol, (ca 1491) 2⁰.

Except for the general description in the *Central Catalogue of Incunabula in Poland,* no special write-up is devoted to this copy. All data presented currently are based on information found in the National Library Catalogue and a study of the book itself. Access to all the material was obtained through the kind assistance of the staff librarian Ms. Eliza Szandorowska.

Data from the catalogue card in English translation:

TRIOD CVETNAJA N[ational] L[ibrary] Inc. F. 1350
[Library of Przemyśl Bishopric]
[Cracow. Sveboldus Fiol, ca. 1491] 2⁰.
Var. A.

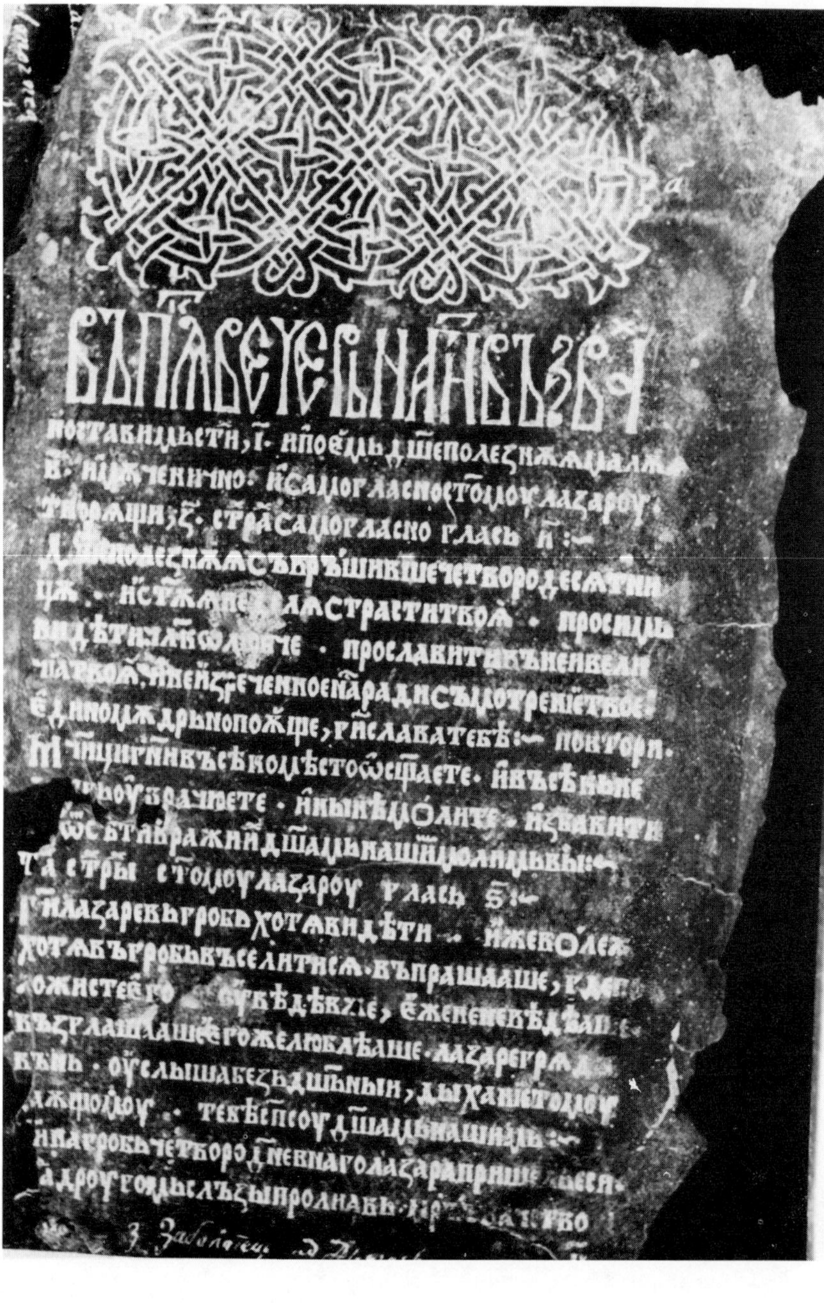

Fiol. *Triod Cvetnaja.* Leaf 3 r. Incipit. Warsaw National Library Copy.

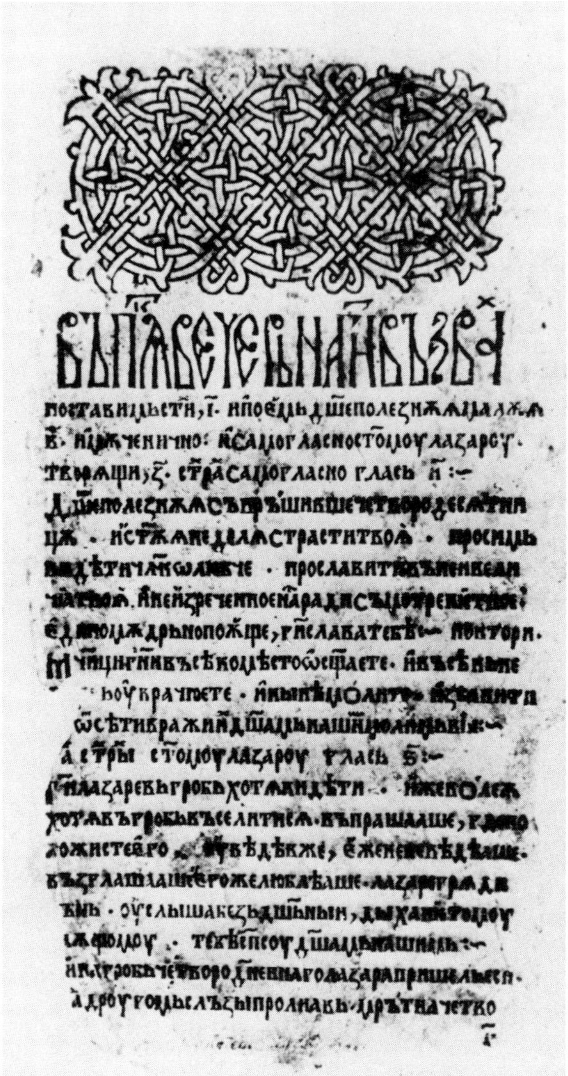

Fiol. *Triod Cvetnaja.* Leaf 3 recto after restoration.

Karataev 5—E[streicher] XXXI. 322–333.
Var.A. different set of sheets:

> Р҃КЗ—127 = leaves 240 and 249/
>
> Р҃МВ—142 = leaves 267 and 270/
>
> Р҃МГ—143 = leaves 268 and 269/

For example:

> leaf 240r. (sheet Р҃КЗ) v. 26:
>
> цолацрѣсаспс҃тнсмдіѿацьнашацѫ ~;
>
> leaf 267r. (sheet Р҃МВ) v. 18:
>
> цѹнацьцоужьснывъдашжсѧ· йдѧволѣгръ,
>
> leaf 268r. (sheet Р҃МГ) v. 17:
>
> боꙗ҇кобя дѣньбы҃, назецлязабл҃гоѥть· ѥоугоу,

The Warsaw copy of *Triod Cvetnaja* was, up to the end of World War II, in the possession of the Uniat (Greek Catholic) bishopric in Przemyśl, Poland. No details are available regarding the provenance of this copy, which would shed light on how and when the book was obtained by the Uniat Chapter's library.

When the book arrived at the National Library in Warsaw, it was in very poor condition. Whether this was due to the wear and tear of old age or war circumstances is not known. Printed pages at the beginning and end which remained were torn, stained and damaged. See page 198. The binding was in impaired condition and torn away from the backbone. The book was then forwarded to the State Relic Conservation Workshop in Warsaw to be reconstructed and restored. The result of this renovation can be considered a masterpiece of workmanship in this field (p. 199). It permits the study of Fiol's typograghy and the material used, such as paper, ink and the binding which was chemically analyzed to reproduce the paper used in the original copy.

Only a few provenance notes in Latin, Polish and Ukrainian exist. Due to cutting of the edges in approximately the seventeenth œntury during the rebinding process the oldest provenance notes could not be completely deciphered. Nevertheless, from the preserved remnants it could be determined that these notes were from the beginning of the seventeenth century or perhaps even earlier, the end of the sixteenth.

Shorter or longer notes and glosses are to be found on the following leaves: 36r, 37r, 47r, 65r-v, 67r, 68r, 69r, 73r-v, 74r-v, 75r, 76r, 77v, 80r-v, 86r-v, 87r, 90v, 93r. On leaf 94r is a drawing of an image of a woman's face (unfortunately the eyes are blotted with ink) on leaf 95r. another drawing of a woman, this time a profile.

103v, 104r-v, 147v, 150v, 151r, 152r, 153v, 154r, 155r, 158r, 160 half of the leaf missing, 171r single letters only, 175r, 178r, 179r, 181r, 192v letters only, 207r, 215v six child-like drawings of animal heads, 216r, 218r-v, 224r-v, 235r, 244r-v, 245r-v, 251r-v, 256r, 257r-v, 258r-v, 259r-v, 260r-v, 261r-v, 262r, 264v, 280r, 288r, 302v, 312v, 319v, 320v, 327v, 334v, 337r.

On leaf 87 some nearly illegible Latin, Polish and Cyrillic letters appear in the margin, apparently from the period before the rebinding. There is a later legible note from 1788 in Polish, however, nothing pertaining to the book and its ownership. This note refers to the price of grain itemizing wheat, rye, barley and buckwheat. This, and also a drawing of a feminine figure on leaf 94r and 95r enables one to surmise that the book, in some period, must have been in possession of a lay person.

This was the period during the Austrian occupation, when the discontinuation of the Catholic orders threw many old books from monastery libraries and collections on the market. Their value was not always recognized and appreciated since feminine images, notes regarding weather conditions or prices of merchandise, also frivolous adages appear in their margins. But, thoughtful people realized that these books must be preserved for posterity. Count Józef Maksymilian Ossoliński first started to collect them. He founded the institution called Ossolineum in 1817, which for 120 years was the most important cultural center with a prominent collection of Polonica in Lwów.[16] After World War II the Ossoliński National Institute was transferred to Wrocław.

At the same time the Greek Catholic (Uniat) Church also collected whatever referred to its past and to Ruthenian history. Most dominant in this action were the bishoprics of Przemyśl and Lwów; the latter became the center of the Ukrainian movement.

Two leaves with a handwritten Latin text are attached at the beginning of the copy; the contents are in no way connected with the book. It was most likely inserted for the purpose of safely preserving a document of the Gołuchowski family pertaining to the management of the inheritance of some sum of money after the death of a relative, Krzysztof Miroszewski. This would indicate the book must have been held in high regard but not used for the purpose for which it was designated, because the estate of Gołuchów, located in central Poland, was a territory with no Orthodox rite followers.

The only important feature of this attachment is the date: "the second day before the feast of purification of the Virgin Mary, the year thousand six hundred eighty." This document is signed by recorder Szydłowski of the Record Office, part of the Offices of the Cracow Castle Captain, who officially recognized the claims to the inheritance.

[16]Ossoliński National Institute, united in 1823 with the Lubomirski Museum, begun its activity in 1827 in Lwów.

On the verso side of the second leaf, in the upper margin appears an inscription in Cyrillic, identification of the book under numbers PN as *Triod Cvetnaja* and the date 1491. This provenance note is of a later date. At the bottom of the page is the National Library number Inc. F. 1350.

The most characteristic feature is that part of this provenance note is preserved on the first printed page of the book, leaf 3r., distinctly indicating the name of the location. This is visible only on the photocopy of the page before the process of its conservation. On the renovated copy this inscription is undecipherable.

The Cyrillic provenance note in Ukrainian states: "Triod Cvetna z Zabolotets od Drogoeva"?. The last word is illegible, in spite of this the inscription has important information. The book came from the locality of Zabolotets, in Polish Zabłodźce, situated in the vicinity of the castle Olesko, in the county of Złoczów, about fifty miles south-east of Lwów. This territory had a mixed Polish-Ukrainian population and according to all indications with a Uniat Greek-Catholic Church. Perhaps the book comes from one of the other places with similar names; but that is not important, all those locations are in the Polish Commonwealth territory with a Ukrainian population.

We do not know in what way the book became the property of the Gołuchowski family. The manner in which the book returned to the Uniat Church and the Library of the Greek Catholic Bishopric in Przemyśl is presently also an enigma since the archives are unavailable for scrutiny. Some conjecture that Count Agenor Gołuchowski (1813–1875), Austrian statesman and governor of Galicia up to 1871, who sympathized with the Ukrainian movement, donated or deposited the book in the Uniat Bishopric Library in Przemyśl.

The attached two leaves at the beginning of the book should be closely scrutinized because the marginalia have some inscriptions in the Latin alphabet. On the left margin of the first page the date 1700 is distinctly visible next to the text which mentions in words the date 1680. The same date 1700, appears in the center of the fourth page beneath the signatures of Gołuchowski and Paszycki, however it is barely visible. Both dates could have some association with the book, but that is difficult to determine without further research.

On page three of the inserted two leaves, in the upper, lower and left margins are a few notes but they are difficult to decipher and understand. The contents, the names and short sentences in the Latin alphabet would indicate some connection with the inheritance record but are not relative to the incunabulum.

During the conservation process much was learned about the way the binding of Fiol's books was done. It consisted of wooden boards covered with leather, to which the ends of the bands holding together the sections were fixed. The leather covering these boards was blind-tooled. The covers were equipped with brass clasps, which in spite of their decorative finish withstood wear and tear during the centuries. Three illustrations obtained through the courtesy of the National Library in Warsaw reveal the before-and-after appearance of the books.

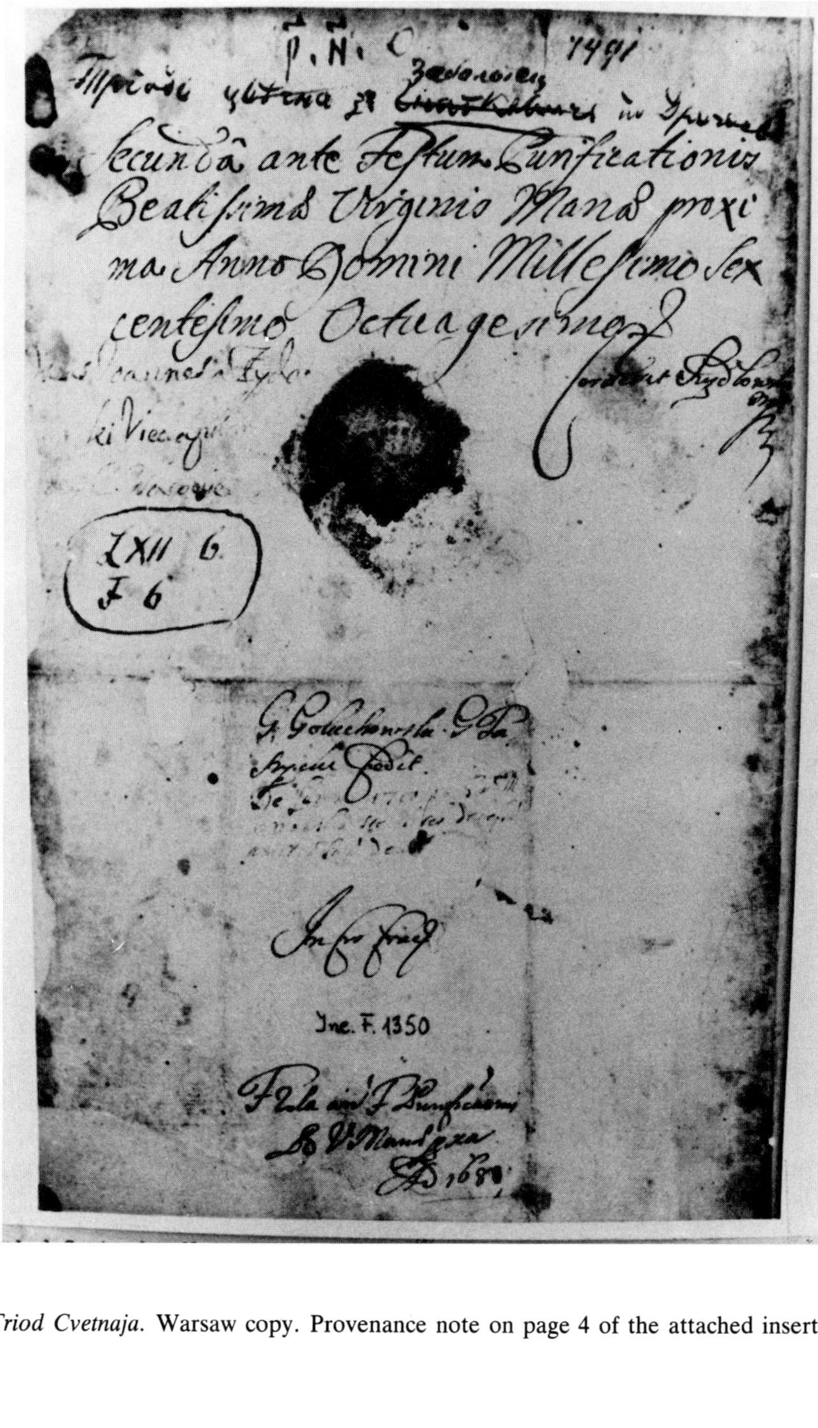

Triod Cvetnaja. Warsaw copy. Provenance note on page 4 of the attached insert.

One illustration shows the outward flaps of the book torn away from the book block with the soiled, stained and frayed first pages. However, with the exception of the few torn out pages in the front and back, the book appears to be firm. How much of this is the original product we cannot determine. No doubt this book had been reconditioned in the seventeenth century.

The other illustration shows the book cover before restoration, soiled to the extent of obscuring the blind-tooled design in the leather. In spite of the worn-out look of the surface the leather and wooden boards were in useable condition.

The third illustration reveals the reconditioned binding of the book with maximum conformity to the old method of workmanship, disclosing the lovely design in the blind-tooling of the leather in the fifteenth century style with floral decorations which also preserved some old linear elements. The backbone which was restored during the process of rebinding reveals some deviation from the original. The reconditioning gave the book the appearance of never having been damaged.

These fragmentary data were obtained through a thorough study of the copy, inc. No. 1350 itself, and also on the basis of material and documents provided by and through the cooperation of the librarians. This copy needs, however, a complete monographic description. The book has been reconditioned after 1950. It would be necessary to get a report with reference to what had been accomplished during the renovating process. Photographs of before and after the reconstruction would be most valuable. A clear picture as to the condition and appearance of the book when it reached the National Library in Warsaw ought to be preserved. These photographs before the reconstruction could be instrumental in deciphering some of the provenance notes that might have been obliterated during the process of renovation. Besides that, worthy of detailed investigation would be the defects, especially the last four unnumbered leaves of quire XXXI (the last one). The first four leaves with signatures 186 through 189 (РПЅ, РПЗ, РПИ, РПΘ) are the original last leaves. The following unnumbered leaves in the present copy are replacements. No report or record from where and by what method these substitutions were incorporated is available. Investigation into this aspect of the book should be pursued further.

American Holdings of Triod Cvetnaja

Only one copy and one fragment* of this book is in the United States. The book is listed by Barbara B. Stillwell in: *Incunabula in American Libraries. A Second Census of Fifteenth-Century Books Owned in the United States, Mexico and Canada.* New York, 1940, under T. 388; and in F. R. Goff: *Incunabula in American Libraries. A Third Census of Fifteenth-Century Books Recorded in North American Collections.* New York, 1964, under T.428.

* The fragment was never listed, recorded or described; what is most important it has never been thoroughly identified.

The citation by Goff reads:

TRIOD' TZVETNAYA. I.e. Liturgy and Ritual of the Eastern Orthodox Church/Russian/Cracow: Swietopolk Fiol, 1491. Folio. Ref: Lam, Stanislas: *Le livre polonais au XV et XVI siècle,* (Varsovie, 1923) p. 63. Of Proctor, p. 693.[17]

It is necessary to clarify a fundamental error in the subject heading. The description given by Goff identifying the Eastern Orthodox Church as Russian is incorrect because when the book was printed in 1491 the Eastern Orthodox Church was Greek and not Russian. Its complete name was The Holy Orthodox Catholic Apostolic Eastern Church, in brief called the Greek Church in contrast to the Roman Church. The insertion of the word Russian is confusing and was introduced much later by Moscow for political purposes. Subject heading should be: Liturgy and Ritual of the Eastern Orthodox Church.

New York Public Library Copy

No special summary is devoted to this copy. All data presented currently are based on inquiries by the author and material obtained through the kind assistance of Mrs. Zofia Głodowska MLS., and other employees of the New York Public Library.

Data in the Main Catalogue Card:

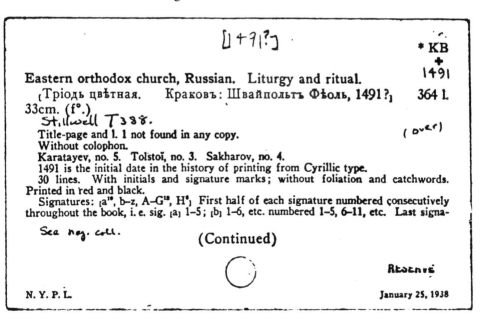

[1491?]

* KB
+
1491

Eastern orthodox church, Russian. Liturgy and ritual.
[Тріодь цвѣтная. Краковъ: Швайпольтъ Фѣоль, 1491?] 364 l.
33cm. (f°.)
Stillwell T388.
Title-page and l. 1 not found in any copy. (over)
Without colophon.
Karatayev, no. 5. Tolstoĭ, no. 3. Sakharov, no. 4.
1491 is the initial date in the history of printing from Cyrillic type.
30 lines. With initials and signature marks; without foliation and catchwords. Printed in red and black.
Signatures: [a¹⁰, b–z, A–G¹², H⁸] First half of each signature numbered consecutively throughout the book, i. e. sig. [a] 1–5; [b] 1–6, etc. numbered 1–5, 6–11, etc. Last signa-

See neg. coll.

(Continued)

Reserve

N. Y. P. L. January 25, 1938

[17] Goff, *Incunabula in American Libraries.* The language is not Russian. It is Old Church Slavonic of Bulgarian and Macedonian origin. T. 428.

Eastern orthodox church, Russian. Liturgy and ritual. ₍Тріодь цвѣтная. (Continued)

ture has 4 leaves numbered. Signature marks 60–63, 124–125 omitted; few signature marks assigned wrongly: 41 instead of 50; 64 instead of 66; 200–201 instead of 140–141.

Binder's title: Тріодь цвѣтная. Краковъ. 1491.

With a few ms. notes.

Imperfect: l. 1–5 and 1 leaf at end wanting; a number of leaves mutilated.

Binding of leather over wooden boards with remains of clasps.

1. Liturgy—Eastern orthodox church, Russian. I. Title: Triod' tzvetnaya.

N. Y. P. L. January 25, 1918

The description of the book given in the catalogue cards should be revised and supplemented by data found in the note placed on a strip of paper across the upper cover of the copy:

> Third leaf after one numbered NΓ:/53/ wrongly bound at the beginning of the book; leaf numbered BI; /12/ and preceding one should be bound before leaf numbered ΓI; /13/.

The catalogue card in the Rare Book Division in which Fiol's *Тріод Чветнауа* is located requires updating. The number of preserved copies is not four but twenty-one plus four fragments.

Triod Tzvetnaya. (The Floral Triodion or Pentecostarion) ca. 1491.

A liturgical work of the Eastern Orthodox Church, this volume is believed to have been printed in Cracow by Schweidpolt Fiol (Viol) in 1491. This is the initial date in the history of printing from Cyrillic type. Only four other copies are extant.

Rare Book Division

Corrections necessary to introduce in the Main Catalogue Card:

1. Subject heading—the same criticism applies to the subject heading as that in Goff's citation from which it was taken. It should be: Liturgy and Ritual of the Eastern Orthodox Church.
2. Square brackets presently should be applied only to the date.
3. Binder's title: it should be explained that the title does not exist in the original binding and was added during the rebinding process at a much later date.

Description of the condition of this copy coincides with the catalogue card. It is a defect: the first five printed leaves and the last leaf are missing. This copy starts with leaf number 6 and ends with leaf 365. A number of leaves had been misplaced during the rebinding process. Altogether the copy is well-preserved and those leaves that had been damaged, had been reconditioned by having page ends and corners added, torn away pages glued-in; holes refilled with paper backing, etc. Nevertheless some leaves are in poor condition due to candle wax stains as well as waterlogged pages; some are mutilated like leaves Р҃МЄ, Р҃ѮИ and few following Р҃ПѲ. Leaf Р҃НЗ verso has very poor impressions giving the appearance that the page was moved during printing. Leaf 112 has a vacant space for an initial.

Glosses are to be found on leaf 13 and next to the last page. A few marginal notes in Cyrillic, most of them however are faint since they were erased and others are difficult to read. Most characteristic samples are located on the following leaves:
Leaf П—in the right margin an illegible note.
Verso of leaf facing leaf KA—a note in Russian written upside down in the lower margin, also illegible.
Leaf МГ—a longer note in the lower section of the right margin.
Leaf 109—a blotted note in the right margin.
Leaf C—the same appears as above.
Leaf 190 verso—in the right upper corner a blurred note.
Leaf 200 verso—a very primitive handwritten blurred inscription.

There are also some other less distinct marginalia. All of the above notes do not contain any concrete information. A monographic study of this copy would necessitate a thorough research of these marginalia.

Provenance notes are of a later date. Notes of earlier dates, if they existed may have been lost during the rebinding process. The blank leaves at the beginning and the end of the book normally used for that purpose, are missing. Both front and back endpapers of the cover have been replaced and have no early notes. The notes now in existence are from the nineteenth century and later.

1. On the endpaper of the upper cover is the mark of ownership in Russian:

Otd. 1.	(Department 1)
Sochineniya	(Works)
Glavnoi Biblioteki	(Main Library)
No. 5	(No. 5)

At the bottom appears an undecipherable oval seal.

2. On the recto of the flyleaf is a stamp with the inscription Biblioteka Saratovskogo Gos. Un-ta im. H. C. Chernyshevskogo (H. C. Chernyshevsky Saratov State University Library). This stamp gives information where the book was located after World War I.

3. The above stamp appears every few pages throughout the whole book.

4. On the first preserved printed page appears the following note: Perl, December 16, 1935, indicating that the copy was at that time the property of a book dealer.

The binding of the book is old. It is not the original from the fifteenth century. Some parts of the original may have been preserved. Indications are that it had been rebound probably sometime in the seventeenth century. The leather over the wooden boards is fragile; some remnants of the clasps remain. During the rebinding process the binder's title (non-existent in the original) was added. The following inscription in Cyrillic appears on the backbone of the book:

Triod Cvetnaya
Cracow
1491.

When and how the book arrived in the United States is unknown. On September 19, 1935, librarian J. Metcalf received a letter from A. Yarmolinsky, head of the New York Public Library Slavonic Division, recommending the purchase of this rare book. The date on the library card is January 25, 1938 which proves that the book was acquired and processed by January, 1938.

Unnoted Fragment Triod Cvetnaja *in U.S.A.*

Location of the fragment: Saint Basil's College
Library and Museum, 161 Glenbrook Road, Stamford, Connecticut 06902
Library item No. 452.
TRIOD CVETNAJA

Cracow, Szwajpolt Fiol. [Circa 1491] 2°.

Fragment: 29 leaves preserved, pages 205–233 from gathering XVIII, XIX, and XX, beginning with leaf showing signature number PH and ending with first unsigned leaf following the one with signature number PKB. The bulk of leaves held together [presumably with the original stitching], however, some leaves are loose, e.g. 10, 11, and 59. This fragment as now preserved does not give any indication from what section of the book it was taken. The pages were marked from one to sixty later by an unknown person. The first leaf marked page one and two is lost, therefore, this fragment presently begins with the third page.

The Catholic University Library in Lublin provided a photocopy of *Triod Cvetnaja,* thus making possible the identification of those 29 leaves. The special chart will facilitate verification of each page. Listing of these 29 leaves of the fragment marked within sixty pages, does not coincide consecutively with the regular arrangement by the printer. Leaf 227 with signature PHI equivalent to pages 47–48 is located at the end of the fragment carrying erroneous markings as page 59 and 60. It can be explained simply that the leaf was loose and had been incorrectly placed at the end of the fragment. It is correctly noted in the chart.

Fragment pages	Lublin Copy			Leaf No.
	Sign. No.		Gathering No.	
3–4	Р҃И	r-v	XVIII	205
5–6	Р҃Ѳ	r-v		206
7–8	Р҃І	r-v		207
9–10	Р҃АІ	r-v		208
11–12		r-v		209
13–14				210
15–16				211

17–18			212
19–20			213
21–22			214
23–24	р҃ві r-v	XIX	215
25–26	р҃гі r-v		216
27–28	р҃ді r-v		217
29–30	р҃єі r-v		218
31–32	р҃ѕі r-v		219
33–34	р҃зі r-v		220
35–36			221
37–38			222
39–40			223
41–42			224
43–44			225
45–46			226
47–48	р҃иі r-v	XX	227
49–50	р҃ѳі r-v		228
51–52	р҃к r-v		229
53–54	р҃ка r-v		230
55–56	р҃кв r-v		231
57–58	р҃кг r-v		232
59–60			233

Identification of a portion of the fragment's subject and text by Monsignor Emil Manasterskiĭ, librarian at St. Basil's College:

Page 3 (205r) "Slava" 5th Tone, for Stichyry na Hospody Vosvach for Vechirnia for Sunday of the Paralytic (Rozslablenoho).

Page 4 (205v) "Slava" 8th Tone, for Stichyry na Stichovny for Vechirnia Rozslablenoho.

Page 4 (205v) Second Sidealen na Pershim Stychosloviu na Utreni Rozslablenoho.

Page 5 (206r) "Slava" for "Stichyry na Chvalytech na Utreni Rozslablenoho."

These few pages can give some orientation for further investigation. At present this suffices as an authoritative statement by an expert that this fragment is part of *Triod Cvetnaja.*

The previously presented chart identifying leaves from the Stamford fragment with coinciding leaves from the Lublin copy proves that the Stamford fragment is from Fiol's *Triod Cvetnaja.*

The condition of this fragment could be described in general as poor. Even a casual examination reveals quite a bit of dirt and grime. The leaf, pages 3–4, which is the first in this fragment, shows in the left center margin in the bottom half of the page a hole through which the next leaf, page 5, can be seen. This first leaf is in a deteriorated condition. The other leaves are less damaged, the corners torn away and so soiled that it is difficult to read the print. There are no signatures due to pages damaged at the bottom. The leaves are so fragile that it is impossible to handle them for closer research. The Museum administration would permit photocopies of the whole fragment to be made only if it would be done by specialists. Nevertheless the administration was cooperative and delivered Xerox copies of a few first leaves, also some of the loose leaves, especially the last one, which have been most helpful in the identification of the fragment. The reproduction of these Xerox copies is attached at the end of this description of the Stamford fragment.

The origin and provenance of the Stamford fragment was presented by Monsignor Emil Manasterskiĭ in his letters to the author, supplemented by information from the Director of the Museum, Professor Wasyl Lencyk, during the author's visit at the Museum to study the fragment *in situ.*

The pages, evidently only a part of the book, were found in Hołyń, county (*povit*) of Dolyna, Galicia, on September 7, 1912 by Reverend Doctor Constantine Bokhachevskiĭ while visiting his father, the Reverend Teodor Bokhachevskiĭ, pastor of the Greek-Catholic Church in Hołyń. In 1924 Reverend Doctor Constantine Bokhachevskiĭ became bishop of the Ukrainian Catholic diocese in Philadelphia and later Archbishop and Metropolitan of the same see. He was the founder of the Ukrainian Museum in Stamford in 1937. The fragment was donated by him to the Museum and has been there ever since.

Further clarification would be helpful relative to the origin of the fragment and its value. Dolyna is situated at the foot of the Carpathian Mountains about one hundred miles south of Lwów. As we recall, Archimandrite Kopystenskiĭ mentioned in his *Palinodia* that in the Church of the Holy Cross, in Łyczaków, a suburb of Lwów, he found *Chasoslovec* printed by Fiol, as well as copies of both *Triod*s in many churches and monasteries of the Lwów area. This fragment in Stamford could be a part of one of these books mentioned by Kopystenskiĭ, preserved throughout the centuries in the small village church as Dolina geographically could be considered in the Lwów area. However, we learned from Sventsitskiĭ that Fiol's *Chasoslovec* was found a hundred kilometers farther south in a church located close to the Hungarian border in Sub-Carpathian Ruthenia. In 1972 Mircea discovered Fiol's *Triod Cvetnaja* in Braşov, Rumania, another couple of hundred miles farther south. That copy was there since the sixteenth century.

The Stamford fragment is a valuable link in establishing the route and destination of Fiol's prints. It appears that they were spread not only throughout Belorussia and Ukraine, but also reached Sub-Carpathian Ruthenia and Transylvania where the Eastern Orthodox religion was dominant.

It is noteworthy that since 1937 no official recording of the fragment was ever reported in bibliophile or bibliographic literature. Only two short notations were made in some periodicals. *America—Ukrainian Catholic Daily* of April 25, 1968, printed on page one an article titled: "Ukrainian Museum and Library in Stamford, Connecticut," informing about the holdings of this notable institution. At the bottom of this page are two photographs, one showing the room with costumes, ceramics, woodcarvings, etc., the other a display of a collection of old books. The description of the second picture is as follows:

> Incunabula (books printed before 1500 A.D.) old missals and antimensia (blessed altar cloths) displayed in Ukrainian Museum and Library in Stamford, Connecticut. In the center, book printed by Schweipolt Fiol in 1491. On the left: Missal of Lviv from 1666 A.D.

This article accidentally came into the author's possession and resulted in further inquiry regarding Fiol's unnoted book. All efforts to obtain detailed information regarding this notice ended with the statement found in Sokolyszyn's article: "There are also a few pages of Fiol's printing in the Ukrainian Catholic Museum in Stamford, Conn."[18] Since this did not suffice, the author then contacted the Museum directly and was informed in detail that this was only a 29 page fragment of Fiol's *Triod Cvetnaja.*

To the author's knowledge this was all that had been reported about the Stamford fragment. Goff, as quoted previously, cites only *Triod Cvetnaja,* the book in the New York Public Library. He was not aware of the existence of the Stamford fragment when his book was published in 1964.

Following an inquiry to the authorities at Saint Basil's College whether there had been any publication in this matter, a March 2, 1973 answer from Monsignor Emil Manasterskiĭ, librarian, stated: "There is no published pamphlet on the Museum outside the publicity occasionally in the press." He also wrote: "Feel free to make mention of the existence of this fragment in our Museum."

A most cordial and cooperative correspondence developed. When the author visited the Museum all courtesies were extended in presenting the fragment for scrutiny and examination. Thanks to this it is now possible to make known the existence of this Fiol incunabulum in the USA besides the New York Public Library copy.

The Saint Basil's College Museum Fragment

Gathering material and information (still unpublished up to the present) we also have the opportunity to present details about the copy of *Triod Cvetnaja* presently

[18] Alexander Sokolyszyn, "First Ukrainian Printer of Books in Cracow," *Ukrainian Quarterly,* XXVIII (Autumn, 1972), 273.

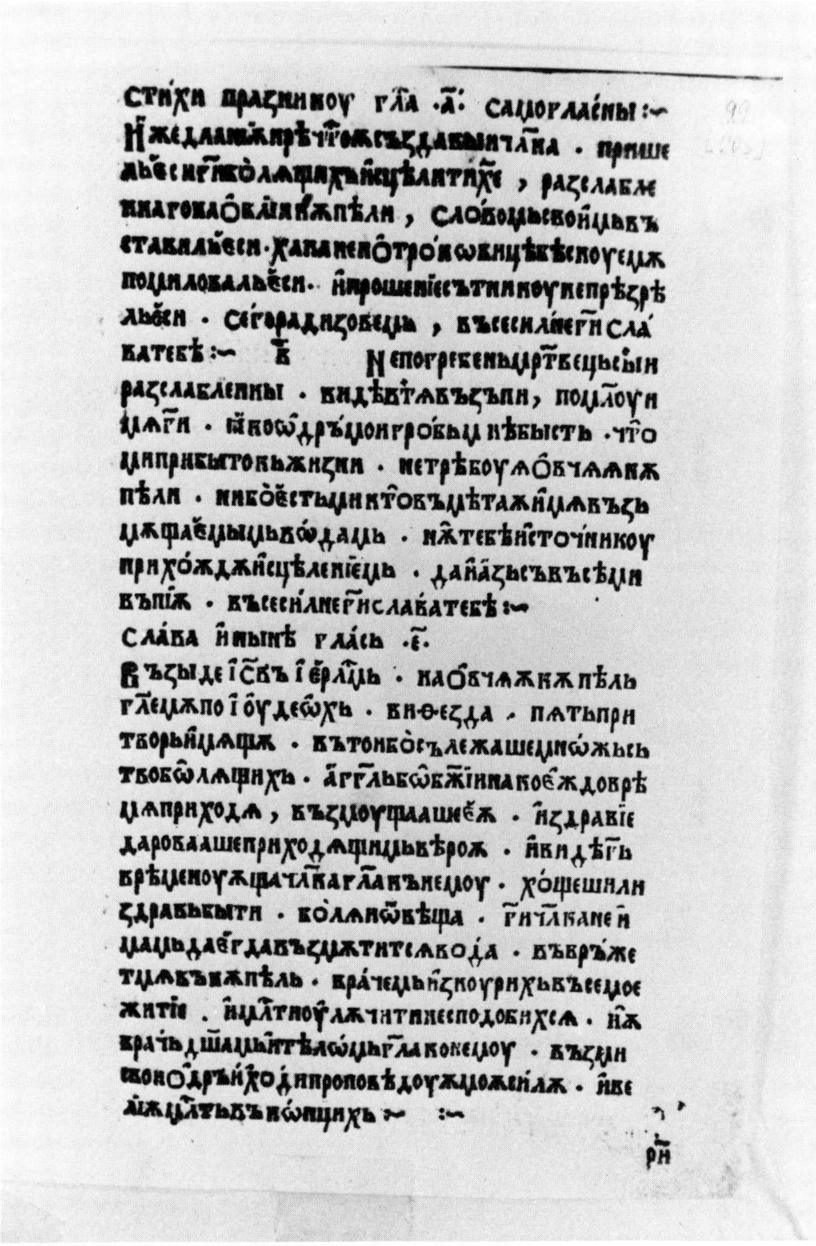

Стихи празникоу гла .а. самогласны :~
Иже дланиѭ прѣчтоѭ създавы члка . прише
лъеси нн҃ѣ ко лѫщимъ ꙗко исцѣлити хс҃ , разслабле
нна гона ѡболѣзни кѫпѣли , свободь своицѣмь въ
ставлѣеси . хапане ѿтроницѣ кѣ сѧ поусемъ
помиловалъ еси . и прошение съ тини моу непрѣзрѣ
лъ еси . сего ради зовемъ , въсеси лне гн сла
ва тебѣ :~ . Непогребень царь твецѣ сыи
разслабленны . видѣвъ тѧ възъпи , помилоуи
мѧ ги . ꙗко ѡдръ мои гробъ ми бысть . что
ми прибыто бѣ жизни . не трѣбоу мѧ ѡбычѧ мѧ кѫ
пѣли . нико есть ми кто бъ да ѣта же имѧ възъ
мѫщаемыцѣ ꙗко ѡдамь . нѫ тебѣ источникоу
прихождѫ и исцѣление ми . да и азь съвъ съ бѣми
въпиѭ . въсеси лне гн слава тебѣ :~
Слава и нынѣ гласъ .е.
Възыде ісъ въ ієрслмь . на ѡбычѧ жк ѫ пѣль
глемѫ по іоудеѡхъ . вивезда . пѧть при
творь имѫщѫ . въ тои бо съ лежаше множьсь
тво болѧщихъ . агглъ бо бжіи на кое ждо врѣ
мѧ приходѧ , възмоущааше ѥѫ . и здравіе
дароваше приходѧщимъ вѣрою . и видѣвъ
врѣменоу жива члка глан ънемоу . хощеши ли
здравъ быти . болѧ ниѡ вѣща . ги члка не и
мамъ да егда възмѫтит сѧ вода . въвръже
тъ мѧ въ кѫпѣль . врачемъ изнурихъ въсе мое
житіе . и милтнѧ оулѫчити не сподобих сѧ . нѫ
врачь дшамъ ите к нѡмоу глаголе немоу . възми
свои одръ и ходи и проповѣдоуи мою милость . и веи
ліи ты дѣ ниѡ изцѣлихъ :~ :~

рн

Fiol. Stamford fragment.

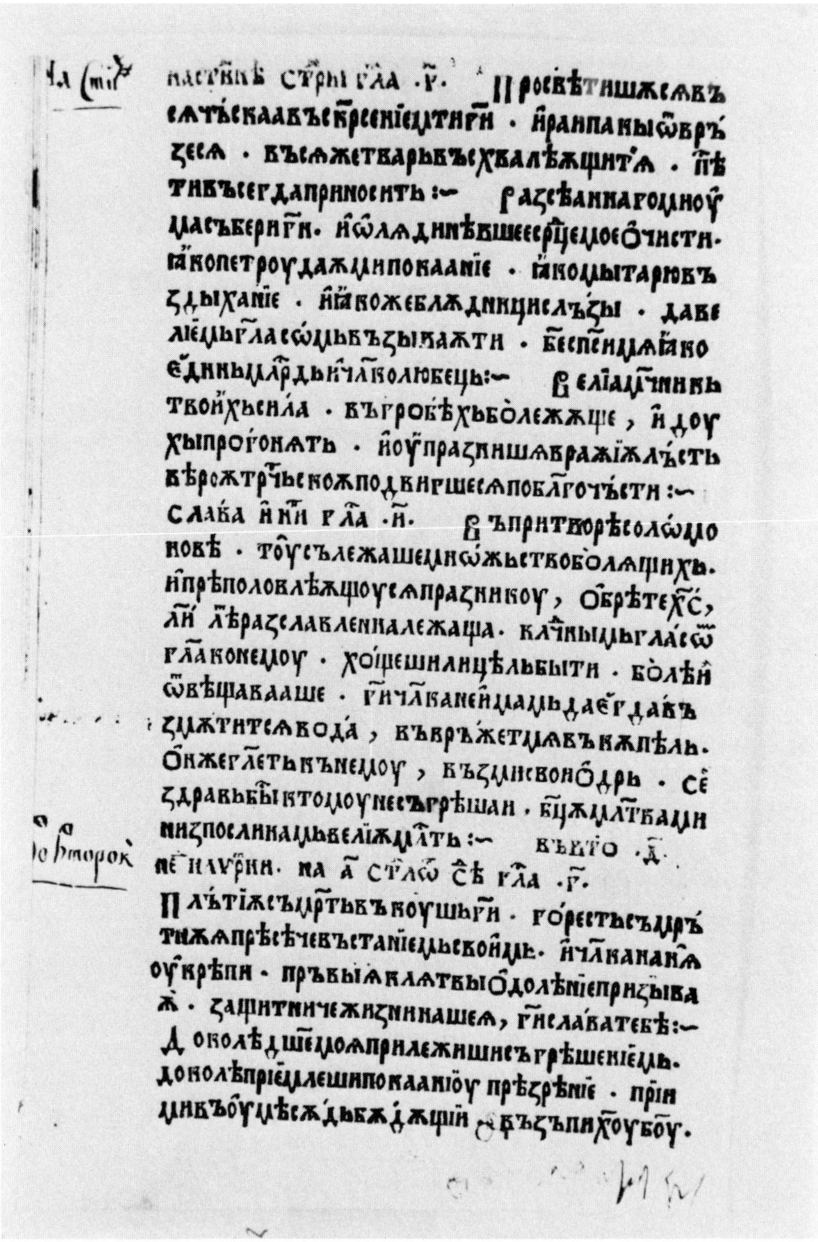

Ча Стих

наст҃ик стр҃ы гла .г҃. Просвѣтишѧжесѧвъ
ѥсѧтѣскаавъскр҃сениѥмтиг҃и . ираипаныѿвръ
зесѧ . въсѧжетварьвъсхвалѧщитѧ . пѣ
тивъсегдаприносить :~ Разсѣаннагомоу
масъберигі҃. иѡлѧдинѣвшеесрцемоеѿчисти.
ꙗкопетроудаждипокаание . ꙗкомытарювъ
здыхание . иꙗкожеблѫдницислъзы . дави
лѥмьглаѥсѡмьвъзыѫжти . беспенмѧꙗко
ѥдинымлрдьичлколюбець :~ Веліамѣчнинь
твоихьсила . въгробѣхьболежѫще, идоу
хыпрогонать . иоупразнишѧвражіжлъсть
вѣрожтрчьскожподвигшесѧпоблгочьсти :~
Слава ини гла .и҃. Въпритворѣсоломо
новѣ . тоусълежашемнѡжьствоболѧщихь.
ипрѣполовлѣѫщоусѧпразникоу, обрѣтехс҃,
лѣ лѣраззлабленналежаща. клчнымьглаѥсѿ
глаконемоу . хощешиланцѣльбыти . болѣи
ѿвѣщаваше . гичлканеимамьдаегдавъ
змѫтитсѧвода, въвръжетмѧвъкѫпѣль.
онжегллетьвънемоу, възмисвоиодрь . сѣ
здравьбыктомоунесъгрѣшаи . бѫжамлтвами
низпослинамьвеліжмлть :~ Въвто .д҃.

во второк

пенлури. на а҃ стлѡ сѣ гла .г҃.
Плътіжесъмртьвкоушьги . горестьсъмръ
тижѧпрѣсѣчевъстаниемьсвоимь. ичлканамѧ
оукрѣпи . пръвыѧклѧтвыѡдолѣниепризыва
ѫ . защитничежизнинашеѧ, гиславатебѣ :~
Доколѣдшемоѧприлежишнесъгрѣшениемь.
доколѣприемлешипокаанію презрѣние . прін
мивъоумѣсѫдьбѫдѫщии ивъзъпихоубоу.

Fiol. Stamford fragment. РИ v.

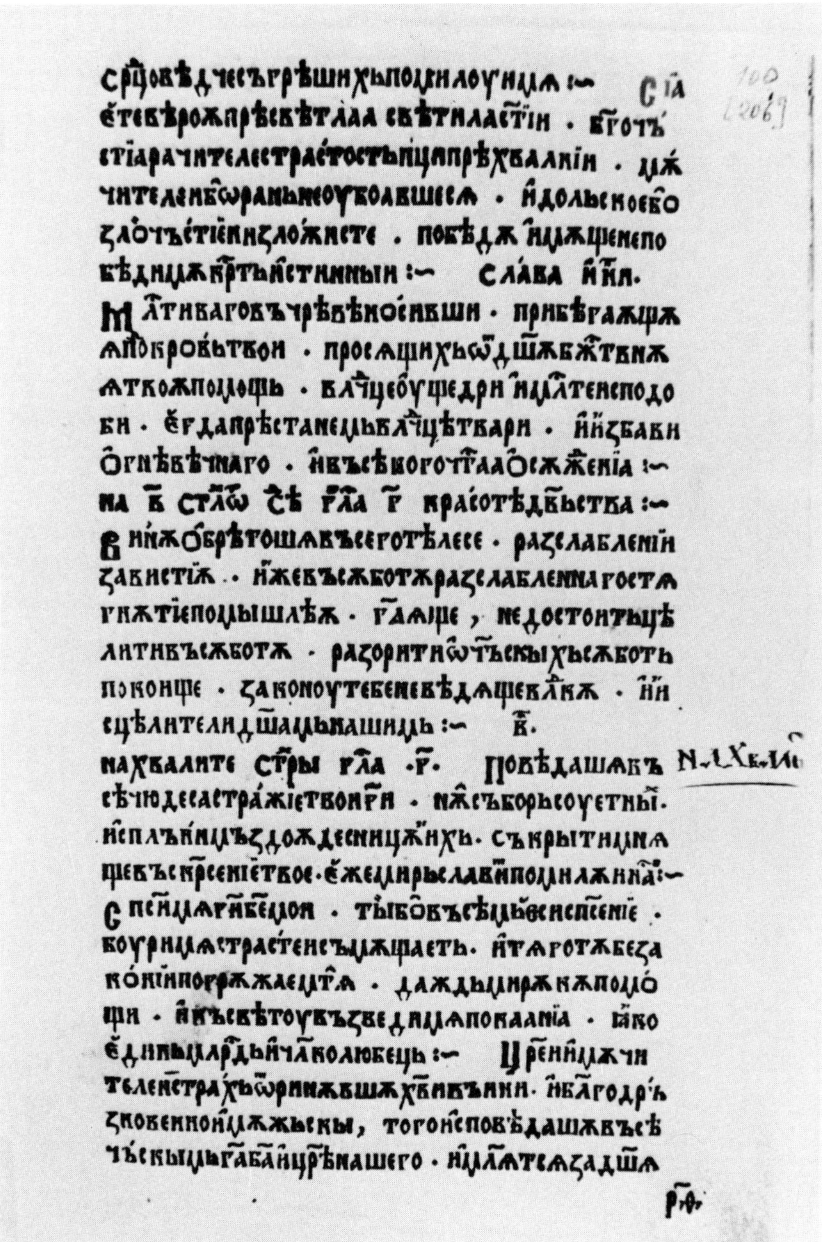

срцовѣдчесъгрѣшнихъıподклилоуницѧ :— с ıа 100 [206]
ѥтебѣрожпрѣсвѣтлаа свѣтиластїи . бготъ
стїарачителестрасѣтостьпцѧпрѣхвалнїи . дѫ
чителенбѡраньнеоукоавшеѥѧ . идольскоебо
ӡлоѣтъстїенизложисте . побѣдѫ идѫщенепо
бѣдицѫкртънестинныи :— слава ини.
М атибагобъчрѣвѣносившии . прибѣгажирѫ
мпокровьтвои . просѧщихьѡ дшжѫбжтвнѫ
мтножпоцѫощь . блицеоущедри идалтенеподо
би . егдапрѣстанецьблицѣтвари . иизбави
огнѣвѣчнаго . иьсѣкогоѣлаа осѫженїа :—
на б стлѡ сѣ гла г красотѣдвьства :—
В нинжобрѣтошѧвъсегоѣлесе . разслабленїи
ӡабистїѫ . ижевъсѫботѫразслабленнагостѧ
гнѫтїепоцышлѣѫ . гамщє , недостоитъцѣ
литивъсѫботѫ . разоритиѡтъскыхъсѫботь
покопще . ӡакоуоутебенесвѣдѧщевлѫ . ии
сцѣлителидшаммнашимь :— в.
нахвалите стры гла г. Повѣдашѧвъ N.A.Xb.Иb
сѣчюдесастражїєтвоигри . нѫсъборьсоуєтны.
испльниѧсъӡдождесницѫнихъ . съкрытиѧнѧ
щевъскрсенїєтвое . ежедарьславиподиажинна :—
С пеимѧгибелон . тыбобъсѣмьвсиспсенїе .
боурицѧстрастенеъдѫщаеть . итмаротѫбеза
конїипорѫжаецтѧ . даждьцирѫнѫпоцо
щи . иикъсвѣтоувъзведимѧпокаанїа . яко
єдиньщаръдьичлколюбецъ :— Црениѧѫчи
теленстрахьѡринѫвшѫхвивъини . иблгодрь
ӡновенноиѧѫжьскы, тогоиспов ѣдашѫвъсѣ
чъскыцьгабанцрѣнашего . иммтеѧзадшѧ
рѳ

Fiol. Stamford fragment. рѳ

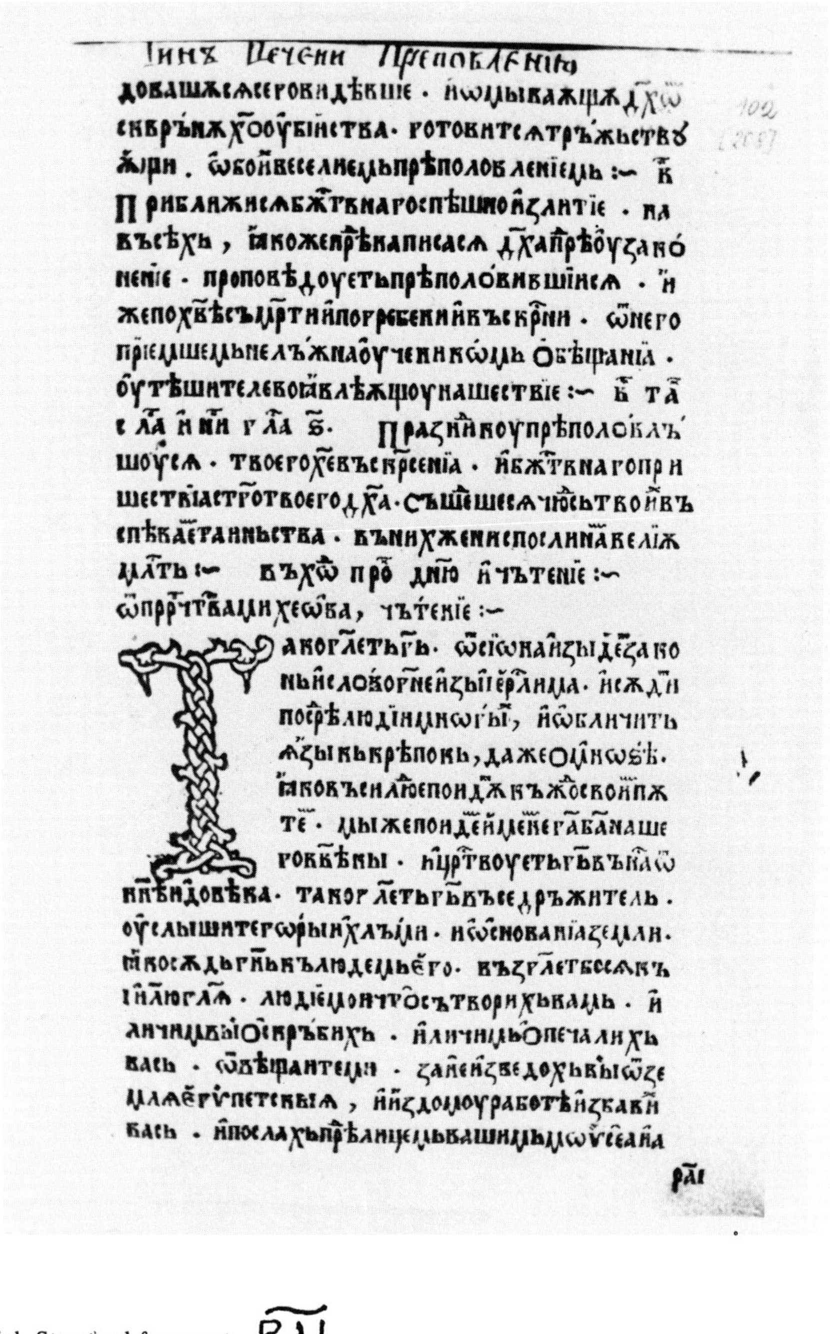
довашжесасеровидѣвше. иѡдывакажірж дхѡ
свръиж хоубіиства. готовитеса тръжьствѹ
жрди. ѡбоивеселинедьпрѣполовленіедь :~ к
Прибльжисабжтвнагоспѣшнои зльтіе. на
въсѣхь, ꙗкожепрѣнаписаса дхапрѣоузако
неніе. проповѣдоуетьпрѣполовившінса. и
жепохвѣсъдртнипогребенииксъкрни. ѡнего
прѣдшедьпелъжнаоучениквдь обѣщаниа.
оутѣшителевоиавлѣжщоунашествіе :~ в та
е ла и ни г ла s. Празникоупрѣполовлъ
шоуса. твоегохевъскрсенїа. ибжтвнагопри
шествіастготвоегодха. съшешесачюсьтвоивъ
спѣвастанныства. въних женисполнивелиж
дать :~ въхѡ про днію ичтеніе :~
ѡпррчтвацихеѡва, чтеніе :~
Такоглетьгь. ѡсеѡнаизыдезако
ньисловогнеизыиерлида. нежди
посрѣлюдінимногы, иѡбличить
азыкькрѣпокь, дажеѡдинѡѣ.
ꙗковъсиаюепонджкъжѡсвоипж
те. дыжепондеидеиегабанаше
рокѣны. ицртвоуетьгьвъкаѡ
ниенидовѣка. такоглетьгьвседръжитель.
оуслышитегѡрыихлъдии. иѡснованіазедлан.
ꙗкосждьгньвълюдедьего. възгаетбесавъ
іналюгла. людиедонитоосътворихьвадь. и
лчидвыѡскръбихъ. иличидьѡпечалихъ
вась. ѡвѣщантеди. зане изведохьвыѡзе
длаегупетскыа, иисдоудоуработѣизбави
вась. ипослахьпрѣлицедьвашидьдѡуееаина
рлі

Fiol. Stamford fragment.

in the Lithuanian Academy of Sciences SSR in Wilno. Nemirovskiĭ had this to say about it: "In the copy of the Lithuanian Academy of Sciences SSSR in Wilno (I–36) missing are leaves 1–8 and 51–102. Binding is new; it was restored and supplied with an ornamental metal buckle and attachments."[19]

In a letter from Dr. Vitaut Tumash to the author, we learn about the provenance of this old Belorussian-Lithuanian copy:

> This copy of *Triod Cvetnaja* was in the private collection of the renowned Belorussian archaeologist I. Luckiewicz up to the year 1919. Upon his death his collection as per his will was bequeathed to the Belorussian Scientific Society in Vilna and during the years between the two World Wars the book was in the Library of the Belorussian Ivan Luckiewicz Museum in Vilna. In 1945 in compliance with a directive from Moscow the Belorussian Museum in Vilna was closed. The Museum Library together with Fiol's *Triod Cvetnaja* and other old prints was transferred to the Central Library of the Lithuanian Academy of Sciences in Wilno.

II. TRIPESNEC—TRIOD POSTNAJA

Triod Postnaja, a large volume in folio, was the second book printed by Fiol. This print has no identification mark. It is probable, that *Triod Postnaja* had the same frontispiece and printer's device as *Triod Cvetnaja,* but this is only a supposition. The first known leaf is the second. On top of the recto side a woodcut vignette identical with that in *Triod Cvetnaja* is impressed in red. Beneath it is the first stylized line of the Incipit also printed in red. Caption letters 3 lines in height form the decorative "clichéd" line, the so-called "Vyaz'." No other illuminative features appear on this first page.

Triod Postnaja is less illuminated than *Triod Cvetnaja.* Only three initials from two knotty woodcuts are used. One seven lines in height "M" (on leaf 179v.) does not appear in any other of Fiol's books. The letter "T" six lines in height, previously used in *Triod Cvetnaja,* was impressed twice on leaves 27 and 117.

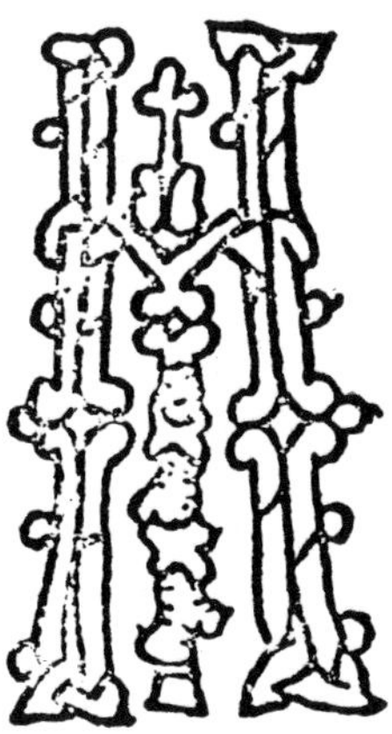

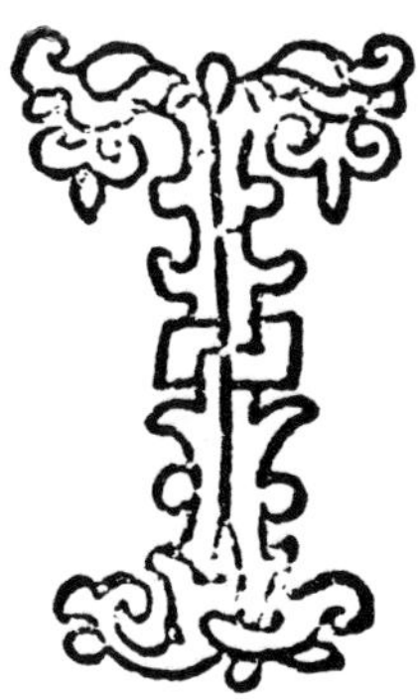

[19]Nemirovskii, "Slavische Inkunabeln . . . ," p. 111.

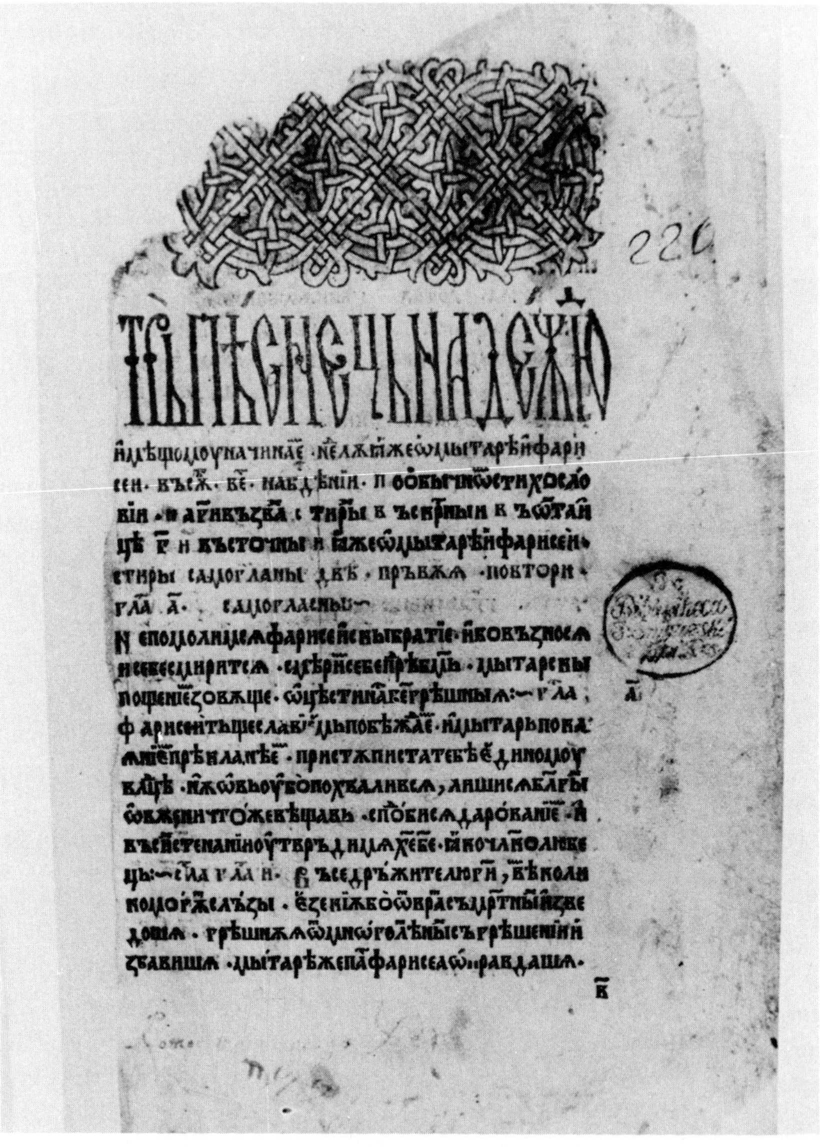

Fiol. *Triod Postnaja.* Leaf 2 r. Warsaw National Library Copy.

The plain floral initials, five and six lines in height, were used altogether about a dozen times.

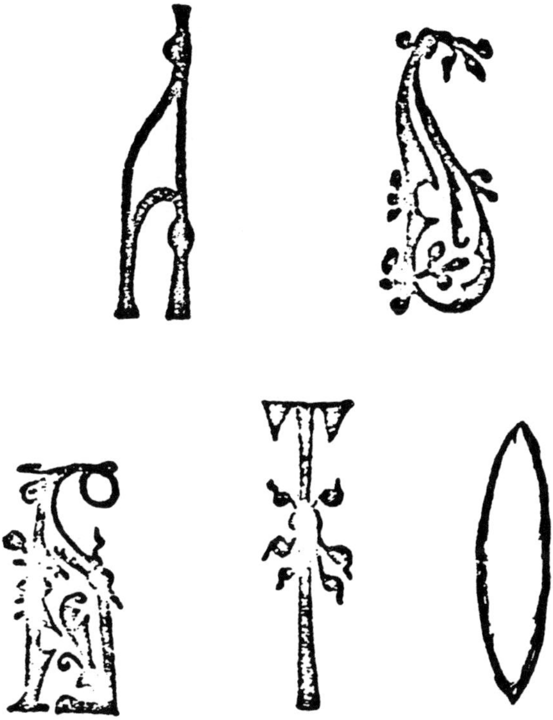

The last initial "O" (on leaf 200) five lines in height, is unique, a fact overlooked by other scholars. Its execution is inferior indicating that it had not been designed by the artist who cut the other four.

Chasoslovec, printed simultaneously, or just following *Triod Postnaja,* also has the similar strange initial, the elongated "O" but with a dot in the center. Sventsitskiĭ in 1908 described the copy of *Chasoslovec* which was in the Greek Catholic Uniat Church Museum in Lwów. He is the only scholar who noticed this feature in the *Chasoslovec*: "The paleographic peculiarity catching our attention is the elongated "O" with one dot in the center. [Leaf 249]."[20] Cutting down on the large knotted and floral initials the printer increased the use of cast-in-metal capital and caption letters as initials. Altogether about ninety imprints two and three lines in height were made; however, not always printed in cinnabar, especially in the third part of the book. No sign of trace of any system or plan for using initials in *Triod Cvetnaja* is apparent, while on the contrary, in *Triod Postnaja* initials are used systematically and their arrangement is more harmonious. The printer must have

[20] Sventsitskiĭ, *Kataloh knih tserkovno-slavianskoĭ pechaty,* p. 46.

concluded that prolific woodcut initials (especially the large ones) were a time and space consuming project and he switched to more economical lombards.

Triod Postnaja does not have a title page or colophon. It has a register of sections on leaf 314v. Since a reproduction of it is not available, a description of sections and signatures based on a study of the Warsaw National Library copy will be given.

Triod Postnaja consists of thirty-two sections (quires)—quinternions, which means five sheets folded once, giving ten leaves—twenty pages. The printer places signatures only on the first five leaves of the folded sheets. Section I has only nine leaves because the first leaf is missing in all preserved copies. The Incipit started on leaf 2 so that the first section has signatures on the first four leaves and next five leaves are without signatures. Sections II–XXXI have ten leaves each, of which the first five are with signatures, the other five without. The last section, XXXII, has only four leaves, two of them with signatures, and two without. In all there are 313 printed leaves and one blank for a total of 314 leaves.

The technical level of printing in *Triod Postnaja* is slightly higher than in *Triod Cvetnaja.* The one difference, a rather important one indicating typographical experience, is the smaller number of decorative elements, woodcuts and more ironcast initials. There is also apparent improvement in setting. Lines are less wavy, right edge evenly aligned; composition of special pages is more harmonious. The best proof is page 277v. which contains the ending of the main text of *Triod Postnaja.* The printer formed an elongated wedge-shaped column, perhaps not perfect, but in comparison with the primitive efforts in *Triod Cvetnaja* it shows distinct progress. (See pp. 222–223).

The Oxford Dictionary of the Christian Church gives the following definition of the *Triod Postnaja*:

> Triodon (Gk.) In the Eastern Rite a liturgical book containing the variable portions of the services from the fourth Sunday before Lent until the Sunday before Easter. It is so named because during this season the canons ordinarily contain only three odes instead of the usual nine.[21]

The Lenten Triodion contains Biblical lection, a biography of Mary of Egypt, *akafist*[22] worshipping Jesus Christ, tales about the power and authority of Chosroes and others. The Lenten Triod covers the services for about seventy days, and is followed by the Flowery Triodion. The contents of *Triod Postnaja* was first given by Karataev.[23]

Two years after K. F. Kalaedovich discovered a copy of *Triod Cvetnaja,* a Polish scholar, J. S. Bandtkie, in 1821 discovered proof sheets of *Triod Postnaja*

[21] F. L. Cross, ed., *The Oxford Dictionary of the Christian Church* (London, 1957), p. 1377.
[22] *Akafist*—religious laudatory hymn sung standing.
[23] Karataev, *Opisanie slaviano-russkikh knig . . . ,*" pp. 10–11.

Конец::

иѿрѫжщи· въсвѣтлостедъсчїи· съклѹбѹкщи
въстыигранеѥрⷭ҇лимь· речегь· въсвѣлика прине
сѫтьсновеилеви, жрътвыи· съѱалмы въдо
мьгнь· иѿнихприемъжинещенникы и левите, рече
гь· ниже обраꙁъ ново бѫдеть ибо новое· и земле
нова· яже аꙁъ творѭ пребѫдевкы предмнож·
такоглетьгь· такостанеть семѧ ваше· и имѧ
вашеглетьгь· и бѫдеть мцъ ѿмца·
и сѫбота ѿсѫботы· и приидеть въ
сѣка плъть поклонити
сѧ предмнож въ ирⷭ҇лимь·
речегь· и иꙁыдѫть и оу
зрѧть тѣлеса чл҇вкаа·
престѫпивших сѧ ѿмене·
ибо чрьвь ихъ не скон
чаетсѧ· и ѿгнь ихъ не
оугасаеть· и бѫдѫ
въвидение всѣкои
плъти:~ п ро г ла
ѕп ол млоуинагри
подманѹинꙗ· с
в ъꙁкедонте
бѣѿчинмон
живѫщо
моунане
беѕе· сеꙗ
коѿчи
рабь·

Конец Триоди Постной

Fiol. *Triod Postnaja.* Leaf 278 v. Warsaw copy

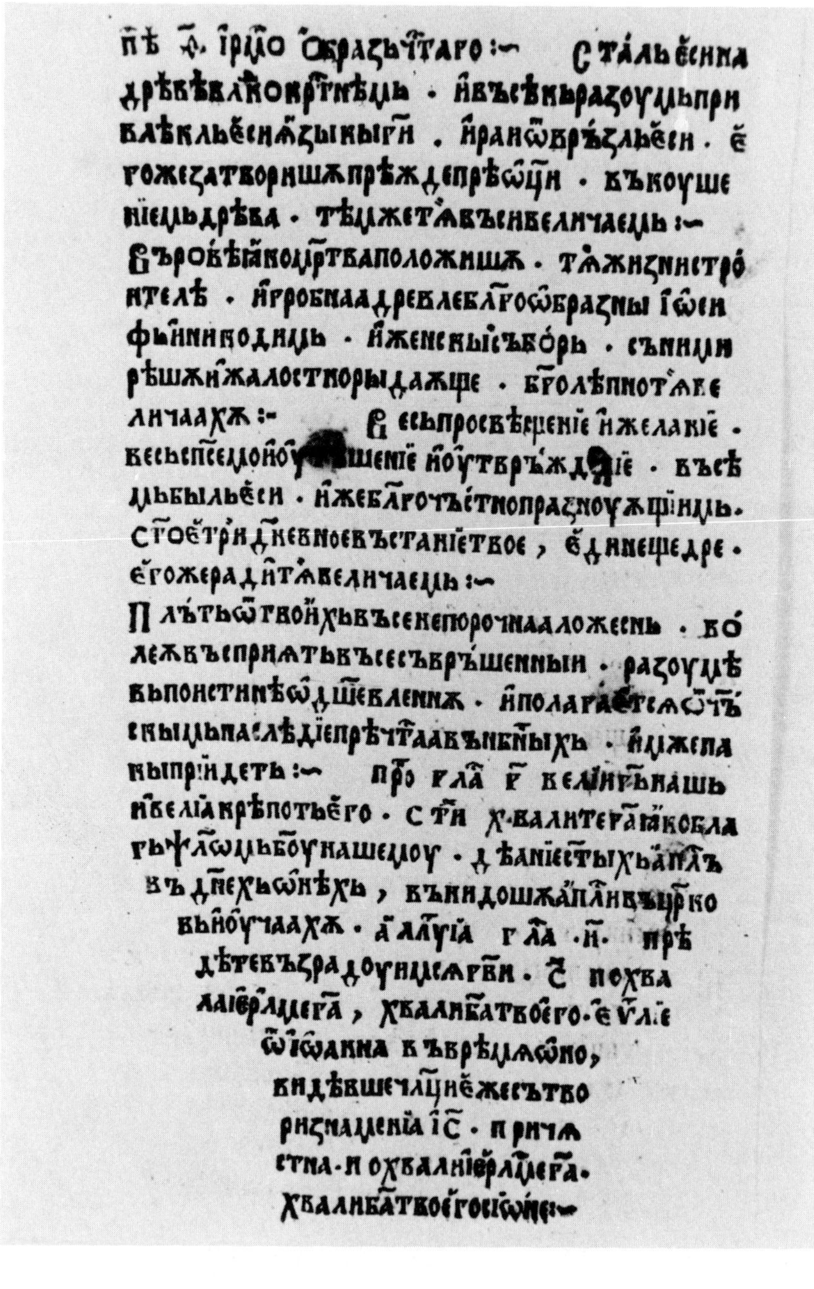
пѣ ѳ. ирмо образъ чтаго :— Стальѣснна
древѣ власоморьтнѣдль . и въсѣмь разоумль при
блѣкльѣсн мозыныгн . и раншбрѣзльѣсн . ѥ
гожезатворишж прѣжде прѣщи . въкоуше
нѥдльдрѣва . тедажетжвъсивеличаѥдь :—
Върокѣмоудртва положишж . тж жизни стро
нтелѣ . и гробнаа древле благо образны іѡсн
фынинподидль . и женѥныѥ събоурь . съникли
рѣшжи жалости порыдажще . бголѣпно тж ве
личаахж :— Весь просвѣщенїе и желаніе .
весь пѣсдоно оу……шенїе и оутвръжд…іе . въсѣ
дльбыльѥсн . и жебгочъстно праздноужщиндль .
стое трид невное въстанїе твое , ѥдинешедре .
егоже радитж величаѥдь :—
Плъть ѿ твоихъ въсенепорочнаа ложеснь . бо
лежвъ приятъ въсесъвръшенныи . разоумлѣ
вьпонстннѣ ѿ дшевленнж . и полагаѥтсм ѿ тъ
сныдльпаслѣдїе прѣчтаа въ нбныхъ . и дажепа
ныприидеть :— прѡ гла г велии гь нашь
и велиа крѣпость ѥго . сти хвалите га ѣко бла
гь ѱ лоудль боу нашемоу . д ѣаніе стыхъ апль
въ дни ѥхьшнѣхь , въ нидошж ап лнвъ цркво
вьноучаахж . а ллуа гла н прѣ
дѣтевъзрадоунцесмрѣни . с похва
лаіерлдега , хвали бга твоѥго . ѥ ѵлїе
ѿ іѡанна въ врѣмм ѡно,
видѣвшечлцнѣжесътво
ризнамденїа ис . причм
стна и охвалніерлдега .
хвалибга твоѥгосіѡне :—

Fiol. *Triod Cvetnaja.* Leaf 59 r. Lublin Copy.

мнащесмкамщеннаго ѿбаленіа . игроуга къ
дроузе глааху . где сжть печати гробныа.
где есть пилатово въинство . ио прасносоутве
ржденіе . бысть же въз вестителы неразоумь
важщи и жены мщь . блистаже сѧ аггль иглан
нищь . что съ рыданіемь ищете живаго . исо
жив лъ шагорода члчьскы . въста хс бъна
шь из мртвых ьіа кобъ вселеные . подаѧ вьсе
мь чамь нетленіе и жизнь . просвещеніе и велі
млость :~ слава гла ѕ.

Мироносица жены къ гробоу твое мѹ дошед
ше . и печати гроб на видешж . и не ѿбреть
ше же пречтго тела твое . рыдажще съ тъщаніе
мь пріидошж глаще . кто оукраде нашж на
деждж . кто въсхать мртва нагапосмирнена .
матери едини оутешеніе . ѿ како иже мр
твых ѿжив деж и оумирает . иже адапле
ни вы и како погребеса . нж въскрсни спасе
самовластно . іако же рекль еси третидн .
спаса доушамъ нашѧ :~
И ныне гласъ .в.
Пре идесе ньзаконнамъ благодати пришедши .
іако бо кжпина несъгараше ѿ палаещ . та
ко два родила еси , и два ж пребысть . въ
место стлъпа ѿгньнаго праведное въснмелъ
ще . въ место моѵсеа хс , спсеніе доуша
мь нашимь :~ на литии.
стихиры . самогласны.
Аще ли не прилоучитсѧ
быти на агрипины.

Fiol. *Triod Cvetnaja. Leaf 60 v. Lublin Copy.*

and *Chasoslovec* in the binding of a Venetian incunabulum "Abbanus Petrus de Abbano. *Conciliator differentiarum philosophorum, etc.*" Venecis, impr: Herbart de Selgenstat. 1483. Hain N. 6."

This small fragment, now in the Jagellonian Library in Cracow, (with proof-readings from *Triod Postnaja* printed on one side and from *Chasoslovec* on the other) is invaluable in the study of Cyrillic typography. Bandtkie's discovery following on the heels of Kalaydowich's resulted in a renewed interest in Fiol and Cyrillic printing and led to the discovery of many copies of the *Triod Postnaja* and other prints. Nemirovskiĭ enumerates twenty-seven copies and two fragments of the *Triod Postnaja* of which twenty-four are in U.S.S.R. libraries.

> Twenty-seven copies of *Triod Postnaja* can be located. The State M. E. Saltykov-Shchedrin Public Library and the State V. I. Lenin Library of the U.S.S.R. each have six copies of *Triod Postnaja* in their collection. The State Historical Museum has four copies; the Lwów State Museum of Ukrainian Art has two copies. One copy is in each of the following institutions: The Central State Archives of Early Russian Historical Records (Moscow); Moscow University Library; Saratov University Library; the Library of the U.S.S.R. Academy of Sciences (Leningrad); State Public Library of the Academy of Sciences of the Ukrainian S.S.R. (Kiev); the Jaroslav Regional Museum (Russia); the Church Historical and Archeological Museum in Sofia (Archeological Museum of the Holy Synod) (Bulgaria); the National Library in Warsaw (Poland); the Pontificio Istituto per gli Studi Orientali Library, Rome. A small fragment of *Triod Postnaja* (four leaves) is in the famous Jagellonian Library in Cracow. There is also a fragment in the Lwów State Scientific Library. Complete copies of the *Triod Postnaja* are not rare.[24]

A full description of *Triod Postnaja* follows:

Tripesnec (Tripyesnyetz/Triod Postnaja/Greek Triodion).
(Cracow: Szwajpolt Fiol, ca. 1491). 2⁰.

314 leaves, 625 printed and three blank pages,—1st and 2nd at the beginning and the last. Printed pages have 30 lines 7.8–7.9 mm in height. The printed area averages 236 x 125 mm., however, some of the lines vary up to 150 mm. A total of 32 sections—quinternions. The last section consists of only four sheets. Signatures—Cyrillic numbers on the first five leaves of the quinternion. Register of sections on the last leaf—314r., 314v.—blank. No foliation. No pagination. Supplementary marks, punctuation marks. Print is black and red. No colophon.

Illuminative features: one knotted frontispiece (woodblock) on leaf 2r. Stylized headpieces and initials throughout the whole book.

Paper with four watermarks three of which are the same as in *Triod Cvetnaja* and one new one.

[24] Nemirovskiĭ, *Nachalo*, p. 146.

TRIOD POSTNAJA

Copy in the Pontificio Istituto per gli Studi Orientali Library in Rome.

Data pertaining to *Triod Postnaja* copy presently in the Library of the Pontifical Oriental Institute in Rome—from the short-title catalogue by Reverend J. Krajcar, S. J.:

2.

Kraków, Svejpolt Fiol; 1491.

2^0; Order of gathering runs: $1–31^{10}$, 32^4, i.e. 314 unnumbered leaves.

First leaf in our copy is signed with number 3 in Cyrillic letter and contains first Ode of the Canon for Sunday of the Pharisee and the Publican. Last seven pages of book contain account of the miraculous defense of Constantinople during the reign of East Roman Emperor Heraclius. Leaf with signature 157 and following unsigned leaf missing. Last leaf with text of gathering 32 is, however, preserved.

Und. 4. Kar. 4. Petkov I. Sven. 77.[25]

This copy has defects. The original flyleaves at the beginning and end of the book are missing, therefore no earlier provenance notes are to be found. The book was rebound and new flyleaves had been added. They contain notations of a later date. On the inner side of the upper cover appears a notation which had been blotted out. On the recto side of the upper flyleaf are a few notations. In the upper part of the leaf written in Cyrillic is the title of the book, place and year of printing.

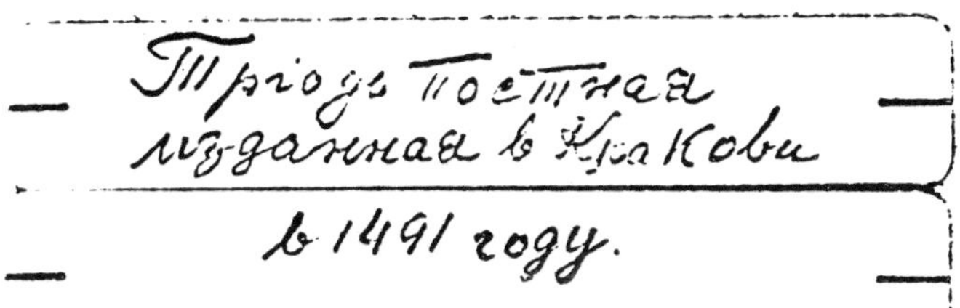

(*Triod Postnaja*, published in Cracow in the year 1491).

Below this on a glued-in slip of paper—a note in Latin:

Pios.
TRIODE (Quadrages. 1491)
Undolski, No. 4

In the lower right section of the leaf the date 27/3/30 and the price R[ubles] 400. No other details. Due to the fact that these notes of dates in both *Triod Cvetnaja* and *Triod Postnaja* are the same except for the last digit (one is a zero and the other is nine), it can be assumed that the discrepancy is in the writing of the digit zero instead of nine, which in the *Triod Cvetnaja* copy is very distinct. Both dates give information when the book was acquired with the sum paid for it.

[25] Krajcar, "Early-Printed Slavic Books . . . ," p. 108.

Very few glosses or notes are to be found within the book. Leaf with signature PSI is the exception having glosses on both the recto and verso sides. In this copy the capital letter which stands for ZH was used as an initial. See leaf ч҃д verso.

The copy is well preserved except for a few missing leaves as stated in the catalogue description. The general appearance of the greater portion of leaves is good, however, some are stained. A few leaves at the end of the book reveal traces of mildew.

The binding is old but not original. Wooden boards are covered with red leather, the clamps are preserved. The covers of the book have traces of insect damage in some places. During the rebinding process, the binder cleverly cut the upper margin thus preserving all the signatures located on the right side of the bottom margin.

Polish Holdings

Data pertaining to Polish holdings of *Triod Postnaja* cited in the *Central Catalogue of Incunabula in Polish Libraries.*

TRIOD'

5398 Triod postnaja. [Cracow, Sveb. Fiol, ante 1491]. 2⁰.

Karataev 4. KJ[Lewicka-Kamińska. Incunabula in the Jagellonian Library. Cracow 1962] 1136. A. Birkenmajer, K. Piekarski: Proof sheets of Szwajpolt Fiol's prints. *Congrès International des Bibliothècaires et des Amis du Livre à Prague 18 VI—13 VII 1926.* K. Heintsch: "Studies regarding Szwajpolt Fiol," Part I. *Annals of the Ossoliński National Institute* Vol. V. 1957 pp. 233–342. N. V. Varbanets, V. I. Lukyanenko: "Slavic Incunabula in the Saltykov-Shchedrin State Public Library in Leningrad." *Kniga*: vol. 2 1960, pp. 196–201. BAL[-E. I. Bobrova: *Catalogue of Incunabula. Academy of Sciences, U.S.S.R.* Leningrad. Moscow, 1963]. 772 (ca 1491). M. Błońska: "Attempt at a New View of the History of Szwajpolt Fiol's Printing Press." *Annals of the National Library.* IV: 1968 pp. 52–62.

Cracow J [Jagellonian Library] (frg.: folia 32a mutilum. 39b, 134a, 137b speciminis loco typis exscripta. Folia 134a, 137b rubro impressa). Warsaw N [Nat. Lib.] (def.).[26]

[26] Kawecka-Gryczowa, *Incunabula . . . ,* p. 921.

5398 Triod' postnaja. [Kraków, Sveb. Fiol, ante 1491]. 2⁰.

Karataev 4. KJ 1136. A. Birkenmajer, K. Piekarski: Korektowe arkusze druków Szwajpolta Fiola. "Congrès International des Bibliothècaires et des Amis du Livre à Prague 18 VI—13 VII 1926." K. Heintsch: Ze studiów nad Szwajpoltem Fiolem. Cz. I. "Rocznik Zakł. Nar. im. Ossolińskich" T. V 1957 pp. 233–342. N. V. Varbanets, V. I. Luk'ianenko: Slavianskie inkunabuly v sobranii Gosudarstvennoj Pulichnoї Biblioteki im. M. E. Saltykova Shchedrina v Leningrade (GPB). "*Kniga*: sb. 2 1960 pp. 196–201. BAL 772 (ca 1491). M. Błońska: Próba nowego spojrzenia na dzieje krakowskiej oficyny Szwajpolta Fiola. "Rocznik Biblioteki Narodowej" IV: 1968 pp. 52–62.

Kraków J (frg.: ff. 32a mutilum, 39b, 134a, 137b speciminis loco typis exscripta. Ff. 134a, 137b rubro impressa). Warszawa N (def.).

Fragment of Triod Postnaja at the Jagellonian Library in Cracow

Data from the Catalogue of the Jagellonian Library Incunabula:

SVEBOLDUS FIOL
Pro Joanne Turzo de Lewocza
1136 [1491?] Triod Postnaja. 2⁰. Frg. The pull of the outer form of sheet 17 and inner form of sheet 69, that is leaves 39v, 134r, 137v, and a strip of the leaf 32r; anopistographe [print on one side] black and red. Compare: BP [Birkenmajer-Piekarski] 1926; E[streicher] XXXI 323; Kar[ataev] 4; E S[treicher] Fiol 59, 5; Heintsch p. 82, footnote 11, table 18; W [Wisłocki, W. Incunabula typographica Bibliothecae Universitatis Jagellonicae Cracoviensis . . . Cracoviae 1900.] 514.
—Inc. 2051 a.[27]

Incunabulum Nr. 1136 is closely related to incunabulum Nr. 1137: see continuation on pp. [240–241.] Both are proof sheets from different books printed on atlas size folio sheets of paper. Description of this very rare incunabulum by Birkenmajer-Piekarski follows:

The first fragment represents one full leaf and a portion of another, both printed only on one side, black and red [as in a final print]. This is the pull of the outer form of sheet number 17 of *Triod Postnaja* (leaf 39v., and a strip of leaf 32r.). There are no differences in the text of this pull and the final print. The second fragment, however, is impressed completely in red ink. On one side there is the inner part of sheet number 69 from *Triod Postnaja* with leaves 134r, and 137v, both slightly clipped from the top. On the pull [proof sheet] letters and words were designated which in the final print were to remain in red, also corrections were made in the text which was to be printed in black. The final print, nonetheless, shows slight differences in comparison with the corrected pull [proof sheet]. On the reverse side [of this fragment] is the pull of the outer form of sheet 67 of *Chasoslovec* [Cracow 1491 in 4⁰] leaves 267r., 168v., 269r., 270v. Only those letters appear on the imprint which in the final print were to be in red—but comparison with the final print shows considerable differences.[28]

Copy of Triod Postnaja *in the Warsaw National Library*

Note regarding this copy:

Except for the general description in the *Central Catalogue of Incunabula in Poland,* no special write-up is devoted to this copy. Information obtained from librarians Eliza Szandorowska and Maria Błońska, as well as from the copy itself studied *in situ,* are the sources of all data presented here.

[27] Anna Lewicka-Kamińska, *Inkunabuły Biblioteki Jagiellońskiej* (Jagellonian Library Incunabula), (Cracow, 1962), pp. 58–59.

[28] Birkenmajer and Piekarski, "Korektowe arkusze druków Szwajpolta Fiola," *Rocznik Biblioteki Narodowej,* IV: 1968, 57.

Catalogue card in English translation.

Triod' Inc. F. 1349

(Library of Przemyśl Chapter)

Triod' Postnaja

(Cracow, Szwajpolt Fiol, ca 1491) 2⁰.

Karataev: description 4.—E[streicher] XXXI 323.

Central Catalogue of Incunabula 5398

Inc. F. 1349—Defect.

When *Triod Postnaja* arrived at the National Library in Warsaw its condition left much to be desired; however, in general it was not as serious as that of *Triod Cvetnaja.* Blank pages in front and at the end of the book are missing. Numerous pages at the beginning and the end were impaired and marred. The unnumbered leaves of quire XXXI corresponding to leaves РНА, РНГ, РНВ, РНД, РНЄ were badly damaged. The first three were torn at the right side only, a fragment of the fourth remained, and the fifth leaf was slightly obliterated. The book was subjected to restoration utilizing a conservation process similar to *Triod Cvetnaja.* The binding of the book is not the original from the the fifteenth century; it is also restored.

Whatever was said previously about *Triod Cvetnaja* inc. no. 1350 regarding the process of renovation should also be applied to *Triod Postnaja,* inc. no. 1349. It would have been desirable to get a report with reference to what had been done during the restoration of the book. Also, it would have been important to have had photographs made before the reconstruction process began.

The first reconstruction leaf of *Triod Postnaja* shows that some markings are at the bottom of the page and in the right-hand margin in the center of the page appears a round stamp with lettering in its circle; both of these markings are undecipherable. A photograph made prior to renovation might have enabled us to decipher these markings as it was possible in the case of *Triod Cvetnaja.*

Approximately one third of the leaves contain marginal notes and glosses in Cyrillic referring to the text of the book. Shorter or longer notes are to be found on the following leaves: 2r, 3r, 6r–v, 7v, 10r, 15r, 16r–v, 17r, 18r, 19r, 20r, 21r, 22r, 23r, 24r, 25r, 26r, 27v, 35v, 37v, 46r, 47r–v, 48r–v, 49r–v, 50r–v, 51r–v, 52r–v, 59r, 60v, 67r, 123v, 171r–v, 218r, 227r, 228r, 229r–v, 230v, 232r–v, 233r, 234r, 236v, 237v, 250r–v, 258r–v, 262r, 275r, 278r–v, 279r–v, 280r, 287r, 288v, 291v, 294r, 300r, 303r, 304r–v, 308r, 309r.

These are only two provenance notes: 1. The most important note in Cyrillic is dated March 30, 1682. It reads as follows:

Во имя отца и сына и с[вя]т[о]го д[у]ха амин. Сию книгу зовемую Триод купил раб [бо]жий благородный Василий Волчишский ватага Волошин ротмистр короля [. . .] з села Местности [?] за отпущение грехов своих и дал за ню золотых 12 [. . .]

до церкви Ковынской до храму Преображениа г[оспод]а б[о]га нашего[. . .]а хто бы важил тую книгу отдалити или д[у]ховный нли [. . .] да будет проклят яко Аріа анафема [. . .] року 1682 м[е]с[я]ца марта дня 30

(In the name of the Father, Son and Holy Spirit, Amen. God's servant the nobleman Vasilii Volchishskiĭ [Volchinskii] Voloshin of the Voloshin branch, captain in the King's cavalry, from the village Mestnost' bought this book called Triod and for the remission of his sins paid 12 gold coins for it and gave it to the Kovno Church of the Transfiguration of our Lord God and whoever would dare to take away this book whether clergymen or [ ] will be cursed as an anathemized Arian the year 1682 month of March day 30).

2. From the middle of the eighteenth century (1756 on leaf 290) is a note in the Latin alphabet which may be either a Polish or Belorussian description of a snowless winter difficult for travelling. This note contributes nothing other than trivial weather information.

Catalogue and accession books of the Greek Catholic Chapter Library in Przemyśl are missing, consequently nothing is available to clarify how and when this book was acquired by the Greek Catholic Chapter in Przemyśl. No provenance notes are to be found anywhere in this matter.

Our study of *Triod Cvetnaja* and *Triod Postnaja* is based on copies presently in the Catholic University Library in Lublin and the National Library in Warsaw. These incunabula were in the possession of the Greek Catholic Chapter Library in Przemyśl up to World War II.

The town of Przemyśl is situated on the river San, 60 miles west of Lwów. First historical notations about this fortified town on the main commercial route to the south appear in 981. This territory was on the borderland between Poland and Ruthenia and its population was mixed.

From the fourteenth century Przemyśl had been an integral part of the Polish Kingdom and obtained a city charter under the terms of the so-called Magdeburg Law in 1389. The city grew in cultural and industrial stature during the following centuries. It was the seat of the Roman and Greek Catholic bishops. Przemyśl was the most western Ruthenian outpost firmly linked politically, economically and culturally with Cracow. The majority of the Ruthenian students and professors at the Jagellonian University were from this area. Close ties with Moldavia in religious matters were established as early as the fifteenth century.

Following the first partition of Poland in 1772 this territory was annexed by Austria in 1773. Przemyśl was returned to Poland in 1918. Up to the outbreak of World War II Przemyśl became, after Lwów, the second most important center of the Uniat Church. The richly endowed Greek Catholic Chapter accumulated 1,400 old manuscripts and prints in libraries that served the Church and the theological seminary as well as the Ruthenian population.

The liquidation of the Uniat Church and Chapter in Przemyśl after World War II was a direct outcome of the Yalta agreement for the gigantic translocation of the population in Central Europe. It was also instrumental in the closing of the Uniat Church libraries which fortunately survived the war but did not fare too well in consequence of the Yalta agreement.

No publication is available to answer the question of what happened to the libraries. A prominent Polish scholar, Maria Błonska, at our request, collected pertinent material which clarified the problem of the fate of the libraries and abolished the rumors that the valuable collection was left without proper care and that most of the collections disintegrated.

Copies of three documents provide sufficient material to give a clear picture of what transpired. Since they are of great value to this research, it is advisable to cite them.

Document Nr. 1. A letter dated August 17, 1946 signed by the Rector of the Catholic University in Lublin:

17 August, 1946

To the Minister of Education in Warsaw.

We have received information, that the Ministry of Education has in its possession the theological library of the Greek Catholic Library and intends to allocate it to a Scientific Institution which is doing research in this field. In this matter our representative was asked whether such books would be needed by the Catholic University.

The Rectorate of the Catholic University in Lublin seeks from the Minister of Education an order authorizing the transfer of the above-mentioned library to the Catholic University in Lublin. The rationale supporting this request is the University's chair of comparative theological studies [for the study of Eastern Christianity] which is the only chair of its kind in Poland. The Institute, due to its geographical location, devotes special attention to the Eastern Christian problems and collects pertinent literature.

Rector

From this letter it appears that as early as the beginning of 1946 the theological collection of the former Greek Catholic (Uniat) Chapter was under the custodianship of local authorities. Then it was placed under the jurisdiction of the Polish Ministry of Education in Warsaw which immediately made an effort to find an appropriate location. And finally, the Catholic University in Lublin responded to this inquiry affirmatively requesting the issuance of the order for transmission and transportation of the collection to Lublin. The reason for this request was the fact that the University had the only existing chair for comparative studies of Eastern Christianity in Poland.

The Catholic University in Lublin received a copy of a letter dated January 21, 1947 from the Ministry of Education in Warsaw to the National Library in Warsaw in January of the following year. The letter contained instructions regarding the disposition and allocation of books from the former Chapter and Theological Seminary of the Greek Catholic Church in Przemyśl. The Catholic University in Lublin was to carry out these instructions.

Document No. 2.
Polish People's Republic
Ministry of Education
No. NDB–3617/46 Warsaw, January 21, 1947

National Library in Warsaw

In regard to the request of the National Library with reference to the allocation of books pertaining to Poland in the library of the former Chapter and Theological Seminary of the Greek Catholic Church in Przemyśl, the Ministry announces it has made efforts at the Ministry of Culture and Arts for the transmission of the complete library collection to the Catholic University in Lublin. After the acceptance of this collection the Catholic University in Lublin shall perform the segregation according to the following plan:

1. Prints (printed matter to the year 1550—to the Jagellonian Library
2. All printed matter pertaining to Poland and the Ukraine up to the eighteenth century inclusive, and
3. All secular printed matter pertaining to Poland and the Ukraine from the nineteenth century to the National Library, which in turn will transmit duplicates in theology (especially the more recent ones) to the library of the Carmelite Order in Przemyśl and to the library of the Roman Catholic Chapter in Przemyśl.
4. The remainder of the collection shall be accepted by the Catholic University in Lublin with the obligation of relinquishing its duplicates in theology to the previously mentioned ecclesiastical libraries in Przemyśl.

[Signature of] Dr. J. Grycz
Director of Libraries

This letter from the Ministry of Education in Warsaw designates the recipients, allocations and the executor of the order. The order was clear and simple, however, unforeseen complications developed. The National Library in Warsaw did not wait for the Catholic University representative from Lublin and took its share from Przemyśl by its own means, however, not without some oversights.

The final processing of the directives from the Ministry of Education is revealed in Document No. 3:

To the Ministry of Education
Department of Libraries

This is to inform you that on September 8, 1947 at 11:00 A.M. upon presentation of the necessary documents, the official in charge gave consent for the transfer of the Greek Catholic Chapter and Theological Seminary Libraries in Przemyśl to the Catholic University in Lublin: later I received the keys to these libraries. [A complete listing appears here of how many persons were employed for how many days, number of freight cars loaded, who worked, among them students of the Pedagogic Lyceum etc.]. The freight cars reached Lublin on September 17. During the day of September 18 these freight cars were unloaded and their contents transported to the Catholic University in Lublin.

During the packing of these books in Przemyśl, I found many manuscripts not taken by the National Library in Warsaw (the stack was one to two meters in height) also museum monuments. I did not take the above mentioned items with me. After the completion of arranging and listing them, I conveyed them to Mr. Leśnik, the Director of the Museum of the Przemyśl Region on September 14.

Representative of the Catholic University in Lublin for the acceptance of Libraries in Przemyśl for the University.

Prof. Doc. Rev. Dr. Bolesław Radomski

Lublin, September 24, 1974

The last document reveals that the acceptance of the libraries had been processed properly and efficiently. It also enlightens one indirectly as to the size of the shipment by the number of freight cars necessary for its transporation. Some manuscripts and museum monuments were left behind. This material was sorted out, arranged and listed. Later it was handed over to Mr. Leśnik, the Director of the Museum of the Przemyśl Region. Thus the Museum in Przemyśl became the fifth recipient of the Greek Catholic Libraries holdings. This report now nullifies all rumors about the destruction and loss of this valuable collection.

Unfortunately there is no information about the catalogues and accession book for these libraries. They would be extremely valuable in establishing details regarding the provenance of books and manuscripts and their heritage. All efforts to locate them are without positive results. It has been determined that neither the Catholic University Library of Lublin nor the Museum in Przemyśl has any of them. However, since the archives of the Przemyśl Greek Catholic Chapter were sent to Warsaw, it is most likely that they were deposited in the National Archives of Contemporary Documents. It would be necessary to verify this supposition. Reverend Ataman who was well acquainted with the holdings of the Chapter Library stated that the Card Catalogue contained a record of 1400 old prints and manuscripts. These are yet to be discovered.

The only source of information regarding some books appeared in the *Catalogue of Church-Slavonic Manuscripts and Books in Cyrillic Located at the Archaeologic-Bibliographical Exhibit,* compiled by A. S. Petrushevich, published in Lwów in 1888.[29] The exhibit commemorated the 300th anniversary of the establishment of the Stavropigijskoe Brotherhood in Lwów.[30] Numerous books and manuscripts from various places, including Przemyśl were brought to Lwów. Among these books we find both *Triod*s, *Cvetnaja* and *Postnaja,* especially mentioned by

[29] A. S. Petrushevich, *Katalog tserkovno-slovenskikh rukopiseĭ i staropechatnykh knig kirillovskogo pis'ma, nakhodiashchikhsia na Arkheologichesko-bibliograficheskoĭ vystavtsev Stavropigiĭskom zavedenii* (Catalogue of Church Slavonic Manuscripts and Books in Cyrillic at the Archaeologic-Bibliographical Exhibit in the Stavropigiiski Institution, (Lvov, 1888).

[30] Historical data however are as follows: the Ruthenian Brotherhood was established in Lwów as early as 1453 at the Orthodox Wallachian Church. In 1784 it was confirmed as Greek Catholic Stavropigiĭskiĭ Institute.

Petrushevich. The catalogue verifies in print that in 1888 these books were in the Przemyśl Greek Catholic Chapter Library. Excerpts from page 24:

CRACOW.
About 1491. *Triod postnaja,* without giving place and year of printing, impressed with Cracow type, most likely somewhere in Hungarian Rus' perhaps in the Grushov monastery. Folio, 313 leaves.
Library of Przemyśl Cathedral, incomplete copy.
About 1491. *Triod cvetnaja.* Without giving place and year of edition, printed with Cracow type, somewhere in the Transcarpathian Rus'. Folio 362 leaves.
Library of Przemyśl Episcopal Cathedral. Incomplete copy.[31]

In conclusion this study confirms that solicitous care was given to this rare and irreplaceable collection; also it informs us of the locations where they could be found. It should be emphasized that both copies of *Triod* in the National Library in Warsaw and the copy at the Catholic University Library in Lublin are of the Uniat Church provenance, *sui generis* historical depository.

III. CHASOSLOVEC (Chasoslovetz)

Chasoslovec (presently known as "Chasoslov" in Russia) was the third book published by Fiol. It was a handy prayer book printed in quarto for complete day and night services and also often used as a primer for teaching purposes. *Chasoslovec* was executed shortly after *Triod Postnaja* or perhaps even printed simultaneoulsy. Indication of this is the proofreading page from each book—*Triod* and *Chasoslovec*—on one folio size sheet.

The first known leaf is the third. At the top of the recto side impressed in red is the same head ornament, woodcut vignette, angular knotty flag as in the previous books. V. I. Lukianenko in her description of Cyrillic incunabula at the Saltykov-Shchedrin Library stated that the knotty flag in *Chasoslovec* was printed upside down.[32] Beneath the head ornament, as in both *Triod*s, the beginning of the Incipit

[31] Petrushevich, *Katalog tserkovno-slovenskikh rukopiseĭ* . . . p. 24.

Краковъ.

Около 1491 г. Тріодь постная, безъ означенія мѣста и года печати, напеч. Краковск. типами, кажется, гдѣ то на Угорской Руси, не въ Грушовскомъ ли монастырѣ. Въ лист. 313 л.
Библ. Перемышльского Собора, неполный эксемплярь.

Около 1491 г. Тріодъ цвѣтная. Безъ означенія мѣста и года изданія, напечат. Краковскими типами, гдѣ то въ Закарпатской Руси. Въ лист. 362 л.
Библ. Перемышл. епископского Собора. Неполн. экс.

The author of the catalogue strongly supports the old erroneous theory that the type was produced in Cracow, but the printing itself was done in some undisclosed place in Subcarpathian Rus'.

[32] N. V. Varbanets and V. I. Lukianenko, "Slavianskiye inkunabuly v sobranii Gosudarstvennoĭ publichnoĭ biblioteki im. M. E. Saltykova-Shchedrina v Leningrade" (Slavonic Incunabula in the M. E. Saltykov-Shchedrin State Public Library in Leningrad), *Kniga-issledovaniia i materialy,* (Moscow, 1960), II, 198.

(also printed in red) gives the title and the name of the author. Caption letters 3 lines in height form the decorative "clichéd" line called "*vyaz'*" commencing the text.

Only two knotted initials: "R" (leaf 7 verso) and "T" (leaf 8 verso) are known from *Triod Cvetnaja.* Floral initials are also rarely used. Captions and capital letters, however, were used extensively in both *Triod*s (both smaller size 12 mm. high, from specially prepared sets of type for print in quarto, and larger ones—18 to 25 mm. in folio). The use of color was predominant in the illumination etc., and cinnabar is distributed lavishly in the text to facilitate legibility.

Chasoslovec consists of 48 sections composed of 2 sheets each folded twice giving together 8 leaves quarto size. Total number 384 leaves—768 pages. According to Karataev 767 pages were printed, one—the last page 768th was blank. Nemirovskiĭ states that 382 leaves were printed, stipulating that the last two leaves were blank; however, in none of the known copies have those blank leaves been preserved. Having no access to a copy with the last printed pages we cannot make any determination, especially since the only copy outside the U.S.S.R. is presently in the Pontificio Istituto Orientale in Rome (defective—ending with leaf 377). Consequently, there are no means of verifying the authenticity of Karataev's or Nemirovskiĭ's statements.

Marking of sections was very simple. The printer marked only the first leaf of the sheet that had been folded twice. The second twice-folded sheet was inserted into the first with the signature on the first quarter. This gave what some scholars call strange or peculiar marking, because only the first and third leaf in the section had signatures with the other six leaves left unmarked. This method appears to be logical and economical. Fiol printed the entire sheet which had not been cut in quarto until after it was folded and sewn together. One number for the whole sheet was enough to facilitate the process of binding.

Section	Leaf No.	Signature Cyril.	Signature Arab.	Section	Leaf No.	Signature Cyril.	Signature Arab.	Section	Leaf No.	Signature Cyril.	Signature Arab.
I.	1	а҃	1	II.	9	г҃	3	III.	17	є҃	5
	2				10				18		
	3	б҃	2		11	д҃	4		19	ѕ҃	6
	4				12				20		
	5				13				21		
	6				14				22		
	7				15				23		
	8				16				24		

On leaf 383v. is the Register of Sections with the following heading:

These are the numbers to this book—how quires should be arranged from the beginning to the end. One quire following the other in succession to the end.[33]

On the attached copy of leaf 383v. with Register of Sections errors in marking signatures are emphasized. They are the following:

Nr. 27—  was used twice
Nr. 72— is missing

Nr. 55—  was used twice, first time in the right place, second time as Nr. 85.
Nr. 88— is missing

Nr. 100—  following Nr. 90 is placed out of consecutive numeration

Nevertheless the last forty-eighth section is correctly marked with numbers 95 and 96. Forty-eight quires, each with two signatures starting with number 1 and ending correctly with number 96, indicate that in spite of all shortcomings the method worked.

Following the Register is the printer's device and colophon on leaf 384 recto. The colophon gives place: Cracow; country and ruler; Poland, King Casimir; printer and his origin; Szwajpolt Fieol, German from Franconia; and year: 1491.

In the colophon, and for that matter, throughout the entire book capital letters were used sparingly. Surnames, names, names of towns and countries and the term for the Christmas holyday were not capitalized. Punctuation marks were used properly and sentences marked distinctly, although print within the sentences is continuous without spacing between words. This could and has caused misinterpretation of meaning. Thus, Estreicher created a man named "Frank" by misunderstanding that the term referred to Franconia.[34]

It should be noted that the publishing date of the books in Fiol's colophon—the year 1491—is given according to the Christian era, from the birth of Christ, and not according to the Byzantine era "from the creation of the world," which was then used in Muscovy and some other Orthodox countries.

The colophon in *Chasoslovec* is printed in seven lines. Language: contemporary Belorussian used in the Chancery of the Grand Duchy of Lithuania. The translation of the colophon follows: "This book was accomplished in the famous city of Cracow during the reign of the great Polish King Casimir. And was executed by a

[33] Transcription of Old Church Slavonic according to *Old Church Slavonic Grammar,* pp. 16–17: č—ch (church); ę—nasalized e; ě—ie; ž—zh (azure); št—shch; š—sh. abbreviation marks.

[34] Karol Estreicher, "Günther Zainer . . . ," pp. 207–211.

ѐгдапрїидетьвъславѣбжествасвоѐгосъ
всѣмистымиангглысвоимиглаашеи. сѫ
нѣщиивъздестсащїи. иженеимѫсѧсъмрти
въкоусити. дондежевидѧтьцртїебожїе
пришедшеевъсилѣ:~

сиѧ, тро. пославословиивелицѣ. вне
сеже гли, ѐгдаѐ гла а г е з,

Д неспсенїевсегомира. поевъскршагоизь
гроба, началникажизни. хабанашего ра
зрѫшивосъмртьипобѣдѫдана. мирьи
велїюмлть:~ асе гли ѐгдаѐгла в д ѕ и:·

В ъскрсьотгроба, ижзырастръза. разрѫ
шилъесиотсоужеиїессъмртигри. ивсѧотсѣ
неприазненыиизбавль. гависебеапло
мьсвоимь, ипославыихьнапро
повѣдь. итѣмимирьсвои
подавселеннѣи. ѐдине
мнсогомлтиве:~

та сокте ниа исопу

Chasoslovec. Fiol. Cracow, 1491. Leaf 383 r. Wedged shaped ending of liturgical text.

Cracow citizen, Szwajpolt Fieol, from Germany, of German extraction, a Frank. The book was completed birth in the year of fourteen hundred ninety and one after Christ's.

The illustration and short description of printer's mark appears on the following page.

Compared to Fiol's first two books, the *Chasoslovec* reveals a degree of typographical improvement which began with *Triod Postnaja.* The lines are straight, both margins are more uniform and the type appears more distinct because of added space between sentences. Captions and capital letters in the text are smaller than in the previously printed books and in proportion to the size of the book, which was printed in quarto. Mastery in typographical technique is shown in the ending of the liturgical text of *Chasoslovec.* On leaf 383r. type ornament is set with finesse in a wedge-shaped column using both colors to emphasize the contents. (See the illustration on p. 236.)

Chasoslovec is a liturgical book containing the unchangeable parts of the daily church offices; the portions of the ecclesiastical office extending throughout the entire year. There were two types—editions actually—of *Chasoslovec,* a short version called the *kratkiĭ* and a longer one (covering more services and including the psalms) called the *velikiĭ.* Fiol's *Chasoslovec* was a *velikiĭ.* The contents of *Chasoslovec* is given very thoroughly by Karataev.[35]

Like *Triod Postnaja, Chasoslovec* was also rediscovered in 1821 by a Polish scholar, J. S. Bandtkie, through a proof sheet found in a lining of another contemporary incunabulum. Soon (as in the case of *Triod Cvetnaja* and *Postnaja*) many copies of *Chasoslovec* were found in Polish, Lithuanian, Belorussian, Ukrainian and Russian territories. At present all of them, except for one copy and one fragment, are within the boundaries of the U.S.S.R.

Nemirovskiĭ located twenty-five copies and two fragments of *Chasoslovec*:

> We established the location of twenty-five copies of the Cracow *Chasoslov* of 1491. Only one copy is beyond the borders of the U.S.S.R. Besides this we are obliged to mention two fragments preserved in different places: one in the U.S.S.R., and one in Poland. The richest holdings are the State Historical Museums and the State M. E. Saltykov-Shchedrin Library. In each of their collections there are five of the Cracow *Chasoslov.* In the State V. I. Lenin Library of the U.S.S.R. are four copies of the 1491 *Chasoslov*; the Central State Archive of Old Russian Historical Records (Moscow) and the Saratov University Library have two copies each. In the Lwów Museum of Fine Arts is a copy with 293 leaves, also an incomplete copy with the leaves partly fastened together; partly with loose leaves in paper envelopes. One copy of the 1491 *Chasoslov* is located in the Central Scientific Library, Ukr.S.S.R. Academy of Sciences, the Library of the Academy of Sciences of the Lithuanian S.S.R., M. Gorkiĭ State Scientific Library in Odessa, the

[35] Karataev, *Opisanie slaviano-russkikh knig . . . ,* pp. 6–7.

Докончана бысиѧ книга оу великомь гра
дѣ оу кракове. при державѣ великаго коро
лѧ полскаго казимира. и докончана бы мѣ
щанином ѿ краковьскымь швайполтомь,
фѣоль, из нѣмець немецкого родоу,
франкь. и скончаша сѧ по божиемь наро
жениѥ. аі сътъ. девѧтьдесѧт и а лѣто.

Chasoslovec. Fiol. Cracow, 1491. (State Public Library in Leningrad). Leaf 384 recto. Printer's mark of Fiol's printing office and colophon. Monograms S and V in two upper corners are initials of Sveybold Viol. The ribbon around the Cracow coat of arms has inscription "z Krakowa" meaning "from Cracow." In the two lower corners are two identical printer's devices. Colophon of *Chasoslov* is set in 7 lines.

Moscow State University Library, and the Pontificio Istituto per gli Studi Orientali Library, Rome.[36]

A complete description of the *Chasoslovec* follows:

Chasoslovec. /Chasoslovetz/ Greek: Horologion/.

Cracow. Szwajpolt Fiol, 1491. 4^0

384 leaves, 763 printed pages and 5 blanks, the 1st, 2nd, 3rd and 4th at the beginning and the last one—764th (leaf 384v.). Printed pages have 19 lines, 7.8–7.9 mm in height. The printed area averages 147 x 104 mm., some lines, however, measure up to 112 mm. in length. There is a total of 48 sections—quaternions. Signatures: Cyrillic numbers in lower right corner of the first and third leaves of the quaternions. Register of sections on leaf 383v. No pagination. Supplementary marks, punctuation marks. The print is black and red.

Illuminative features: woodblock frontispiece on the first printed page as in Fiol's other books. Three imprints from two woodblock initials. Stylized head-pieces and smaller initials throughout the whole book. On leaf 384r. a woodblock print presenting the coat of arms of the city of Cracow with printer's mark as a decorative element to the colophon appearing beneath it.

Paper with three different watermarks, two of them identical with those used in both *Triod*s.

CHASOSLOVEC

Copy in the Pontificio Istituto per gli Studi Orientali Library in Rome

Data in reference to this copy prepared by Reverend J. Krajcar, S.J. in the Catalogue of Early Printed Slavic Books:

1.

Krakow, Svejpolt Fiol, 1491.

4^0, 382 unnumbered leaves. (See Kar. and an article on Slavic Incunabula in *Kniga* II, 1960, p. 197). 48 gatherings, 8 leaves each except for last of only 6.

Our copy begins with fol. 9 (100th verse of Ps. 118, midnight service), ends with fol. 377 (*Stikhiry na stikhovne,* Tone 6, matins on Monday). Also missing ff. 15, 16, 367.

Und. 2, Kar. 2, Petrov 2, Str.-Toł. I, Sven. 162, Mil. I.[37]

The copy is a defect with missing front and back leaves also some within the book as noted in the catalogue description. The preserved leaves in the book are generally in good condition; those damaged are patched with white paper and the missing texts, words and letters are handwritten inserts. Leaf 69 is mounted with white paper. There is an inscription but illegible due to the cut off margins.

[36] Nemirovskiĭ, *Nachalo,* p. 124.

[37] Krajcar, "Early-Printed Slavic Books . . . ," p. 108.

Provenance notes: The original flyleaves are missing therefore no early notes. Relatively new inscriptions are on the cover and flyleaf. On the inner side of the upper cover is the Cyrillic inscription: Krakovskiĭ Chasoslov, 1491 [Cracow Chasoslov, 1491]. On the verso side of the first flyleaf the number 415-1-22 appears to be the Institute marking. There is also a glued-in piece of paper with a handwritten note in Latin:

Pios.
Horologion, 1491
Undolskij. Number 2.

The binding of this copy needs special attention. It is bound in off-white linen cloth, and the format is smaller than quarto. This is due to the cutting off of the upper margin and trimming of the right-hand margin. The bottom margin was not cut or trimmed, therefore signatures of quires were generally preserved. The binding is quite recent.

Upon closer study of this copy in Rome, it was possible to notice a few more capital letters used as initials in addition to those presented while describing *Triod Cvetnaja* (see p. 171).

The provenance of all three of Fiol's books in the Pontifical Oriental Institute in Rome cannot be traced in detail because some were acquired after the revolution in Russia and it is difficult to determine their previous whereabouts. Most incunabula collected in the Institute were donated; some were purchased. As to Fiol's prints Reverend J. Krajcar, S.J. author of the short-title catalogue states:

> Because the register of accessions was introduced as late as 1927, ten years after the foundation of the Institute, it is often impossible to trace the manner in which some old books were acquired. This holds for the three incunabula printed in Cracow in 1491 or earlier. . . . A fair number of books of West Russian presses were bought from the antiquarians of Lwów and Vilna; the National Ukrainian Museum of Lwów also sold several duplicates to the Institute.[38]

Polish Holdings

Data pertaining to Polish holdings of *Chasoslovec* cited in the *Central Catalogue of Incunabula in Polish Libraries.*

CHASOSLOVEC (Chasoslovetz).
1446 Chasoslovec, Cracow, Sveb. Fiol, 1491. 2°.
E[streicher] XIV 550. Karataev 6. KJ [Lewicka-Kamińska] 1137. A. Birkenmajer, K. Piekarski: Proof sheets of Szwajpolt Fiol's prints, in: *Congrès International des Bibliothécaires et des Amis du Livre à Prague.* 18 VI-13 VII 1926.

38 Krajcar, "Early-Printed Slavic Books . . . ," pp. 105-106.

Cracow J/frg.: ff. 267r., 269r., 270v., Plagula, *speciminis loco typis rubro descripta*/.[39]

Data in reference to the above fragment are based on information from the Jagellonian Library Incunabula catalogue. It covers both sides of the same sheet, on one side is a pull (proof sheet) from *Triod Postnaja,* on the other from *Chasoslovec,* under two different catalogue numbers 1136 and 1137. Incunabulum 1136 as closely related to incunabulum 1137 should be simultaneously discussed. Data given presently will refer only to *Chasoslovec* to avoid repetition.

To avoid misunderstanding the sign 2⁰ used in both catalogues needs to be clarified. *Chasoslovec* was printed in quarto (4⁰). Cataloguers took only size of the paper used for the proofreading into consideration; therefore, describing it as in folio.

Data in reference to the fragment of *Chasoslovec* in the Jagellonian Library Catalogue. Incunabulum nr. 1137:

1491 *Chasoslovec.* 2⁰ Frg. Proof sheets of the outer form of the 67th quire, that is leaves; 267r., 268v., 269r., 270v., only of those letters that in the final print were to be in red. Trial imprint done in red on the reverse side of the sheet contains similar pull of leaves 134r., and 137v., of *Triod Postnaja.*
Compare with BP [Birkenmajer-Piekarski] 1926 and incunabulum nr. 1136; E[streicher] XIV 550; Kar. 6; E[streicher] Fiol 56, 2; W[isłocki] 514.—Inc. 2051b.[40]

This fragment—the earliest one of Fiol's prints—was discovered in Poland by Jerzy Samuel Bandtkie about 1821. It was found in the binding of an Italian incunabulum: "Abbanus Petrus de Abbano. *Conciliator differentiarum philosophorum* etc. Venecis, impr. Herbert de Selgenstat. 1483. Hein Nr. 6." This binder's volume was done in Poland about 1493. A thorough investigation and description was presented in 1926 at the Congrés International des Bibliothécaires et des Amis du Livre held in Prague from June 28 to July 3, by two Polish scholars, Aleksander Birkenmajer and Kazimierz Piekarski.[41]

IV. OSMOGLASNIK (Oktoikh—Gk. Oktoechos).

Osmoglasnik, a folio size volume, was in all probability the last book printed by

[39] Kawecka-Gryczowa, *Incunabula . . . ,* p. 244.
[40] Lewicka-Kamińska, *Inkunabuły Biblioteki Jagiellońskiej,* p. 59.
1491 Časoslovec. 2. Frg. Próbne odbicie zewnętrznej formy 67 arkusza tj. kart: 267a, 268b, 269a, 270b, tylko tych liter, które w czystodruku miały być czerwone. Odbicie próbne wykonano w druku czerwonym na odwrocie karty 134a i 137b takiegoż odbicia *Triod Postnaja,* por. BP 1926 i wyżej poz. 1136; E XIV 550; Kar 6; E. Fiol. 56, 2; W 514,—*Inc. 2051b*
[41] Birkenmajer and Piekarski, "Korektowe arkusze druków Szwajpolta Fiola," II, 57–58.

Доконьчана бꙑсиѧ книга оу великомь градѣ оу
краковѣ при державѣ великаго королѧ полского
казимира. И доконьчана бꙑ мѣщанином краковь
скꙑмь швайполтомь, фѣоль, изъ нѣмець не
мецкого родоу, франкь. И скончаша по божием
нарожениемь. ДI сътъ девѧтьдесѧт на лѣто.

Osmoglasnik. Fiol. Cracow. 1491.
Printer's mark of Fiol's printing office. Colophon identical in text with Czasoslow, but slightly different in topographical setting, having only 6 lines.

The Incipit of *Osmoglasnik* revealing the name of the author and title of the book: "S Bohom poczynajem osmohlasnik tworenie prepodobnaho otca naszeho Joana Damaskyna w subotu weczer na hospody, etc." "With God we begin the Oktoich, a book by Our Blessed Father Ivan Damaskin . . . ." [According to Golowatzkij, *op. cit.*, p. 428.]

Fiol. The first page is blank, on the second page [leaf 1v.] is the illustration—the Crucifixion, the same that recently had been found in *Triod Cvetnaja.* There is no printer's mark beneath the frontispiece.

On leaf 2r. at the top is the same knotty vignette as in both *Triod*s. Beneath it, as in all other prints, is the first stylized and clichéd line of the Incipit molded in a "Vyaz'," as the vignette impressed in cinnabar. This first printed page is also illuminated with the knotted initial "V," seven lines in height, a unique woodcut especially prepared for *Osmoglasnik* and not repeated in any other book. The entire page is colorful with cinnabar used in the text.

No other knotted initials are found in *Osmoglasnik.* Lukianenko, who studied all four Fiol prints, determined that besides the one knotted initial "V" there also were used: "seven other initials of simple design slightly different from the minuscule letter."[42]

Lukianenko when later describing decorative elements in *Triod Cvetnaja* believed that it was printed after *Osmoglasnik.* She mentioned that next to the thirteen knotted initials there were used: "Few initials of simple design impressed from the same woodblocks which were used in *Osmoglasnik.*"[43] This would lead one to believe that the five floral initials used in *Triod Cvetnaja* (presented by this author when describing illumination of the print) were used in *Osmoglasnik* as well as in all of the other Fiol books. Having no access to the original books we must rely in this instance solely on Lukianenko's statement until such time when a study of the original texts will be available.

According to Nemirovskiĭ three lines and sometimes also two lines in height caption and capital letters were used extensively as initials—especially the letters "B," "V," "K," "R," "S," with some variations because of differences in duplicated woodcuts.

All captions of parts, chapters and paragraphs are formed in "*vyaz*" and as initials printed in cinnabar. This is all *Osmoglasnik* has for illumination unless the printer's mark located at the end of the book could also be considered a decorative element.

Unfortunately none of the preserved copies of *Osmoglasnik* contains the colophon. The above is a facsimile of the Wrocław copy which perished during World War II. The printer's mark is situated above the colophon similar to that in *Chasoslovec,* but not identical. Technically the woodcut is as good as that in *Chasoslovec.* (See p. 242.)

The penultimate page [leaf 169r.] as in all other Fiol prints contains a Register of Sections. Each section consists of 8 leaves [4 sheets folded once]. Signatures are located on the first 4 leaves, the other 4 are unmarked. This was the most advanced system of marking signatures commonly accepted by printers. Section I has only

[42] Varbanets and Lukianenko, "Slavianskie inkunabuly . . . ," p. 198.
[43] *Ibid.,* p. 199.

three numbers—1, 2, 3, starting on leaf 2r. because the first page [leaf 1r.] was blank. All other twenty sections [II–XXI] have the first four leaves with signatures. The last four leaves are unmarked. Altogether there are 172 leaves—344 pages, of which 337 are printed and 7 blank, the first and the last six.

The technical level of the printing is as good as in *Chasoslovec*. Proportions of the width to the length of the column are more harmonious in comparison to those in the *Triod*s which are slightly elongated. The printer tried to keep the line straight and of the same length; nevertheless, some were too long and the edges so uneven it was necessary to correct these irregularities.

V. I. Lukianenko determined two variants among the copies of *Osmoglasnik* presently in the M. E. Saltykov-Shchedrin Public Library in Leningrad. In the fourth quire, leaves one and eight [first sheet of the quaternion] variant "A" has an uneven right margin while in variant "B" the right margin is uniform and even, almost like the left margin. This is only a typographical improvement. In her article Lukianenko presents the same page from both variants without deriving any conclusion.[44]

The comparative illustration shows a professional awareness of the typesetter in the variant "B" copy. This differs from the two variants of *Triod Cvetnaja* mentioned on p. 172 where corrections on three sheets were made but with no typographical improvements. Thus words and sentences were changed; but the uneven right margin remained uncorrected as originally set. This indicates that *Triod Cvetnaja* was set by an inexperienced craftsman and implies that it was executed before *Osmoglasnik*.

The contents of Fiol's *Osmoglasnik* was described by Karataev.[45] The definition of the book given by Cross:

> The *Osmoglasnik* is a liturgical book which contains the variable parts of the service from the first Sunday after Whitsun until the tenth Sunday before Easter. Since these variable parts recur every eight weeks in the same order, only eight sets of tones, one for each week, are provided, hence the name (Gk. *Oktoechos* = The book of eight tones).[46]

Osmoglasnik constitutes the service book used by the lector and choir. It contains the canons and hymns for Little and Great Vespers, Compline, Midnight Service, Matins, the hymn for the day (*Troparion*), and the Collect hymn (*Kondiakon*). All Byzantine Church music is based upon eight melodies or tones. Each week, beginning with Pentecost, is assigned a tone with the following week taking the next tone. The book is printed in two volumes. The first part, Odes I–IV, is

[44] *Ibid.*, p. 198.

[45] Karataev, *Osmoglasnik 1491 g. napechatannyǐ w Krakove kirillovskimi bukvami* (Osmoglasnik of 1491, Printed in Cracow with Cyrillic Type), (St. Petersburg, 1876).

[46] Cross, *The Oxford Dictionary of the Christian Church*, p. 975.

called Osmoglasnik pervoglasnik; the second part containing Odes V–VIII is called Osmoglasnik petoglasnik. *Osmoglasnik* may also be condensed into one volume, as was Fiol's print, and called *Paraklitik*.

According to Nemirovskiĭ only six copies of *Osmoglasnik* still exist, and all are now in the U.S.S.R. He writes:

> We are able to locate six copies and one small fragment which has not been described up until the present time. There are two copies of the Cracow *Oktoich* in both the M. E. Saltykov-Shchedrin Public Library in Leningrad and in the State Historical Museum in Moscow. The State V. I. Lenin Library of the U.S.S.R. in Moscow has one copy and also a small fragment consisting of two leaves. A copy discovered in 1965 in Arkhangelsk is now in the Scientific Library of Leningrad State University. It is the most complete.[47]

Few copies of *Osmoglasnik* survive probably because few were actually published by Fiol, due to the closing of the shop by the Inquisition during the printing process. Indirectly, this also supports our contention that it was the last of Fiol's prints published.

Nemirovskiĭ, of course, concludes that Fiol's *Osmoglasnik* has much in common with the *Osmoglasnik* manuscripts produced in Moscow, Pskov and Novgorod in the second half of the fifteenth century, but has failed to take into consideration other Slavic *Osmoglasnik*s produced during that era. Also, he tends to forget his own statement that the book was called *Shestodnev* in Russian territories. In Belorussia, Ukraine and in the South, *Shestodnev* was the translation of the *Hexameron* by St. Basil the Great, and has nothing in common with the title *Osmoglasnik*.

Although six copies of *Osmoglasnik* are preserved, nonetheless the full description of this book was possible only through the "ghost copy" of *Osmoglasnik*, previously the property of the City Library in Breslau-Wrocław, which mysteriously disappeared during World War II.[48] All six copies are defective due to the missing first leaf containing the illustration and the missing last leaf bearing the colophon and printer's mark. Whatever we learned about the missing leaves was from the Wrocław copy which eyewitnesses claim was in excellent condition.

There are many different descriptions of *Osmoglasnik*. A short summary is given of those who contributed most and their work should be considered valuable reference material:

1. Jerzy Samuel Bandtkie. *De primis Cracoviae in arte typographica incunabulis. Cracoviae* 1812.

Bandtkie was the first scholar who discovered, located, identified and gave a

[47] Nemirovskiĭ, *Nachalo*, pp. 79–80.

[48] Since some artistic items lost during World War II have emerged lately, the hope remains that someday this valuable copy will also be rediscovered.

short description of the Wrocław copy of *Osmoglasnik*. It was primarily the property of the cloister of the Catholic Elizabethan Sisters (followers of Saint Elizabeth, 1207–1231) who were devoted to charity. When Bandtkie visited Wrocław the book was in the possession of the Rehdiger Library. Later the collection became part of the City of Wrocław Library. The balance of the collection was allocated to the University Library after World War II.

2. Adam Junosza Rościszewski (1774–1844). Spis XXX foliatów . . . (List of XXX volumes . . .) Manuscript number 2443—III in the library of the Ossoliński National Institute in Wrocław.

The study by Rościszewski was not made *in situ* but was based on a facsimile delivered by a Bohemian professor of Breslau (Wrocław) University, Dr. Jan Evangelist Purkyne. Among many details discussed which will be more explicitly defined later, two are not mentioned by anyone else.

Primo: he presented a reproduction from the facsimile of an inscription impressed on the cover of the book. It represents complicated and not easily decipherable abbreviations forming a "*vyaz*." Rościszewski states that the great authority in these matters, the canon of the Przemyśl Diocese, O. G. Ławrowski, deciphered this inscription (composed in sophisticated abbreviations) as "Sije Swiatłomu Joannu Predteczy."

The second item is a provenance note some place in the book—most difficult to decipher from the facsimile. The only thing that can be established is that the inscription is in the Latin alphabet.

3a. Karol Estreicher (1827–1908). "Günther Zainer i Świętopełk Fiol." (Günther Zainer and Świętopełk Fiol). *Biblioteka Warszawska.* Vol. III, pp. 199–220. Warsaw 1867. Also reprint.

b. Karol Estreicher. *Bibliografia Polska XV–XIX wieku* (Polish Bibliography of the XV–XIX Centuries). Cracow, 1875 and continuation until 1908. Vol. I–XXI. Data regarding Fiol—Vol. XIV, Cracow 1896, p. 550. Vol. XV, Cracow, 1897, pp. 22–23.

c. Stanisław Estreicher (1869–1939). *Polish Bibliography*—Vol. XXI–XXXIII. Data regarding Fiol, Vol. XXXI. pp. 322–323. Information by Stanisław Estreicher is not based on examination of the Wrocław copy.

The next scholar after Bandtkie who based his study of *Osmoglasnik* on the Wrocław copy was Karol Estreicher. For many years his works were the main source of knowledge about Fiol's prints. The description of *Osmoglasnik,* especially the first and last leaves (which are missing in all preserved copies) discloses the true substance of what was there. Many other scholars had the opportunity but none of them revealed anything about the elaborately executed illumination of the Crucifixion and other decorative elements.

The details of multicolor rubrication given by Estreicher could be explained in the same manner as the coloring of the initial "V" on leaf 2r. previously discussed. The Wrocław copy of *Osmoglasnik* never left Central Europe. There is no mention of any Cyrillic provenance notes or glosses on its margins. This was a rare book among Latin and Polish collections in the Catholic church and monastic libraries. Since the original book was printed only in two colors, cinnabar and black, to improve its appearance the multicolor additional decoration was applied in the Western manner and style. Estreicher was not aware this copy was exceptional. In his description (not being familiar with other copies) he presented what he had seen without any reservations.

The newly discovered *Triod Cvetnaja* in Rumania containing the illustration of the Crucifixion identical with that in *Osmoglasnik* proves that Estreicher actually studied the Wrocław *Osmoglasnik in situ,* however, his description can be applied only to that one copy.

Estreicher was a prominent bibliographer, therefore his notes from this point of view are trustworthy and correct. He was not however, a Slavic philologist. In this capacity Fiol's books were better presented by Karataev and Golowatzkiĭ. Estreicher's main contribution, in addition to his collection of bibliographical data, was the awakening of interest in Fiol's Cyrillic incunabula among Slavic scholars.

In 1874 the Wrocław copy was taken to St. Petersburg to reconstruct those missing leaves from copies which were in Russian libraries. What method was used for these reproductions is uncertain. Some mention facsimile, others lithography and still others photographs. It is characteristic that having such an opportunity no efforts were made to copy the whole book (which was like new), and no complete description of this special copy was made. After the book was returned to Wrocław, four works appeared devoted to Fiol's incunabula, by two prominent scholars:

Jakow Fiodorowitsch Golowatzkij, "Sweipolt Fiol und seine Kyrillische Buchdruckerei in Krakau vom Jahre 1491." *Sitzungsberichte der Kaiserlichen Akademie der Wissenschaften zu Wien,* Vol. 83 (Wien, 1876); three studies by Ivan Karataev: *Opisanie slaviano-russkikh knig napechatannykh kirillovskimi bukvami. 1491–1730. I ot 1491 po 1600* (Description of Slavic-Russian Books Printed with Cyrillic Type. One from 1491 to 1600) (Sanktpeterburg, 1878; *Opisanie slaviano-russkikh knig napechatannykh kirillovskimi bukvami. T. I ot 1491 po 1652* (Description of Slavic-Russian Books Printed in Cyrillic Type. Vol. I from 1491 to 1652). (Sanktpeterburg, 1883); and, *Osmoglasnik 1491 g. napechatannyj v Krakove kirillovskimi bukvami* (Osmoglasnik of 1491 Printed in Cracow with Cyrillic Type), (Saint Petersburg, 1876).

Osmoglasnik was given much attention by both scholars in the cited works. Their research, however, was not based on direct studies *in situ* of the Wrocław copy. Golowatzkij, who published the first monograph about Fiol's life and achievements, used material given to him by H. Nehring, professor at Wrocław University. His description of *Osmoglasnik* is considered the most accurate since he also took advantage of Estreicher's findings.

Karataev, a prominent Slavic scholar, in his description of *Osmoglasnik* used the facsimile or lithograph from the Wrocław copy. His presentation of Fiol's incunabula is regarded as the best despite its being outdated. This refers to *Osmoglasnik* only, since with its disappearance from the Wrocław Library, Estreicher, Golowatzkij and Karataev are the only sources of information about the all-important first and last leaves of this book.

A complete description of Fiol's *Osmoglasnik* follows:

OSMOGLASNIK; Oktoich; Ochtai. (Gk. Octoechos).

Szwajpolt Fiol. Cracow. 1491. 2⁰.

172 leaves, 337 printed and 7 blank pages, the first page at the beginning and the last six. Printed pages have 25 lines 7.8–7.9 mm in height. The printed area averages 195 x 120 mm however some lines are up to 135 mm. There is a total of twenty-two sections, quaternions. Signatures in the lower right corner of the first four leaves of each section. The first section consists of only three leaves. Index of quaternions on leaf 169r. No pagination. Supplementary marks, punctuation marks. Print is black and red. Colophon on the last page.

Illuminative features: one woodblock illustration, Crucifixion on leaf 1v. One knotted frontispiece—vignette on leaf 2r. One big (7 lines in height) knotted initial "V" on leaf 2r. Printer's mark on the last page above the colophon. Stylized headpieces and lombards throughout the whole book.

Two known variants of *Osmoglasnik,* A and B exist. Changes on leaf 8 of section 4. Technical improvements were made in variant B to even out the right margin.

The paper contains seventeen watermarks, all different from those used in other prints.

PSALTIR SLEDOVANNAIA (?)

Some Eastern Slavic scholars list a fifth book purported to have been printed by Fiol. It is called the *Psaltir Sledovannaia* and means Psalter with Chasoslovec. This supposition is based upon a statement by Archbishop Pitirim. Golowatzkij states:

> Archbishop of Nizhni Novgorod Pitirim mentioned in his book *Praścica protivo voprosov raskolničeskich* (St. Petersburg, 1721, vopr. 140) a *Psalter Sledovannaia* from the year 1491. Perhaps he had in mind the Cracow *Chasoslovec,* or there is a possibility that Fiol also printed a Psalter as many bibliographers hold certain. However, to date, no copy of it has ever been found. There is the most likely probability that the entire edition of this book was destroyed by the Cracow Holy Inquisition.[49]

[49] Golowatzkij, "Sweipolt Fiol . . . ," p. 441.

Based entirely upon the mention by Archbishop Pitirim, many, even a majority, of Eastern Slavic scholars, Ukrainian, Belorussian and Russian, enumerate and specify the *Psalter* as a fifth book of the Cracow printing shop in 1491. To date not one copy, not even a page or a proof sheet of this *Psalter Sledovannaia* has ever been found. Furthermore, no contemporary documents which mentioned Fiol and his books record its existence nor was there any note of it in the sixteenth or seventeenth centuries. In addition, Kopystenskiĭ did not list a Psalter as being among Fiol's prints. Therefore we feel that no such Psalter was ever produced by Fiol.

The argument that all copies of the book were destroyed by the Inquisition is not valid. Why would the Psalter be singled out for destruction and the others allowed to survive.

Pitirim's book in three editions—1721, 1726 and 1752, became so influential that for almost a century all four books actually produced by Fiol were forgotten and only the *Psalter* that never existed was cited in the bibliographies throughout the eighteenth century.

Not until 1790 were Fiol's actual accomplishments brought to the attention of Czech and Polish scholars by the founder of Czech philology, Vaclav Fortunat Dürich. They then became interested in Cyrillic incunabula and soon came to the conclusion that Pitirim had confused the *Psalter* with *Chasoslovec* and that Fiol printed only the latter.

The renowned Czech scholar, Josef Dobrovský, elaborated on this hypothesis which later was accepted and proved by Samuel Bandtkie. The latter, an authority on the history of printing, discovered several documents in Cracow pertaining to Fiol and his printing activities. In his correspondence with Dobrovský (edited by V. A. Francev) Bandtkie accepted Dobrovský's theory that only *Chasoslovec* was printed by Fiol. Dobrovský states: "Because in the Eastern Church the *Chasoslovec* and the *Psalter* are commonly printed together, Pitirim had taken it for granted that Fiol had also printed the *Psalter*."[50]

Polish scholars prudently decided to ignore the *Psalter* as long as there was no proof—not even a proof sheet—that it ever existed. Eastern Slavic scholars, as previously mentioned, still support Pitirim's theory by accepting that the *Psalter* printed in Jewie in 1638 has, in addition to the Polish text, one in Cyrillic which they say is a reprint of Fiol's *Psalter*. They also consider other Psalters of the sixteenth and seventeenth centuries to be reprints of the Cracow Psalter.[51] Ukrai-

[50] V. A. Francev, *Korrespondence Josefa Dobrovskeho, Dil II. Vzajemne dopisy Josefa Dobrovskeho a Jiriho Samuele Bandtkeho z lat 1810–1827* (Correspondence of Josef Dobrovský, Vol. II, Exchange of Letters Between Josef Dobrovský and Jerzy Samuel Bandtkie in the Years 1810 to 1827), (Prague, 1906), p. 56.

[51] Vatslaŭ Lastoŭski, *Historyia belarusk ıĭ knihi* (History of the Belorussian Books), (Kovno, 1926), p. 558.

nian scholars have always accepted the theory that Fiol printed five books in Cracow.

Thus Kuziela stated "because this undated print was not preserved, it should not be ruled out that it was mistaken for the *Horologion.*"[52] Among nineteenth and even twentieth century Russian scholars there was simply no doubt a Psalter was printed in Cracow in 1491 because Pitirim said it had been, and because Backmeister, an eighteenth century authority, listed it in his bibliography.[53]

M. Bošnjak, a Croatian scholar, retains this outmoded view in his *A Study of Slavic Incunabula,* published in translation in 1968, believes Fiol printed a Psalter in Cracow. Nemirovskiĭ, on the contrary, in his 1971 work, definitely accepts the conclusion reached by Dobrovský and Bandtkie some 150 years earlier: that Fiol did not print the Psalter and that it was confused with *Chasoslovec* which contains many Psalms. He contends convincingly that the confusion stems from a list of questions that the Raskolniks, an Orthodox heretical sect, sent to Pitirim during the course of a religious dispute. In question 140 the Raskolniks cite a verse from Fiol's print stating that it is from the *Psalter.* The citation was correct but the source was the *Chasoslovec.* Pitirim tried to obtain a copy of Fiol's Psalter; but naturally he could not obtain that which did not exist. Having failed to do so, he meticulously mentioned the Psalter which subsequently misled those who accepted Pitirim's work literally. Nemirovskiĭ used the unpublished papers of A. E. Viktorov, a connoisseur bibliophile, and his studies are complete—concluding that the Psalter never existed.[54]

Errors are not confined to Slavic scholars however. In the 1978 spring edition of the *Quarterly News-Letter* published by the Book Club of California, David Henderson in his article "An Introduction to Slavic Letter Forms and Printing" states: "The first books printed in Cyrillic were the *Psalter* and the *Ochtoechos*; they were issued in 1491 at Cracow, then the capital of Poland, by Sweybold Veil, a master embroiderer and ingenious inventor. Both contained the printer's mark and had bibliographic information in a colophon.[55]

Henderson not only perpetuates the error about the non-existent *Psalter,* but omits the *Triod*s and the *Chasoslovec* printed by Fiol, and then invents a printer's mark and colophon for the Psalter which no one has ever previously mentioned and one hopes that no one else ever will.

In the same article when discussing Skaryna's prints a few discrepancies appear: "He wanted to translate the Bible into Russian. He went to Prague and set up a press, since it was still forbidden in Russia to translate the Bible from Church

[52] Zeno Kuziela, "Der Deutsche Schweitpold Fiol als Begründer der ukrainischen Buchdruckerkunst (1491)," *Gutenberg-Jahrbuch* (Mainz, 1936), p. 80.

[53] Karataev, *Opisanie slaviano-russkikh knig . . . ,* pp. 8–9.

[54] Nemirovskiĭ, *Nachalo,* pp. 188–190.

[55] David Henderson, "An Introduction to Slavic Letter Forms and Printing," *Quarterly News-Letter of Book Club of California,* vol. XLIII, Nr. 2, 33.

Slavic . . . . His freely done translation was a mixture of Church Slavic and Belorussian."[56] The basic and cardinal error is the supposition that Skaryna wanted to translate the *Bible* into Russian. First, Skoryna was Belorussian not Russian; second, his native language was Belorussian, and third, he was a free citizen of the Polish Commonwealth of which Belorussia and his native town of Polotsk was an integral part. Another point should be clarified. Skaryna's translation of the *Bible* cannot in any shape or form be treated as some composite or mixture. Skaryna's *Bible* is the first vernacular Slavic Bible. His translation was into the native Belorussian. Only the Psalms were translated into Old Church Slavonic which most likely was intended for use in churches throughout all East Slavic nations.

Henderson started with the commonly held truism: "There is very little information available in English on the writing system of the two-thirds of the Slavic population whose alphabets are not based on the Roman."[57] Regrettably he confuses the obvious information with the name of Peter the Great, who only two hundred years after the magnificent development of Cyrillic printing in Belorussia, Ukraine, Rumania and the Balkans introduced some minute changes in the form of Cyrillic script. Actually it was an adaptation of Cyrillic to the Roman script or vice versa.

Henderson ends his article with the sentence: "By the middle of the eighteenth century the basic design of Cyrillic type had been established."[58] Unfortunately, three centuries of Cyrillic printing are passed over without proper recognition.

Henderson's comments in spite of all his blunders are not dangerous since he is not an authority in Slavistics. It is necessary however to be cautious with what is presented by well-known authorities. The last publication of 1979, *Opisanie izdaniĭ tipografii Shvaĭpolta Fiola* (Description of Publications of Shvajpolt Fiol's Printing Shop) by E. L. Nemirovskiĭ is a summary of all his studies in this field over the last ten years. Unfortunately nothing new is revealed, in spite of important discoveries and publications which have appeared in the meantime. No revisions were made and the author remains steadfast to the theories and concepts expressed in his book of 1971, *Nachalo slavianskogo knigopechataniia* (The Beginning of Slavic Printing).

In the foreword to this last publication it is emphasized: "Information about bookbinding and notes [provenance] on the pages of the book do not pretend to be fully comprehensive."[59] It is distressing that what may be most valuable for the

[56] *Ibid.*, p. 33.
[57] *Ibid.*, p. 31.
[58] *Ibid.*, p. 34.
[59] E. L. Nemirovskiĭ, "Opisanie izdaniĭ tipografii Shvaĭpol'ta Fiola" (Description of Publications from Fiol's Printing Shop), *Opisanie staropechatnykh izdaniĭ kirillovskogo shrifta* (Description of Old Printed Publications in Cyrillic Print) (Moscow, 1979), pp. 6–7.

Сведения о переплете и о записях на страницах книг не претендуют на исчерпываю-

background and history of each copy continues further to remain obscured.

No evidence is shown of an in-depth research on the copy recently found in Braşov. The Crucifixion on leaf 2 which in itself is a revelation because it is the only presently available illustration in its original form, has not been presented in full. Nemirovskiĭ gave separately the Crucifixion and the printer's device so that the reader does not get a true picture of leaf 2 in its entirety. Besides this he has taken it upon himself to pencil-in the upper and right hand frame around the printer's device which in the original does not appear. This arbitrariness is unorthodox in a scholarly publication.

Although the above discussed printer's device is evidence that *Triod Cvetnaja* had been printed at the same time as *Oktoikh* using the same illustration, Nemirovskiĭ insists that *Triod Cvetnaja* was printed with *Triod Postnaja* in 1493. Persistent with his theory in describing *Triod Cvetnaja* as the last book printed in 1493 despite all new evidence, he still puts the name, place, and date in square brackets.

In spite of many excellent publications by M. Błońska and other scholars regarding different variants in Fiol's publications this is completely ignored by Nemirovskiĭ.

Characteristically when he describes Polish holdings of *Triod Postnaja* and *Triod Cvetnaja* in the National Library in Warsaw he does not mention that both copies came from the Greek Catholic Bishopric Library in Przemyśl, only when describing the copy in the Catholic University Library in Lublin he cites the provenance note from the inner side of the book cover—Ex bibliotheca Capituli Ritus graeco-catholici Premisliensis" without any explanation.

To avoid any misunderstanding the above comments are not to diminish Nemirovskiĭ's contribution to the studies of Cyrillic printing, but the great contributions of other scholars should also be acknowledged.

It is time to learn the truth. Americans deserve to be informed about all Slavic nations and their cultural contributions. If this book would be instrumental in presenting the facts and information regarding this field, it would fulfill its purpose and obligation. Since the very important achievement of Gutenberg and his followers have been glorified, it is time to give full recognition to Fiol, the two Makarios, Skaryna, Mstislavetz and Fedorov.

щую полноту. Воспроизводя текст записей, мы не ставили перед собой задачу паучной публикации древнерусских текстов. Приводимые в этом случае сведения носят сигнальный характер и предназначены служить лишь самой первичной информацией для исследователей. При воспроизведении текстов применена транслитерация кирилловского шрифта знаками современного русского алфавита. Мы сохраняем, однако, знаки «омега», «ять», «и десятеричное», «фита» и не сохраняем «юсы», «иси», «кси». Как «зело», так и «земля» передаются знаком «з». Не сохраняются нами и знаки ударения и придыхания. Титла и сокращения, как правило, раскрываются. «Юс большой» мы передаем знаком «у», «юс малый»—знаком «я».

Appendix II
Statistical Tables

Attached is a set of statistical tables to facilitate better understanding of the fluctuation in location and possession of Fiol's incunabula in the past.

STATISTICS OF 1971
(According to Nemirovskii)

I.

Place	Triod Cvetnaja		Triod Postnaja		Chasoslovec		Osmoglasnik		Total	
	Copies	Frag.	Copies	Frag.	Copies	Frag.	Copies	Frag.	Copies	Frag.
U.S.S.R.	14	1	24	1	24	1	6	1	68	4
Beyond U.S.S.R.	6	2	3	1	1	1	0		10	4
Total	20	3	27	2	25	2	6	1	78	8

STATISTICS OF 1939

II.

U.S.S.R.	10		22		21		6	1	59**	1
Beyond U.S.S.R.	10	3	5	2	4	2	1*		20	7

* Wrocław copy

** two copies — one of *Chasoslovec,* one of *Osmoglasnik* are in Kiev, Ukraine. Taking this under consideration, we could establish that on ethnic Russian territories in 1939 there were fifty-seven copies and one fragment of Fiol's prints.

STATISTICS OF 1620
(Based on Zakharii Kopystenskii's data)

III.

	Triod Cvetnaja	Triod Postnaja	Chasoslovec	Osmoglasnik
Russia	0	0	0	0
Belorussia Ukraine Lithuania	5+	5+	4+	3+

The first statistical table indicates how many of Fiol's incunabula are presently in the U.S.S.R. and how many are outside its boundaries.

The second statistical table shows the location of these incunabula before World War II. As can be seen, the ratio changes quite distinctly. If we take under consideration the two copies located in East Ukraine (Kiev, Odessa) in 1939, the copies located in ethnic Russia were only 57 compared to 22 elsewhere; one fragment in Russia and seven elsewhere.

The third statistical table goes back to the date of the beginning of the seventeenth century, disregarded by Nemirovskii. It reveals the location of Fiol's books by the normal process of acquisition through purchase immediately after the printing of the books. Kopystenskii reveals information pertaining to holdings only in Belorussia and Ukraine. A high church official, Kopystenskii was well informed as to the location of ecclesiastical books throughout all Eastern Slavic territories. He knew the books from autopsy and found them in numerous places which gives evidence of their existence and wide use in the territories connected with Poland.

Below is a final statistical table which takes into consideration the recent discoveries.

STATISTICS OF 1975

Place	Triod Cvetnaja		Triod Postnaja		Chasoslovec		Osmoglasnik		Total	
	Copies	Frag.	Copies	Frag.	Copies	Frag.	Copies	Frag.	Copies	Frag.
U.S.S.R.	14	1	24	1	24	1	6	1	68	4
Beyond U.S.S.R.	7*	3**	3	1	1	1	0		11	5
Total	21	4	27	2	25	2	6	1	79	9

*Newly discovered copy in Rumania.
**Newly reported fragment in U.S.A.

Bibliography

Books:

Anichenka, Uladzimir Vasilevich. *Belaruska-ukrainskiia pis'mova-mounia suviazi* (Relations between Written Belorussian and Ukrainian Languages). Minsk, 1969.

A comparative study of the Belorussian and Ukrainian languages.

Badalić, Josip. Inkunabule u Narodnoj Republici Hrvatskoj (Incunabula quae in Populari Republica Croatia asservantur). Zagreb, 1952.

A richly illustrated catalogue of incunabula in the libraries of Croatia. Introductory five chapters throw light upon the collection as an example of the country's culture.

Bandtkie, Georgius Samuel. *De primis Cracoviae in arte typographica incunabulis.* Cracoviae, 1812.

The announcement of a discovery of Fiol's prints in this article commenced Polish studies in Cyrillic incunabula and influenced other Slavic nations. First description of the Wrocław *Osmoglasnik.*

Bandtkie, Jerzy Samuel. *Historia drukarń krakowskich* (History of Cracow Printing Presses). Cracow, 1815.

A historical survey of Cracow's first Cyrillic printing presses. A valuable contribution to the studies of Fiol and his achievements. Chapter about Fiol was translated by a Russian, M. T. Kachenovskii and published in Moscow in 1819. It initiated intensive studies of Slavic Cyrillic prints.

Bandtkie, Jerzy Samuel. *Historia drukarń w Królestwie Polskim i w Wielkim Księstwie Litewskim . . .* (History of Printing Presses in the Kingdom of Poland and the Grand Duchy of Lithuania). Vols. 1–3. Cracow, 1826.

Comprehensive study on the subject.

Barazny, L. *Hraviury Frantsyska Skaryny* (Woodcuts of Francis Skaryna). Minsk, 1972.

Album of illustrations of all woodcuts from Skoryna's prints preserved in various libraries in the USSR. A comprehensive work with description and annotations in Belorussian and Russian. A valuable edition on good paper, beautifully bound.

Barwiński, E. *Katalog inkunabułów Biblioteki Uniwersyteckiej we Lwowie* (Catalogue of Incunabula in the University Library in Lwów). Lwów, 1912.

Catalogue obsolete because of changes in the post-World War II era.

Bauch, Gustaw. *Deutsche Scholaren in Krakau in der Zeit der Renaissance, 1460–1520* (German Scholars in Cracow during the Renaissance Period, 1460–1520). Breslau, 1901.

Better, A. *Polskie ilustracje książkowe XV i XVI wieku (1490–1525)* (Polish Book Illustrations of the Fifteenth and Sixteenth Centuries, 1490–1525). Lwów, 1929.

Biernat of Lublin, *Raj duszny — Hortulus animae.* Cracow, 1513.

Blades, William. *The Biography and Typography of William Caxton, England's First Printer.* Totowa, N.J., 1971.

Bobrova, E. I. *Katalog inkunabulov.* Akademiia nauk SSSR. Biblioteka. (Catalogue of Incunabula. Library, Academy of Sciences USSR.) Moscow, 1963.

Bodeman, Eduard. *Xylographische und typographische Inkunabeln der Königlichen öffentlichen Bibliothek zur Hannover.* Nr. 54. Hannover, 1866.

Bohatta, H. *Einführung in die Buchkunde.* Vienna, 1927.

Bośnjak, Mladen. *A Study of Slavic Incunabula.* Trans. F. Dobrovolsky, Leyden, 1968.

A study by a Croatian scholar of Slavic incunabula to 1500. In general a valuable book. However, information pertaining to the Cracow printing press is misleading due to the acceptance of the unverified Kuziela theory. English translation is very helpful.

Bray, R. G. A. de. *Guide to the Slavonic Languages.* London, 1969.

Braha, Symon. *Lakalizatsyia zhyts'tsiapisu doktara Skaryny* (Localization of Doctor Skaryna's Biography). Munich, Belaruski Instytut Navuki i Mastatstva, 1965. Offprint from *Zapisy,* vol. 3.

Geographical locations instrumental to the biography of Doctor Francišak Skaryna.

Briquest, C. M. *Les filigranes. Dictionnaire historique des marques des papier, des leur apparition vers 1282 jusque'en 1600.* The Briquet-Jubilee edition, J. S. G. Simmons, gen. ed., Amsterdam: The Paper Publication Society, Labarre Foundation, 1868.

A collection of papermarks known worldwide.

Cambridge Medieval History, vol. VI. New York, 1936.

Candea, Virgil. *Livres anciens en Roumanie.* Bucharest, 1962.

Description of old book collections in Rumania.

Catalogue of Books Printed in the XV-th Century Now in the British Museum. London, 1908–1962. Part I–IX. (Part I–VIII lithographic print. London, 1963).

Cherepnin, L. V. *Russkaia paleografiia* (Russian Paleography). Moscow, 1965.

A comprehensive study on this subject matter.

Chmiel, Adam, ed. *Album Studiosorum Universitatis Cracoviensis.* Vols. 1–2. Cracoviae, 1887–1892.

Chwalewik, Edward. *Zbiory polskie, archiwa, biblioteki, gabinety, galerie, muzea i inne zbiory pamiątek przeszłości w ojczyznie i na obczyźnie* (Polish Collections, Archives, Libraries, Studies, Galleries, Museums and other Collections of Memorabilia of the Past in Poland and Abroad). 2nd ed., 2 vols. Warsaw-Cracow, 1926.

A comprehensive work listing Poland's cultural treasures seized by Russia during the occupation of Polish territories from 1772 to 1917.

Clair, Colin. *An History of Printing in Britain.* London, 1965.

Copinger, W. A. *Supplement to Hain's Repertorium Bibliographicum.* Part 1–3. London, 1895–1902; reprint, Berlin, 1926.

Cross, F. L. *The Oxford Dictionary of the Christian Church.* London, 1937.

Dąbrowski, Jan. *Czasy świetności miasta. Kraków. Jego dzieje i sztuka* (Period of the City's Splendor. Cracow. Its History and Art). Warsaw, 1965.

Presenting the city of Cracow, its history, cultural splendor and art.

Diringer, David. *The Illuminated Book, Its History and Production.* New York, 1958.

Dobrovský, Josef and Bandtke, Jíři Samuel. *Korrespondence Josefa Dobrovského, dil II. Vzájemne dopisy Josefa Dobrovského a Jiřiho Samuele Bandtkeho z let 1810–1827. K vydáni upravil V. A. Francev* (Josef Dobrovský's Correspondence. Part II. Exchange of Letters between Josef Dobrovský and Jíři S. Bandtkie between 1810–1827). Edited and prepared by C. A. Francev. Prague, 1906.

The "Patriarch of Czech and all Slavic philology," Josef Dobrovský thoroughly discussed Fiol's printing with Bandtke, and agreed that there was no evidence of the *Psalter* being printed as a separate book.

Duff, E. G. *The Printers, Stationers and Bookbinders of Westminster and London from 1476 to 1535. Cambridge, 1906.*

Dürich, F. *Bibliotheca slavica antiquissimae dialecti communis ecclesiasticae universae Slavorum gentis.* Vol. I. Vindobonae, 1795.

With this book Dürich became the forerunner of Slavic philology. Later in correspondence with Josef Dobrovský he discussed the revelation of the discovery of Fiol's *Chasoslovec.*

Ehrenberg, R. *Das Zeitalter der Fugger.* Vol. I. Jena, 1896

A comprehensive study of the Fugger banking family and its impact on the history of Germany. Another book by Ehrenberg was translated in 1928 by H. Lucas: *Capital and Finance in the Age of the Renaissance: A Study of the Fuggers and Their Connections.*

Estreicher, Karol. *Bibliografia polska XV–XVI stulecia* (Polish Bibliography of the Fifteenth and Sixteenth Centuries). Cracow, 1875.

Monumental bibliography of Polish literature and writings. It also includes foreign literature pertaining to Poland. Continued by Estreicher's successors, main source of bibliographical data up to this date. Vol. XXX — 1936, pp. 382–383, description of *Triod Cvetnaja* and *Postnaja.*

Estreicher, Karol. *Bibliografia Polska* (Polish Bibliography) Part I, Vol. 1–7 bibliographical items from 1800–1880; Part II, Vol. 8–11, chronological register of literature from 1455–1889; Part III, Vol. 12–22 critical description of literature from the fifteenth to eighteenth century in alphabetical order. This bibliography was continued by his son Stanisław who published eleven volumes 22 through 33 by

1939. Stanisław Estreicher was killed in the Oświęcim concentration camp, but his work was and is continued by his son Karol.

Feigelmans, N. *Lietuvos inkunabulai* (Incunabula in Lithuania). Vilnius, 1975.

Fournier, Pierre Simon. 1712–1768. *Manuel typographique.* 2 vols. Paris, 1764–1766.

Handbook of engraving and type founding, printing and examples of type faces.

Gesamtkatalog der Wiegendrucke. Herausgegeben von der Kommission für den Gesamtkatalog der Wiegendrucke. Vols. 1–7. 8-Lief, 1. Leipzig, 1925–1940.

Goff, Frederick Richmond. *Incunabula in American Libraries. A Third Census of Fifteenth Century Books Recorded in North American Collections.* New York, 1964.

Goldsmith, Ernest Philip. *Gothic and Renaissance Bookbindings.* Vols. 1–2. London, 1928.

A brilliant historical survey-analysis of Renaissance bookbinding with a valuable contribution to the history of bookbinding in Poland. Author's emphasis on the use of gold embossing in Polish bookbinding as the first in Central Europe.

Haebler, Konrad. *Die deutschen Buchdrucker des XV Jahrhunderts im Auslande.* Munich, 1924.

———. *Typenrepertorium der Wiegendrucke.* Abt. I–V. Halle a. S.–Leipzig, 1924.

———. *Handbuch der Inkunabelkunde.* Leipzig, 1925.

———. *German Incunabula Text. West European Incunabula.* 60 original leaves. Described by Konrad Haebler. Tr. Andre Barbey. Munich, 1928.

———. *The Study of Incunabula.* Tr. Lucy Osborn with a Foreword by Alfred W. Pollard. New York, 1933.

Hain, Ludwig. *Repertorium bibliographicum . . . .* Vols. 1–2. Stuttgartiae, Lutetiae Parisiorum, 1826–1838.

Hoffman, Johannes Daniel. *De Typographiis earumque initiis et incrementis in Regno Poloniae et Magno Ducatu Lithvaniae cum observationibus rem literariam et typographicam utriusque gentis aliqua ex parte illustrantibus.* Dantisci, 1740.

Horodyski, Bogdan. *Podręcznik paleografii ruskiej* (Manual of Russian Paleography). Cracow, 1951.

A historical survey and presentation of subject matter illustrated with holdings in Poland.

Hrushevskyi, M. *Istoriia ukrains'koi literatury* (History of Ukrainian Literature). Kiev, 1927.

A comprehensive study by the great Ukrainian scholar and historian.

Iur'ev, Panteleimon. *Pervopechatnik v Krakove. Iz istorii pervopechatnykh sviazei slaviano-russkikh* (The First [Cyrillic] Printer in Cracow. History of Early Slavic-Russian Printing Relations). Warsaw, 1967.

Revived theory of Fiol's Ukrainian descent with the introduction of a new location of the place of his birth in Lemkoland.

Jędrzejewska, H. and Pelczarowa, M. *Katalog inkunabułów Biblioteki Gdańskiej Polskiej Akademii Nauk, II. Uzupełnienia i dodatki (Nr. 665–696).* (Catalogue of Incunabula in the Gdańsk Library of the Academy of Sciences. II. Supplements and Additions, (Nr. 665–696)). Gdańsk, 1967.

Juszyński, H. *Dykcjonarz poetów polskich* (Dictionary of Polisth Poets). 2 vols. Cracow, 1820.

One of the initial works in this field. Valuable with information regarding some books that have not survived to the present day.

Kaczmarczyk, K. *Księgi przyjęć* do prawa miejskiego w Krakowie 1392–1506 (Libri iuris civilis civitatis Cracoviensis). Cracow, 1913.

A thorough presentation of valuable documents, among them some pertaining to Fiol.

Karataev, Ivan. *Osmoglasnik 1491 goda napechatannyi v Krakove kirillovskimi bukvami* (Osmoglasnik of 1491 Printed in Cyrillic in Cracow). St. Petersburg, 1876.

A thorough description of Fiol's *Osmoglasnik* based on autopsy.

Karataev, Ivan. *Opisanie slaviano-russkikh knig napechatannykh kirillovskimi bukvami, 1491–1730* Vol. I: *Ot 1491 po 1600.* (Description of Slavic-Russian Books Printed in Cyrillic. Vol. I: From 1491 to 1600). St. Petersburg, 1878.

Although outdated, a valuable and useful list, due to reliable, objective and accurate description of Fiol's prints based on a thorough examination of the subject. In 1883 the book was revised and enlarged.

Karskii, Evfimii F. *Russkaia dialektologiia* (Russian Dialectology). Moscow, 1928.

———. *Belorussy. Iazyk belorusskogo naroda* (The Belorussians. The Language of the Belorussian People). Part I. Moscow, 1955.

A brilliant study of the Belorussian language by the most prominent specialist in this field.

Kawecka-Gryczowa, Alodia. *Katalog starych druków Biblioteki Publicznej M. st. Warszawy.* I: *Inkunabuły* (Catalogue of Old Prints at the Warsaw Public Library, Part I: Incunabula). Warsaw, 1949.

———. *Katalog inkunabułów Biblioteki Zakładu im. Ossolińskich we Wrocławiu* (Catalogue of Incunabula in the Library of the Ossoliński Institute in Wrocław). Wrocław, 1956.

———. ed. Maria Bohonos and Elisa Szandorowska, comps. *Incunabula quae in bibliothecis Poloniae asservantur.* Bibliotheca Nationalis Polona. Vratislaviae-Varsaviae-Cracoviae. Ex Officina Instituti Ossoliniani, 1970.

The Union Catalogue of Incunabula in Polish Libraries includes descriptions of 5,768 editions represented by 19,207 copies which are found in 107 state, church, monastery and private libraries. The Latin version of the catalogue makes it accessible to everyone interested in incunabula.

Kłosińska, J. *Ikony. Katalog zbiorów. Muzeum Narodowe w Krakowie* (Icons. Catalogue of Holdings. National Museum in Cracow). Cracow, 1973.

Analytical description of icons from the earliest days collected in the National Museum in Cracow.

Kocowski, Bronisław. *Katalog inkunabułów Biblioteki Uniwersyteckiej we Wrocławiu. Catalogus incunabulorum typographicorum Bibliothecae Universitatis Vratislaviensis.* I: *Alfabetyczny wykaz druków* (An Alphabetical List of Prints), II: *Konkordancye, indeksy, ilustracje* (Concordances, Indexes, Illustrations). Wrocław, 1959.

A comprehensive two volume catalogue, restored after World War II, arranged according to the latest scientific requirements.

Kopera, Feliks. *Spis druków epoki Jagiellońskiej w zbiorze Emeryka hrabiego Hutten-Czapskiego w Krakowie* (List of Prints from the Jagellonian Era in the Count Emeryk Hutten-Czapski Collection). Cracow, 1900.

First list and general description of printed books from the fifteenth and sixteenth centuries in the Czapski Collection.

Kopystenskii, Zakharii. *Besedy Ioanna Zlatoustogo na poslanie apostola Pavla* (Sermons of St. John Chrysostom Concerning the Epistles of the Apostle Paul). Kiev, 1623.

An Orthodox religious work which incidentally mentions the locations of Fiol's books in Belorussia and the Ukraine.

Lastouski, Vatslau. *Historia belaruskai knihi* (History of the Belorussian Books). Kovno, 1926.

A general presentation of the development of Belorussian book production.

Lelewel, Joachim. *Bibliograficznych ksiąg dwoje* (Two Volumes of Bibliography). Warsaw, 1823.

The first serious bibliographical work at the beginning of the nineteenth century, the only one of its kind for the following fifty years.

Lenhart, John M., O.F.M. *Introduction to Checklists of Names and Places Where Typography was Applied, of Master Printers, Workmen, Publishers, Promoters, etc.* St. Louis, Mo., The Central Bureau of Catholic Central Union, 1959.

A unique work documenting the Catholic Church's participation in the development of the production of books in the fifteenth century.

Lewicka-Kamińska, Anna. *Inkunabuły Biblioteki Jagiellońskiej* (Jagellonian Library Incunabula). Cracow, 1962.

The Catalogue of Incunabula in the Jagellonian Library revised after World War II. The most modern and scholarly edition.

Likhachev, Nikolai Petrovich. *Paleograficheskoe znachenie bumazhnykh vodnykh znakov* (Paleographic Significance of Paper Watermarks). 3 vols. St. Petersburg, 1899.

A superb collection of watermarks by a prominent Russian scholar.

Lunt, Horace G. *Old Church Slavonic Grammar.* 2nd ed. The Hague, 1959.

McMurtrie, Douglas C. *The Book, the Story of Printing and Bookmaking.* New York, 1943.

Miłosz, Czesław. *The History of Polish Literature.* London, 1969.

A recent survey of Polish literature, excellent textbook by a contemporary Polish philosopher and poet teaching at University of California, Berkeley.

Molé, W. *Sztuka Słowian południowych.* (The Art of the Southern Slavs). Wrocław-Warsaw, 1962.

Morawski, Kazimierz. *Historia Uniwersytetu Jagiellońskiego* (History of the Jagellonian University). 2 vols. Cracow, 1900.

First comprehensive history of the University of Cracow.

Muczkowski, Josephus. *Statuta nec non liber promotionum philosophorum ordinis in Universitate studiorum Jagellonica ab anno 1402 ad annum 1849.* Cracoviae, 1849.

Important list of student degree conferments in the Jagellonian University in Cracow during the Renaissance.

Muszkowski, Jan. *Życie książki* (Life of the Book), 2nd ed., illustrated and revised. Cracow, 1951.

A huge work devoted to the world of books and all that is connected with it: such as publisher, printer, editor, book collector, librarian, etc. The history of writing and printing also included. *Vade mecum* for bibliophiles.

Napierski, Karl E. *Russische-Livländische Urkunden* (Russko-Livonskije akty). St. Petersburg, 1869.

Nemirovskii, Evgenii L'vovich. *Nachalo slavianskogo knigopechataniia* (Beginning of Slavic Printing). Moscow, 1971.

Socio-realistic monograph concerning Fiol and his printing endeavors using dialectical materialism to convince the world that Russia was instrumental in the development of the first Cyrillic printing press. Positive side of the book — new data of three known items, more descriptive details of known holdings. Fine background of Cracow as one of the greatest cultural centers in the Renaissance era.

Panaitescu, P. P. *Liturghierul lui Macarie* (The Missal by Macarie). Bucharest, 1961.

An interesting theory of the Moldavian origin of Fiol's prints.

Pares, Bernard. *A History of Russia.* New York, 1965.

Paszkiewicz. Henryk. *The Origin of Russia.* New York, 1954.

Petrushevich, A. S. *Katalog tserkovno-slovenskikh rukopisei i staropechatnykh knig kirillovskogo pis'ma, nakhodiashchikhsia na Arkheologichesko-bibliograficheskoi vystave: Stavropigiiskom zavedenii* (Catalogue of Church Slavonic Manuscripts and Books in Cyrillic at the Archaeologic-Bibliographical Exhibit in the Stavropigiiskii Institution). Lvov, 1888.

Piekosiński, Franciszek. *Średniowieczne znaki wodne. Wiek XIV.* (Medieval Watermarks. XIV Century). Cracow, 1893.

Collection of watermarks in manuscripts from the fourteenth century in Polish libraries.

———. *Wybór znaków wodnych z XV stulecia* (Selected Watermarks of the Fifteenth Century). Cracow, 1896.

Collection of watermarks found in manuscripts and books from the fifteenth century in Polish collections.

Popov, P. H. *Pochatkovyi period knyhodrukuvannia u slovian* (The Initial Period of Slavic Printing). Kiev, 1958.

Studies regarding early Cyrillic printing.

Proctor, R. *An Index to the Early Printed Books in the British Museum: From the Invention of Printing to the Year MD. With Notes of Those in the Bodleian Library.* London, 1898. 1–4 Supplements 1899–1902. Part II: 1501–1520. Section I: Germany. London, 1903; (2nd ed., 1954).

Ruppel, Aloys, *Stanislaus Polonus. Polski drukarz i wydawca wczesnej doby w Hiszpanii* (Stanislaus Polonus. An Early Polish Typographer and Publisher in Spain). Cracow, 1970.

This is an enlarged, magnificently executed Polish edition prepared by Tadeusz Zapiór. It is devoted to the work of a distinguished Polish typographer who between 1491 and 1504 ran a printing press at Seville and Alcala de Henares. With the author's consent, the editor, a Cracow scholar, revised and translated the original German text adding an afterword and extensive notes. The Polish edition includes new findings. This is one of the most valuable editions of Stanislaus Polonus, richly illustrated and artistically published.

Sakharov, I. P. *Obraztsy slaviano-russkogo knigopechataniia s 1491 goda* (Examples of Slavic-Russian Printing since 1491). St. Petersburg, 1849 (not distributed then). Reprint 1891.

A valuable collection of typographical samples of the first Cyrillic prints from various presses by an unidentified Russian scholar.

Sedov, Valentin V. *Slaviane verkhnego Podneprov'ia i Podvin'ia* (Slavs of the Upper Dnieper and Dvina). Moscow, 1970.

Seruga, Józef. *Jan Haller, wydawca i drukarz krakowski 1467–1525* (Jan Haller, Cracow Publisher and Printer, 1467–1525). Cracow, 1933.

A monograph about the founder of Polish typography, Jan Haller.

Shchelkunov, M. I. *Istoriia, tekhnika, isskustvo knigopechataniia* (The History, Technique and Art of Printing). Moscow-Leningrad, 1920.

Shevchenko Scientific Society. *Entsyklopediia ukrainoznavstva* Encyclopedia of the Ukraine). Vol. I. Munich, 1949.

Shitsgal, A. *Russkii grazhdanskii shrift, 1908–1958* (Russian Plain Type). Moscow, 1959.

———. *Russkii tipografskii shrift* (Russian Graphic Type). Moscow, 1974.

Simmons, J. S. G. *Incunabula in the U.S.S.R.: Supplementary Notes.* [Photocopy of manuscript prepared for print for *The Book Collector,* Summer, 1967].

Sopikov, Vasilii. *Opyt rossiiskoi bibliografiii* (Outline of Russian Bibliography). St. Petersburg, 1813; reprint ed. 1904.

The first Russian bibliography in the nineteenth century including incunabula. Outdated and antiquated for research purposes.

Stasov, Vladimir Vasil'evich. *Razbor rukopisnogo sochineniia g. Rovinskogo: "Russkie gravery i ikh proizvedeniia"* (An Analysis of Mr. Rovinski's Manuscript "Russian Engravers and Their Works"). St. Petersburg, 1864.

An early study of first printings by a Russian scholar, with many valuable notes.

Steinberg, S. N. *Five Hundred Years of Printing.* 3d ed. Edinburgh, 1974.

Stillwell, M. B. *Incunabula in American Libraries. A Second Census of Fifteenth Century Books Owned in the United States, Mexico and Canada (*Bibliographical Society of America. Monograph series, no. 1). New York, 1940.

Sventsitskii, Ilarion S. *Kataloh knih tserkovno-slavianskoi pechaty* (Catalogue of Church Slavonic Printing). Zhovkva, 1908.

A listing of Ukrainian holdings of Cyrillic books located in the Greek Catholic Church Museum in Lwów before World War II.

Szwejkowska, Helena. *Książka drukowana XV–XVIII wieku. Zarys historyczny* (The Printed Book from the Fifteenth to the Eighteenth Century. A Historical Outline). Warsaw, 1961.

Review of the history of the development of book printing in Poland.

Talev, Ilya. *Some Problems of the Second South Slavic Influence in Russia.* München, 1973. Slavistische Beiträge. Band. 67.

A comprehensive study of the Second South Slavic influence stimulated by two great Metropolitans of Bulgarian origin. Weakness of this valuable work is in its chaotic historical presentation of the territories covered by three nations Belorussians, Ruthenians (Ukrainians) and Russians. Author's terminology may be highly misleading.

Tobolka, Z. *Česke prvotisky. Knihopis československych tisku. Od doby nejstarsi az do konce XVIII stolet.* I: *Prvotisky do r. 1500* (Czech Incunabula. A List of Czechoslovak Prints from the Oldest Period to the End of the Eighteenth Century. I: Incunabula to 1500). Prague, 1925.

Review of the development of printing in Bohemia.

Ukraine: A Concise Encyclopedia. Prepared by the Shevchenko Scientific Society. Edited by Volodymyr Kubijovyc. Vol. I. Toronto, 1963.

Ulewicz, Tadeusz. *Wśród impresorów krakowskich doby renesansu* (Among Cracow Printers in the Renaissance). Cracow, 1977.

Undol'skii, V. *Katalog slaviano-russkikh knig tserkovnoi pechati Biblioteki A. H. Kasterina* (Catalogue of Slavonic-Russian Church Books in the A. H. Kasterin Library). Moscow, 1848.

Vladimirov, P. V. *Doktor Frantsisk Skorina: Ego perevody, pechatnye izdaniia i iazyk* (Dr. Francis Skorina: His Translations, Printed Publications and Language). St. Petersburg, 1888.

Wapowski, Bernard. *Polish Chronicle to 1535* (in Latin). Vol. II in series of the Polish Academy of Arts and Sciences *Scriptores rerum polonicarum,* ed. by Józef Szujski, 1874.

First Polish cartographer who influenced European cartography in the sixteenth and seventeenth centuries. Author of the Polish Chronicle from the earliest period to 1535.

Wierzbowski, Teodor. *Bibliographia Polonica XV ac XVI sc.* Vols. 1–3. Warsaw, 1889–1894. Reprint. 1961.

Wroth, Lawrence C. *A History of the Printed Book.* New York, 1938.

Zathey, J. and Reichan, J. *Indeks studentów Uniwersytetu Krakowskiego w latach 1400–1500* (Index of Students Attending Cracow University in the Years 1400–1500). Wrocław, 1974.

Zernova, Antonina Sergeevna. *Knigi kirillovskoi pechati, khraniashchiesia v zagranichnykh bibliotekakh i neizvestnye v russkoi bibliografii* (Cyrillic Books in Foreign Libraries Not Cited in Russian Bibliography). Trudy 4, Vol. II. Moscow, 1959.

———. *Nachalo knigopechataniia v Moskve i na Ukraine* (The Beginnings of Printing in Moscow and the Ukraine). Moscow, 1947.

Zhurauski, A. I. *Historyia belaruskai literaturnai movy* (History of the Belorussian Literary Language). Vol. I. Minsk, 1967.

A recent study of the Belorussian literary language and its historical development by a prominent Belorussian scholar.

Zigrosser, Carl. *Six Centuries of Fine Prints.* New York, 1937.

Periodical literature:

Adam, P. "Über polnische Einbandkunst im XVI Jahrhundert," *Allgemeiner Anzeiger für Buchbindereien* (Leipzig, 1925), no. 32.

A valuable contribution to the history of European bookbinding. Adam stresses the original style of the Polish art of bookbinding, an amalgam of eastern and western elements with local ingenuity.

Atanasov, Pet″r. "B″lgarski tekstove v p″rvite slavianski kirilski inkunabuli" (Bulgarian Texts at the Outset of Slavic Cyrillic Incunabula), *Ezik i literatura* (Sophia, 1966), vol. 21, no. 5, pp. 17–32.

An interesting study by a Bulgarian scholar noting Bulgarian influences in Fiol's prints.

Birkenmajer, Aleksander and Piekarski, Kazimierz. "Korektowe arkusze druków Szwajpolta Fiola" (Proofsheets of Szwajpolt Fiol's prints), *Congrès international des bibliothécaires et des amis du livre tenu à Prague du 28 juin au 3 juillet, 1926. Procès-verbaux et mémoires* (Prague, 1928), vol. II, pp. 57–58.

A careful analysis of a fragment of Fiol's print found to be proofsheets from *Triod Cvetnaja* and *Chasoslovec.* Exceptionally important due to the revelation of the method of dual color printing.

Birkenmajer, Aleksander. "Rzut oka na historię drukarstwa krakowskiego w ciągu XV–go i XVI–go stulecia" (A Glance at the History of Printing in Cracow in the Fifteenth and Sixteenth Centuries), *Biblioteka Jagiellońska. Katalog wystawy druków krakowskich XV–go i XVI–go wieku* (Jagellonian Library. Catalogue of Exhibition of Prints from the Fifteenth and Sixteenth Centuries) (Cracow, 1936).

A concise outline to the history of Cracow printing in the fifteenth and sixteenth centuries.

Błońska, Maria. "Druki cyrylickie w Polsce. Problemy i zadania" (Cyrillic Books in Poland. Problems and Tasks), *Przegląd Biblioteczny (*Library Review) (Warsaw, 1962), vol. XXX, pp. 229–236.

A study of problems and tasks connected with Cyrillic printing due to their ties and links with other countries.

———. "Próba nowego spojrzenia na dzieje krakowskiej oficyny drukarskiej Szwajpolta Fiola (około 1483–1491)" (An Attempt at a New View of the History of Szwajpolt Fiol's Printing Press, circa 1483–1491), *Rocznik Biblioteki Narodowej* (Yearbook of the National Library) (Warsaw, 1968), vol. IV, pp. 51–62.

A new approach to the problem relating to the founding of Cracow's Cyrillic printing press and requirements of a closer scrutiny of the problem by Polish historians and church historians. Polemics with V. J. Lukianenko on the chronology of Fiol's prints.

Borski, Lucia Marecka. "A Short History of Early Printing in Poland," *Bulletin of the New York Public Library* (New York, 1942), no. 2, pp. 74–86.

Braha, Symon. "Doktar Skaryna ŭ Maskve" (Doctor Skaryna in Moscow), *Zapisy* (New York-Munich, Whiteruthenian Institute of Arts and Sciences, 1963), vol. 2, pp. 9–36.

A study pertaining to Dr. Skaryna's unverified visit to Moscow and the burning of his book by the authorities.

———. "Doktar Frantsishak Skaryna, 1485(?)–1540" (Doctor Francis Skaryna, 1485(?)–1540), *Zapisy* (New York-Munich, Whiteruthenian Institute of Arts and Sciences, 1970), vol. 5, pp. 11–33.

A biographical sketch and description of Skaryna's deeds and printing achievements, based on old and recent archival discoveries published in 1965: Symon, Braha, "Liakalizatsiia zhytstsiapisu Doktara Skaryny" (Doctor Skoryna — Review of Sources to a Biography), Whiteruthenian Institute of Arts and Sciences, New York-Munich, 1965.

———. "Partrèty doktara Skaryny" (Dr. Skaryna's Portraits), *Konadni* (New York-Munich, 1963), no. 7, pp. 138–151.

A survey and analysis of all known portraits of Skaryna.

———. "Review of E. L. Nemirovskii, *Nachalo slavianskogo knigopechataniia*" (Beginning of Slavic Printing), "1971", *Zapisy* (New York-Munich, Whiteruthenian Institute of Arts and Sciences, 1974), no. 12, pp. 117–127.

A most thorough and knowledgeable review of Nemirovskii's book emphasizing all its faults and shortcomings, also revealing an *a priori* established "ideological purpose" of this Soviet scholar.

———. "Rètsenzyia na: E. Nemirovskii, *Vozniknovenie knigopechataniia v Moskve*" (Review of E. Nemirovskii's "Beginning of Printing in Moscow"), *Zapisy* (Munich, 1964), vol. 3, pp. 239–242.

———. "Uhodki druku na belaruskai ziamli" (Jubilee of Printing on Belorussian Territory), *Belarus* (New York, 1972), no. 186.

Brückner, Aleksander. "Monumenta Poloniae Typographica I. Cracovia Typographorum," *Przegląd Warszawski* (Warsaw Review) (Warsaw), vol. III.

A presentation of the first printing presses in Cracow and their achievements.

Chojecka, Ewa. "Wokół wyposażenia graficznego druków słowiańskich Szwajpolta Fiola" (Shwaipolt Fiol's Slavic Printing and His Graphic Equipment), *Bulletin of the History of Art* (Warsaw, Art Institute of the Polish Academy of Sciences, 1978), vol. XL, no. 3, pp. 223–240.

Latest comprehensive and thorough study of graphic features in Fiol's incunabula. Known literature discussed and analyzed. However, the Mircea 1971 discovery is overlooked.

Demeny, L. "L'imprimerie cyrillique de Macarios de Valachie," *Revue Roumaine d'Histoire* (Bucharest, 1969), vol. VII, no. 3.

A study by a Rumanian scholar regarding the first Cyrillic printing in Walachia by the monk Makarios.

Estreicher, Karol. "Günther Zainer i Świętopełk Fiol," *Biblioteka Warszawska* (Warsaw, 1867), vol. III, pp. 161–220.

An article about the first printing presses in Cracow and their printers. Numerous valuable data, also some erroneous theories.

Fijałek, Jan. "Początki cenzury prewencyjnej w kościele rzymsko-katolickim i w Polsce" (The Beginnings of Preventive Censorship in the Roman-Catholic Church and in Poland), *Studia staropolskie* (Studies of Ancient Poland) (Cracow, 1928).

A historical survey-analysis of censorship in Poland by an authoritative writer in the field of church affairs in Poland.

Friedberg, Helena. "Leonard Vitreatoris z Dobczyc," *Polski Słownik Biografiiczny* (Wrocław, 1972), vol. XVII/I, pp. 71–72.

A valuable contribution to the study of the relationship between Borchtrop, Fiol's type engraver, and the Jagellonian University professor Leonard Vitreatoris de Dobczyce.

Gębarowicz, Mieczysław. "Ivan Fedorow i jego działalność w latach 1569–1583 na tle epoki. Część I. Poprzednicy" (Ivan Fedorov, His Activities in the Years 1569–1583 and the Historical Background of the Era. Part I. Predecessors), *Roczniki Biblioteczne* (Library Annals) (Wrocław-Warsaw, 1969), vol. XIII, pp. 5–95.

Comprehensive historical study about Fedorov, the first Russian and Ukrainian printer, by a Polish scholar currently living in Lwów, USSR.

Golowatzkij, Jakow Fiodorowitsch. "Sweipolt Fiol und seine Kyrillische Buchdruckerei in Krakau vom Jahre 1491," *Sitzungsberichte der Kaiserlichen Akademie der Wissenschaften zu Wien. Philosophisch-Historische Klasse* (Vienna, 1876), vol. 83, pp. 425–448.

The finest study of Fiol's and his workshop. Although a century old, still valuable thanks to its objectivity and scholarly approach.

Hoskins, Janina W(ojcicka). "Printing in Poland's Golden Age," *The Quarterly Journal of the Library of Congress* (Washington, 1966), vol. 23, no. 3.

A general review of the printing presses in Poland during the fifteenth and sixteenth centuries.

Heintsch, Karol. "Ze studiów nad Szwajpoltem Fiolem. Część I. Materiały do życiorysu i działalności Fiola" (From Studies Regarding Szwajpolt Fiol. Part I. Materials toward Fiol's Biography and Activities), *Rocznik Zakładu Narodowego imienia Ossolińskich* (Yearbook of the Ossoliński National Institute) (Wrocław, 1957), vol. V, pp. 233–342.

The best to date study pertaining to Fiol and his achievements in Poland. Most comprehensive and scholarly work.

———. "Fragment druku Świętopełka Fiola w Bibliotece Zakładu im. Ossolińskich we Wrocławiu" (Fragment of a Fiol Print in the Library of the Ossoliński Institute of Wrocław), *Ze skarbca kultury* (From the Treasury of Culture) (Wrocław, 1953), vol. 2, no. 5, pp. 78–94.

The most precise, accurate, complete presentation and description of the fragment of *Triod Cvetnaja* currently in the Ossolineum Institute Library in Wrocław.

Henderson, David. "An Introduction to Slavic Letter Forms and Printing," *Quarterly Newsletter, The Book Club of California* (Spring, 1978), vol. XLIII, no. 2, pp. 31–39.

Latest article regarding the writing system of two-thirds of the Slavic peoples. Many cardinal errors.

Hubko, O. "Do pochatkiv ukrains'koho drukarstva" (Beginning of Ukrainian Printing), *Arkhivy Ukrainy* (Archives of the Ukraine) (Kiev, 1969), no. 3, pp. 12–28.

A speculative article of another follower of the theory of Fiol's Lemko-Ukrainian origin.

Isaevich, Ia. D. "Kirillovskie staropechatnye knigi v kollektsiiakh Polskoi Narodnoi Respubliki —Varshava, Krakov, Vrotslav" (Early Cyrillic Printed Books in the Collections of the Polish People's Republic), *Kniga* (Moscow, 1963), vol. VIII, pp. 291–296.

An informative article disclosing where Fiol's prints are located in Poland.

Jagic, I. V. "Ein Nachtrag zum ersten Cetinjer Kirchendruck vom J. 1494," *Archiv für Slavische Philologie* (1903), vol. 25, pp. 628–637.

Jurginis, Juozas. "Vilnius. Pierwsze przekłady książek polskich na język litewski i ich znaczenie kulturalne" (Vilno. The First Translations of Polish Books into Lithuanian and Their Cultural Importance), *Dawna książka i kultura (*Old Books and Culture (Wrocław-Warsaw, Ossolineum, 1975), pp. 316–329.

A historical survey of the first Polish Lithuanian literary relations.

Kaldor, I. L. "The Genesis of the Russian Grazhdanskii Shrift or Civil Type," *Journal of Typographic Research* (1969), vol. III, no. 4 and (1970), vol. IV, no. 2.

Kawecka-Gryczowa, Alodia. "Kłopoty z inkunabułami w skali międzynarodowej i polskiej" (International and Polish Problems Regarding Incunabula), *Przegląd Biblioteczny* (Library Review) (Warsaw, 1961), pp. 148–158.

Kocójowa, Maria. "Zarys historii zbiorów Emeryka Hutten-Czapskiego" (Outline of the History of the Emeryk Hutten-Czapski Collection), *Rozprawy i sprawozdania Muzeum Narodowego w Krakowie* (Transactions and Reports of the National Museum in Cracow) (Cracow, 1976), vol. XI, pp. 123–184.

First comprehensive biographical study of Emeryk Hutten-Czapski and the history of his collection.

Koliada, G. J. "Iz istorii knigopechatnykh sviazei Rossii, Ukrainy i Rumynii v XVI i XVII vekakh" (From the History of Printing Ties of Russia, the Ukraine and Rumania in the Sixteenth and Seventeenth Centuries), *U istokov russkogo knigopechataniia* (At the Beginning of Russian Printing) (Moscow, 1959).

A comparative study of first Cyrillic printing in Rumania, the Ukraine, and Russia.

Kopystenskii, Zakharii. *Palinodiia,* November 21, 1621. Printed for the first time in *Pamiatniki polemicheskoi literatury v Zapadnoi Rusi* (Literary Monuments of Polemical Literature in Western Rus' [Ruthenia]) (St. Petersburg, 1878), vol. I.

A religious, polemical book in which for the first time the dissemination of Fiol's prints throughout Belorussian and Ukrainian territories linked to the Polish-Lithuanian Commonwealth is revealed.

Kozłowska-Budkowa, Zofia. "Fiol," *Polski słownik biograficzny* (Polish Biographical Dictionary (Cracow, 1948), vol. VI, pp. 470–471.

Krajcar, J., S.J. "Early-printed Slavonic Books in the Library of the Pontifical Oriental Institute," *Orientalia Christiana Periodica* (Rome, 1968), vol. XXXIV, no. 1, pp. 105–108.

A thorough presentation of Slavonic early printing among them Fiol's books, *Triods* and *Chasoslovec.*

Krynicka, Maria. "Elementy figuralne dekoracji polskich opraw książkowych i ich związki z grafiką w pierwszym trzydziestoleciu XVI wieku, Komunikat" (Decorative Figural Elements in Polish Bookbinding and Their Graphic Associations in the First Thirty Years of the Sixteenth Century. A Communiqué), *Dawna książka i kultura* (Old Books and Culture) (Wrocław-Warsaw, 1975), pp. 169–183.

A valuable presentation of figural decoration in the embossed bookbinding in Poland.

Kuziela, Zeno. "Der deutsche Schweitpold Fiol als Begründer der ukrainischen Buchdruckerkunst (1491)," *Gutenberg Jahrbuch* (Mainz, 1936), pp. 73–81.

A treatise by a Ukrainian scholar endeavoring to establish the Cracow incunabula as a Ukrainian achievement and to present Fiol as the first German-Ukrainian cultural pioneer.

Lewicka-Kamińska, Anna. "Dzieje oprawy książkowej w Polsce. Stan badań, problematyka i postulaty" (The History of Bookbinding in Poland. The Status of Research, Problems and Postulates), *Dawna książka i kultura* (Old Book and Culture) (Wrocław-Warsaw, Ossolineum, 1975), pp. 144–168.

A brilliant review of the history of bookbinding, the state of present studies and the outline of future research in a symposium, "The Old Book and Culture" in commemoration of the five-hundredth anniversary of Polish printing.

———. "Z dziejów średniowiecznej oprawy książkowej na Śląsku" (From the History of Medieval Bookbinding in Silesia), *Roczniki Biblioteczne* (Library Annals) (Wrocław, 1977), vol. XXI, pp. 27–90.

A thorough study of bookbinding in Silesia during the fourteenth and fifteenth centuries of whatever was found after the devastation of World War II. Bookbinding shops were located in various cities such as Wrocław, Zgorzelec, Głogowa, Legnica and also in monasteries. Discussion at great length of the contrast in workmanship of simple plain leather binding with the elaborate binding using gold leaf, embossed and decorated with brass clips. At the end of the fifteenth century Western European, Cracow and Islamic influences appeared in the Silesian bookbinding industry. Numerous illustrations although some of them are of poor quality.

———. "Początki drukarstwa w Krakowie" (The Beginnings of Printing in Cracow), *Księga pamiątkowa ku czci Karola Estreichera* (Festschrift in Honor of Karol Estreicher) (Cracow, 1964), pp. 233–257.

———. "Zagadka drukarza *Kazań* papieża Leona I, tzw. Typographus Leonis I Papae: *Sermones*" (The Riddle Regarding the Printer of Pope Leon I's *Sermons*), *Roczniki Biblioteczne* (Library Annals) (Wrocław, 1976), vol. XX, pp. 495–561. (Offprint from Library Annals).

The latest and most thorough study of Typographus's prints based on a review of the entire literature and the forty-three of the fifty-one extant copies. Each is described accurately with a complete set of watermarks and nineteen plates.

Maleczyński, Kazimierz. "Z dziejów górnictwa śląskiego w epoce feudalnej" (From the History of Mining in Silesia during the Feudal Period), *Szkice z dziejów Śląska* (Sketches from the History of Silesia), ed. Ewa Maleczyńska (Warsaw, 1953).

A historical survey-analysis of the mining industry in Silesia by a Polish historian.

Micu, Emil and Mircea, Ion-Radu. "Un incunabulul unicat in bibliotecile noastre" (The Unique Incunabulum in Our Library), *Scinteia* (Bucharest, February 4, 1972), no. 9048, p. 4.

The first announcement in a newspaper regarding the discovery of Fiol's *Triod Cvetnaja* in the Braşov Library.

Mircea, Ion-Radu. "De la Cracovia de la Braşov: incunabulul din 1491" (From Cracow to Braşov: an Incunabulum of 1491. Pentacostal Triodion in the Museum of Rumanian Culture in Braşov), *Magazin Istoric* (Bucharest, 1972), vol. 8, no. 65, pp. 50–51.

An article by a Rumanian scholar announcing the finding of an unknown copy of *Triod Cvetnaja* printed by Fiol.

———. "Considérations sur les premières oeuvres imprimées à caractères cyrilliques," *Bulletin Association Internationale d'Etudes du Sud-Est Européen* (Bucharest, 1972), vol. X, no. 1, pp. 111–120.

A study by a Rumanian scholar about the commercial, cultural and religious connections of Moldavia with its northern neighbors, Poland and Ruthenia. Important feature is the first reprint of leaf 2 v. of Fiol's *Triod Cvetnaja* with the illustration of the crufixion and printer's mark beneath it.

———. "Primele Tiparituri Chirilice şi incunabulul cracovian de la Braşov," *Tirgovişte, cetate a culturii Românesti.* Part I: *Studii şi cercetări de bibliofilie* (Bucharest, 1974), pp. 111–127.

A study revealing in detail the characteristics of the newly-discovered copy of *Triod Cvetnaja* in Braşov.

Mošin, Vladimir. "Vodeni znaci najstarijih srpskih štampanih knjiga" (Watermarks of the Oldest Printed Serbian Books), *Zbornik, Muzej primenjene umetnosti* (Belgrade, 1967), pp. 7–23.

A collection of watermarks found in old Serbian books.

Muscan, Catinca. "Incunabulul de la Şcheii Braşovului," *Magazin* (Braşov, March 4, 1972), no. 722, p. 5.

News item in a local weekly on the discovery of a rare incunabulum, Fiol's *Triod Cvetnaja.*

Muszkowski, Jan. "Początki drukarstwa w Krakowie. Stan badań i problematyka aktualna" (The Beginnings of Printing in Cracow. The State of Research and Current Problems), *Prace Polonistyczne* (Polish Studies) (Warsaw-Łódż, 1951), pp. 9–63.

Muszkowski devotes the last part of the article to an outline of accomplishments and tasks of researchers of Fiol's Cyrillic printing.

Myl'nikov, A. S. "Na puti k resheniiu 'krakovskoi zagadki'" (On the Road to Solving "The Cracow Riddle"), *Kniga; Issledovaniia i materialy* (The Book: Research and Materials) (Moscow, 1973), vol. XXVI, pp. 222–226.

A Russian scholar's subtle and discreet review of Nemirovskii's book, *The Beginning of Cyrillic Printing,* Moscow, 1971. The reviewer notes that the fundamental theories of Nemirovskii are based on suppositions lacking documentation; therefore he suggests further study and research for a better documentation of the "Cracow Riddle."

Nadson, Alexander. "The Memoirs of Theodore Jeułaseuski, Assessor of Navahrudak (1546–1604)," *Journal of Byelorussian Studies* (London, 1968), vol. I, no. 4, pp. 269–348.

The whole volume is devoted to the publication of the memoirs, both in Belorussian and in English translation with an introduction, "Jeułaseuski and his Times." Included are important notes to the introduction and to the memoirs.

———. "Kniha Skaryny ŭ Kapenhahene" (Skaryna's Book in Copenhagen), *Bozhym Shliakham* (London, 1971), no. 5, p. 128.

An article announcing the discovery of a complete copy of Skaryna's print *Malaia podorozhnaia knizhitsa* in Copenhagen by Professor Moshe Altbauer of the Hebrew University in Jerusalem.

———. "Padruchnik Fedarava i Skaryna" (Fedorov's Primer and Skaryna), *Bozhym Shliakham* (London, 1972), vol. XX, no. 5–6, pp. 8–11.

An article proving that Fedorov, the first Muscovy printer, was well acquainted with Skaryna's prints and exploited this knowledge in his own works.

———. "Skaryna's Prayer Book," *The Journal of Byelorussian Studies* (London, 1972), vol. VIII, no. 2, pp. 339–358.

A historical survey-analysis and full description of Skaryna's prayer book, *Malaia podorozhnaia knizhitsa* based on the latest discovery of a complete copy in Copenhagen by the prominent Belorussian scholar.

Nemirovskii, Evgenii L. "Slavische Inkunabeln in kyrillischer Schrift. Die Geschichte ihrer Erforschung und die noch erhaltene Exemplare," *Beiträge zur Inkunabelkunde,* second series (Berlin, 1969), pp. 81–111.

The most valuable of all of Nemirovskii's scholarly work covering the basic data of Fiol's 75 prints, copies and fragments. German translation facilitates interest in this field in the West. No provenance notes cited; only location of the books.

———. "Pervopechatnik Ivan Fedorov v Krakovskom Universitete" (Early Printer Ivan Fedorov at Cracow University), *Sovetskoe Slavianovedenie* (Soviet Slavic Studies) (Moscow, 1969), no. 1.

Interesting treatise promoting the theory that Fedorov studied at the Jagellonian University in Cracow. Not substantiated by documents, only the obvious influence of Polish culture on the prominent printer.

———. "Slavianskie inkunabuly" (Slavic Incunabula), *Sovetskoe Slavianovedenie* (Soviet Slavistics) (Moscow, Akademiia Nauk USSR, Institut Slavianovedenia, 1969), no. 1.

Studies in early Slavic printing.

———. "Izdaniia Sh. Fiolia, F. Skoriny i I. Fedorova v knigokhranilishchakh Varshavy i Krakova" (Publications of Fiol, Skaryna and Fedorov in the Libraries of Warsaw and Cracow), *Sovetskoe slavianovedenie* (September-October, 1975), no. 5, pp. 69–75.

Review of Polish holdings of Fiol's prints, books and fragments during Nemirovskii's studies in Polish libraries. A critical evaluation of what has been done and what is still to be done.

———. "Die slawischen Inkunabeln in kyrillischer Schrift. Beschreibung," *Beiträge zur Inkunabelkunde* (second series) (Berlin, 1975), vol. 6, pp. 75–80.

Itemized description of Fiol's four prints.

———. "Rasprostranenie krakovskikh izdanii Shvaipol'ta Fiola v Russkom Gosudarstve v XVI–XVII vekakh" (Distribution of Fiol's Cracow Prints in the Russian State during the Sixteenth and Seventeenth Centuries), *Kul'turnye sviazi narodov vostochnoi Evropy v XVI veke. Problemy vzaimootnoshenii Pol'shi, Rossii, Ukrainy, Belorussii i Litvy v epokhe vozrozhdeniia* (Cultural Ties of Eastern European Nations in the Sixteenth Century. Problems of the Interrelations of Poland, Russia, the Ukraine, Belorussia and Lithuania in the Renaissance) (Moscow, 1976), pp. 187–191.

Author consistently endeavors to include Russia into the Renaissance movement through implication of cultural connections with Polish-Lithuanian Commonwealth. However, history reveals that first cultural influences appeared on the brink of the sixteenth and seventeenth century.

———. "Opisanie izdanii tipografii Shvaipolta Fiola" (Description of Publications by Shvajpolt Fiol's Printing Shops), *Opisanie staropechatnykh izdanij kirilovskogo shrifta.* (Description of Old Publications of Cyrillic Printing) (Moscow, 1979), vol. I.

This recent publication by E. L. Nemirovskii regarding Shvajpolt Fiol's typography is the first issue of a large project encompassing description of all old Cyrillic prints. This summary of previous findings does not introduce anything new; as a matter of fact it repeats all previous misconceptions in spite of newly discovered material. It would have great value if he had not insisted on including his unsubstantiated theories and if he had incorporated the latest findings of others.

Paszkiewicz, Henryk. "Are the Russians Slavs?," *Antemurale* (Rome, 1970), vol. XIV, part II.

Historical survey-analysis of Muscovite Russia's position among Slavic nations. This study created an interest even in China, where it was translated.

Piekarski, K. "Inwentarz inkunabułów w bibliotekach polskich" (Inventory of Incunabula in Polish Libraries), *Prace Krakowskiego Koła Związku Bibliotekarzy Polskich* (Studies of the Cracow Chapter of the Association of Polish Librarians), (series 1) (Cracow, 1925).

First effort to establish a comprehensive catalogue of incunabula in Poland.

Pieradzka, Krystyna. "Przedsiębiorstwa kopalniane mieszczan krakowskich w Olkuszu od XV–go do początków XVII wieku" (Mining Enterprises of Cracow's Townsmen in Olkusz from the Fifteenth to the Beginning of the Seventeenth Centuries), *Zeszyty naukowe Uniwersytetu Jagiellońskiego. Historia* (Research Papers of the Jagellonian University. History) (Cracow, 1958).

A valuable contribution to the history of mining in Poland.

———. "Rozkwit średniowiecznego Krakowa w XIV i XV wieku" (The Flowering of Medieval Cracow in the Fourteeenth and the Fifteenth Centuries), *Kraków, studia nad rozwojem miasta* (Cracow, Studies on the Development of the City), ed. Jan Dąbrowski (Cracow, 1957).

Study of the cultural development of Cracow in the fourteenth and fifteenth centuries.

Pirożynski, Jan. "Z badań nad drukarstwem krakowskim XV wieku. Przegląd nowszych publikacji" (From the Studies of Cracow Printing in the Fifteenth Century. Review of Recent Publications), *Studia historyczne* (Historical Studies) (Warsaw, 1971), vol. XIV, pp. 563–577.

Review of recent studies regarding Cracow's first printing presses.

Popov, P. M. "Pochatok knyhodrukuvania u slov'ian, XV–XVI st." (Beginning of Slavic Printing, the Fifteenth and Sixteenth Centuries), *Knyha i drukarstvo na Ukraini* (The Book and Printing in the Ukraine) (Kiev, 1965), vol. 1, pp. 9–23.

A fine contribution to the study of early Slavic printing in the Ukraine.

Polkowski, Ignacy. "Nieznany druk krakowski z XV wieku: Dzieło Franciszka de

Platea's Opus restitutionum), *Rozprawy Wydziału Filologicznego Akademii Umiejetności* (Transactions of the Philological Section of the Academy of Arts and Sciences) (Cracow, 1880), vol. VIII.

A marginal announcement of the discovery of Fiol's fragments in an article about Franciscus de Platea's incunabulum.

Ptaśnik, Joannes. "Cracovia impressorum XV et XVI saeculorum," *Monumenta Poloniae Typographica XV et XVI saeculorum* (Leopoli, Sumptibus Instituti Ossoliniani, MCMXXII), vol. I.

An exceptional study, unique for its time. Contains information about printers, bookshops, papermakers, playing card manufacturers, engravers, bookbinders and all that is connected with book production. The descriptive section (pages 10 to 22) deals with Fiol's biography based upon collected documents. In the section of source materials among 300 documents from 1475 to 1526, 50 documents pertain to Fiol.

———. "Cracovia artificium 1300–1500," *Źródla do historii sztuki i cywilizacji w Polsce* (Sources for the History of Art and Civilization in Poland) (Cracow, 1917), vol. IV.

A collection of documents pertaining to the history of Cracow's economy and industry. Among others, 37 documents referring to Fiol compiled by Ptaśnik and other scholars.

———. "Turzonowie w Polsce i ich stosunki z Fuggerami. Kartka z dziejów Krakowa w epoce humanizmu" (The Turzos in Poland and Their Relationship with the Fuggers. A Leaf from the History of Cracow during the Renaissance), *Przewodnik Naukowy i Literacki* (Scholarly and Literary Guide) (Lwów, 1905), vol. XXXIII, pp. 829–1124.

A valuable monograph about the Turzo family, industrial barons in Poland and Hungary and their connections with the Fuggers, the renowned German bankers and industrialists.

Radojićić, D. S. "Die erste Walachische Druckerei (1506–1512)," *Gutenberg-Jahrbuch* (Mainz, 1960), vol. 35, pp. 248–254.

Valuable article on the first Walachian printing press set up by Makarios.

Siczyńskij, V. "Die Anfänge der Ukrainischen Gravierkunst im XV und XVI Jahrhundert," *Gutenberg-Jahrbuch* (Mainz, 1940), pp. 238–247.

A study endeavoring to find a connection between Ukrainian and German woodcut art in the fifteenth and sixteenth centuries.

Sidorov, A. A. "Khudozhestvenno-tekhnicheskie osobennosti slavianskogo pervopechataniia" (Artistic and Technical Peculiarities of Early Slavic Printing), *U istokov russkogo knigopechataniia* (Beginning of Russian Book Printing) (Moscow, Akademiia nauk USSR, 1959).

The first thorough study of the technical and artistic aspects of Cyrillic typography in the fifteenth and sixteenth centuries.

Simmons, J. S. G. "Incunabula in the U.S.S.R. 1. Russia and the Ukraine. 2. The

Baltic Republics, Addenda, and Concordances," *The Book Collector* (Autumn, 1965), pp. 311–323 and (Spring, 1966), pp. 19–34.

Sobolevskii, A. I. "Zamietka o jazyke pechatnykh izdanij Shvaipolta Fiola i Skoryny" (Notes Regarding the Language of Shvaipolt Fiol's and Skaryna's Publications), *Chteniia, IONL* (Kiev, 1888), vol. 2, pp. 192–193.

A study of the language of the first Cyrillic prints by a prominent Russian scholar, a great authority in this field.

———. "Starshie perevody russkikh katolikov" (Older Translations of Russian Catholics), *Materialy i issledovania v oblasti slavianskoi filologii i archeologii* (Materials and Research in the Fields of Slavic Philology and Archeology) (St. Petersburg, 1910).

A study of Old Orthodox Russian linguistic monuments.

Sokolyszyn, Aleksander. "Sweipolt Fiol: The First Slavic Printer of Cyrillic Characters," *American Slavic and East European Review* (1959), vol. 18, pp. 88–94.

One of the few articles published in the United States pertaining to Cyrillic printing. Author unfortunately accepted Iur'ev's theory of Fiol's Ukrainian descent.

———. "First Ukrainian Printer of Books in Cyrillic," *The Ukrainian Quarterly* (1972), vol. XXVIII, no. 3, pp. 286–293.

Swierk, Alfred, "Der Krakauer Buchdruck im XV Jahrhundert," *Börsenblatt für den deutschen Buchhandel* (Historical Section) (May 29, 1970), vol. LXXVIII, no. 43, pp. 1193–1200.

A valuable presentation of Cracow's first printing presses.

———. "Inkunabelnforschung in Polen," *Gutenberg-Jahrbuch* (1972), pp. 117–127.

Szandorowska, Eliza. "Tajemnicza oficyna drukarska XV wieku" (A Mysterious Fifteenth Century Press), *Rocznik Biblioteki Narodowej* (Yearbook of the National Library) (1967), vol. III, pp. 321–346.

The "typographus Leonis papae I sermones" (HC–10015) is one of the anonymous printers of the fifteenth century. A valuable contribution to the study of this printing press by a prominent Polish scholar leads to locating it in Poland.

———. "Czy w Chełmnie nad Wisłą drukowano inkunabuły?" (Were Incunabula Printed in the Town of Chełmno-on-the-Vistula River?) *Rocznik Biblioteki Narodowej* (Yearbook of the National Library) (1968), vol. IV, pp. 23–49.

A study of the subsidiary Order of Brethren of the Common Life from Zwolle in Holland, located in Chełmno. A school of higher learning was established. Szandorowska theorizes that here "typographus Leonis papae I sermones" produced his seven books with Dutch characters.

———. "A Dutch Printing Office in Fifteenth Century Poland," *Quaerendo* (Amsterdam, July 1972), vol. II, no. 3, pp. 162–172.

A study about the anonymous printer called "typographus Leonis papae I sermones." In addition to previous arguments locating this enigmatic press in Chełmno, Szandorowska added another one: the two "Turkish texts" produced by this printing press could also indicate Pomerania as their printing location, for a plan was conceived there to transfer the Teutonic Knights from the north of Poland to Hungary as a defense against Turkish attacks.

———. "List do Redakcji w sprawie nieznanego sygnetu drukarskiego Szwajpolta Fiola" (Letter to the Editor in Reference to the Unknown Printer's Device of Szwajpolt Fiol), *Biuletyn Historii Sztuki* (Bulletin of the History of Art) (Warsaw, 1979), vol. XLII, pp. 230–232.

Important article about the Braşov copy of Fiol's *Triod Cvetnaja* by Eliza Szandorowska who studied the book *in situ*. This is the first announcement in Polish as well as in West European incunabulistic literature regarding the discovery of Fiol's *Triod Cvetnaja* in Braşov. Although brief, nevertheless this article represents a very important and thorough study of this precious finding.

Tarnawsky, M. "The Founding Fathers of Ukrainian Printing: Shvaipolt Fiol and Ivan Fedorov," *The Ukrainian Quarterly* (1965), vol. 21, no. 3.

Tomkowicz, Stanisław. "Drukarnia kirylicka Świętopełka Fiola w Krakowie . . . " (Świętopełk Fiol's Cyrillic Printing Press in Cracow . . .), *Przewodnik Bibliograficzny* (Bibliographical Guide) (Cracow, 1884), vol. VII, no. 8.

Valuable article about Cyrillic printing in Cracow. Important for its accurate notations about correspondence between Sommerfeld and Celtes.

Tumash, Vitaut. "Bibliiahrafiia skaryniiany" (Bibliography of Scoriniana), *Zapisy* (Munich, Whiteruthenian Institute of Arts and Sciences, 1970), vol. 5, pp. 181–268.

The most comprehensive bibliography devoted to Skaryna. Divided into sections: Acts and Documents; Skaryna's prints; Skaryna in Literature and Art. All compiled in chronological order. Altogether 1176 items.

———. "Drèvaryty nastaŭnika Diurera ŭ Padarozhnai Knizhitsy Doktara Skaryny" (Wood Engravings of Dürer's Teacher in Doctor Skaryna's Traveler's Book), *Zapisy* (New York, Whiteruthenian Institute of Art and Sciences, 1978), vol. 16, pp. 3–41.

———. "Drukarnia Piotry Ms'tsislaŭtsa" (The Printing House of Piotr Mstsislavets), *Zapisy* (New York, Belorussian Institute of Arts and Sciences, 1975), vol. 13, pp. 3–29.

A thorough survey-analysis of archival documents, type faces and printing materials revealing that the Vilno printing house in the years 1574–1576 belonged to Ms'tsislavets and not to Mamonich.

———. "Hetman Ryhor Khadkevich i iahonae vydavetstva" (Hetman Ryhor Khadkevich and His Publishing House), *Zapisy* (New York, Belorussian Institute of Arts and Sciences, 1976), vol. 14, pp. 3–42.

The latest results of research by this author reveal that the initiator and editor of the printing house in Zabłudów was Hetman R. Chodkiewicz. Ivan Fedorov was technical executor.

Ulanowski, Bolesław, ed. "Acta capitulorum nec non iuduciorum ecclesiasticorum selecta, vol. 1: Acta capitulorum Gneznensis, Poznaniensis et Vratislaviensis

(1408–1530)," *Monumenta Medii Aevi Historica res gestas Poloniae illustrantia* (Cracow, 1894), vol. V, XIII, no. 2329.

A thorough study and presentation of Acts and Documents pertaining to church affairs. Among them Ulanowski found important documents about Turzo's participation in Fiol's enterprises.

Varbanets, N. V. and Luk'ianenko, V. I. "Slavianskie inkunabuly v sobranii Gosudarstvennoi Publichnoi Biblioteki im. M. E. Saltykova-Shchedrina v Leningrade" (Slavic Incunabula in the Collection of the Saltykov-Shchedrin State Public Library in Leningrad), *Kniga: Issledovaniia i materialy* (The Book: Research and Materials) (Moscow, 1960), vol. II, pp. 187–208.

A valuable contribution to the study of Polish incunabula in Latin and Cyrillic located presently in the Saltykov-Shchedrin Public Library.

Vladimirov, L. I. "Litovets Dzhon Lettov — londonskii pervopechatnik" (The Lithuanian John Lettov — London's Early Printer), *Kniga: Issledovaniia i materialy* (The Book: Research and Materials (Moscow, 1973), vol. XXVI, pp. 183–190.

A study of the identity of John Lettov with Johannes Bremer. Also a discussion regarding Kuntrym, an unverified Lithuanian pupil of Gutenberg.

Vladimirov, P. V. "Nachalo slavianskogo i russkogo knigopechataniia v XV i XVI vekakh" (The Beginnings of Slavic and Russian Printing in the Fifteenth and Sixteenth Centuries), *Chteniia v istoricheskom obshchestve Nestora-letopistsa* (Kiev, 1894), vol. VIII, pp. 11–34.

A study of the language and origin of texts in the first Cyrillic printings.

Wutke, K. "Schlesiens Bergbau und Huttenwesen. Urkunden (1136–1528)," *Codex diplomaticus Silesiae* (Breslau, 1900), vol. XX.

A comprehensive collection of acts and documents pertaining to mining in Silesia. Unique work in this field.

Wynar, Lubomyr R. "History of Early Ukrainian Printing, 1491–1600," *Studies in Librarianship* (Denver, University of Denver, 1962), vol. 1, no. 2.

A study representing the Ukrainian point of view regarding the development of Cyrillic printing.

Zernova, Antonina Sergeevna. "Tipografiia Mamonichei v Vil'ne" (Mamonich's Typography in Vilno), *Kniga: Issledovaniia i materialy* (The Book: Research and Materials) (Moscow, 1959), vol. I, pp. 174–176.

A valuable contribution by a Russian scholar to the study of the famous printing establishment in Vilno.

———. "Metodika opisaniia staropechatnykh knig kirillovskoi pechati" (Methods of Describing Old Cyrillic Prints), *Trudy Gosudarstvennoi Biblioteki SSSR* (Studies of the State Library of the USSR) (Moscow, 1960), vol. 4.

A comprehensive survey-analysis of the subject by a prominent Russian scholar, a specialist in early prints.

———. "Pervopechatnik Petr Timofeevich Mstislavets" (Early Printer Petr Timofeevich Mstislavets), *Kniga: Issledovaniia i materialy* (The Book: Research and Materials) (Moscow, 1964), vol. IX, pp. 80–92.

A valuable contribution to the study of this early printer and pioneer of Russian and Belorussian printing.

Zimmer, Szczepan K. "Polskie druki cyrylickie" (Polish Cyrillic Prints), *Wiadomości* (News) (London, November 9, 1969), no. 1232.

An article on the development of Cyrillic printing in Cracow and Fiol's achievements.

———. "Pierwszy polski drukarz — Kasper Elyan" (The First Polish Printer — Kasper Elyan), *Polish Congress of Contemporary Science and Culture in Exile* (London, 1970), pp. 315–329.

A historical and linguistic survey-analysis of the first printer in Wrocław, determining the Polish origin of the printer, Kasper Elyan.

———. "Cracow's First Printing Press," *Antemurale* (Rome, 1970), vol. XIV, pp. 173–192.

Outline of the first Polish printing press in Cracow in 1474–1477 and the description of four incunabula in Latin produced by an unidentified "Printer of Turrecremata."

Index

J

K

L

M

N

O

T

U

BROOKLYN COLLEGE STUDIES ON SOCIETY IN CHANGE
Distributed by Columbia University Press (except No. 5)
Editor-in-Chief: Béla K. Király

No. 1
Tolerance and Movements of Religious Dissent in Eastern Europe. Edited by B. K. Király, 1975. Second Printing, 1977.

No. 2
The Habsburg Empire in World War I. Edited by R. A. Kann, B. K. Király, P. S. Fichtner, 1976. Second Printing, 1978.

No. 3
The Mutual Effects of the Islamic and Judeo-Christian Worlds: The East European Pattern. Edited by A. Ascher, T. Halasi-Kun, B. K. Király, 1979.

No. 4
Before Watergate: Problems of Corruption in American Society. Edited by A. S. Eisenstadt, A. Hoogenboom, H. L. Trefousse, 1978.

No. 5
East Central European Perceptions of Early America. Edited by B. K. Király and G. Barany. Lisse, The Netherlands: Peter de Ridder Press, 1977. Distributed by Humanities Press, Atlantic Highlands, N.J.

No. 6
The Hungarian Revolution of 1956 in Retrospect. Edited by B. K. Király and P. Jónás, 1978. Second Printing, 1980.

No. 7
Brooklyn U.S.A.: Fourth Largest City in America. Edited by R. S. Miller, 1979.

No. 8
János Decsy. *Prime Minister Gyula Andrássy's Influence on Habsburg Foreign Policy During the Franco-German War of 1870–1871,* 1979.

No. 9
Robert F. Horowitz. *The Great Impeacher: A Political Biography of M. Ashley,* 1979.

* * *

Nos. 10–19
Subseries: War and Society in East Central Europe (See Nos. 30–40 also)

No. 10 — Vol. I
Special Topics and Generalizations on the Eighteenth and Nineteenth Centuries. Edited by B. K. Király and G. E. Rothenberg, 1979.

No. 11 — Vol. II
East Central European Society and War in the Pre-Revolutionary Eighteenth Century. Edited by G. E. Rothenberg, B. K. Király and P. Sugar, 1982.

No. 12 — Vol. III
From Hunyadi to Rákóczi: War and Society in Late Medieval and Early Modern Hungary. Edited by J. M. Bak and B. K. Király, 1982.

No. 13 — Vol. IV
East Central European Society and War in the Era of Revolutions, 1775–1856, edited by B. K. Király, forthcoming.

No. 14 — Vol. V
Essays on World War I: Origins and Prisoners of War. Edited by P. Pastor and S. R. Williamson, Jr., 1982.

No. 15 — Vol. VI
Essays on World War I: Total War and Peacemaking, A Case Study on Trianon, Edited by B. K. Király, P. Pastor and I. Sanders, 1982.

No. 16 — Vol. VII
Thomas M. Barker. *Army, Aristocracy, Monarchy: War, Society and Government in Austria, 1618–1780,* 1982.

No. 17 — Vol. VIII
The First Serbian Uprising, 1804–1813. Edited by Wayne S. Vucinich, 1983.

No. 18 — Vol. IX
Kálmán Janics. *Czechoslovak Policy and the Hungarian Minority, 1945–1948,* 1982.

No. 19 — Vol. X
At the Brink of War and Peace: The Tito–Stalin Split in Historic Perspective. Edited by Wayne S. Vucinich, 1983.

* * *

No. 20
Inflation Through the Ages: Economic, Social, Psychological and Historical Aspects. Edited by N. Schmukler and E. Marcus, 1982.

No. 21
Germany and America: Essays on Problems of International Relations and Immigration. Edited by H. L. Trefousse, 1980.

No. 22
Murray M. Horowitz. *Brooklyn College: The First Half Century,* 1982.

No. 23
Jason Berger. *A New Deal for the World: Eleanor Roosevelt and American Foreign Policy,* 1981.

No. 24
The Legacy of Jewish Migration: 1881 and Its Impact. Edited by D. Berger, 1982.

No. 25
Pierre Oberling. *The Road to Bellapais: Cypriot Exodus to Northern Cyprus,* 1982.

No. 26
New Hungarian Peasants: An East Central European Experiment with Collectivization. Edited by Marida Hollós and Béla Maday, 1983.

No. 27
Germans in America: Aspects of German-American Relations in the 19th Century. Edited by E. Allen McCormick, forthcoming.

No. 28
Linda and Marsha Frey. *A Question of Empire: Leopold I and the War of Spanish Succession, 1701–1705,* forthcoming.

No. 29
Szczepan K. Zimmer. *The Beginning of Cyrillic Printing — Cracow, 1491. From the Orthodox Past in Poland.* Edited by Ludwik Krzyżanowski and Irene Nagurski, 1983.

* * *

Nos. 30–40
Subseries: War and Society in East Central Europe (Continued) (See Nos. 10–19 also)

No. 30 — Vol. XI
The First War Between Socialist States: The Hungarian Revolution of 1956 and Its Impact. Edited by Béla K. Király, Barbara Lotze, Nándor Dreisziger, forthcoming.

No. 31 — Vol. XII
István I. Mocsy. *Effects of World War I: The Uprooted: Hungarian Refugees and Their Impact on Hungarian Domestic Politics: 1918–1921,* forthcoming.

No. 32 — Vol. XIII
Ivo Banac. *Effects of World War I: The Class War after the Great War: The Rise of Communist Parties in the East Central European "Red Wave": 1918–1921.* 1983.

No. 33 — Vol. XIV
The Crucial Decade: East Central European Society and National Defense: 1859–1870. Edited by Béla K. Király, forthcoming.

No. 34 — Vol. XV
The Political Dimensions of War in Romanian History. Edited by Ilie Ceausescu, 1983.

No. 35 — Vol. XVI
East Central European Classics of Military Thought: Rákóczi and Kosciuszko. Edited by B. K. Király, E. Halicz and J. Decsy, forthcoming.

* * *

BOOKS IN THE PLANNING STAGE

No. 36 — Vol. XVII
East Central European Society and War, 1870–1911.

No. 37 — Vol. XVIII
East Central European Society and the Balkan Wars, 1912–1913.

No. 38 — Vol. XIX
East Central European Society in World War I.

No. 39 — Vol. XX
East Central European Society in Revolutions and Counter Revolutions, 1918–1920.

No. 40 — Vol. XXI
East Central European Society and War, 1750–1920. Bibliography and Historiography. Compiled and edited by Dr. László Alföldi.